MW00560294

The Book of Jesse

Also By Michael Rowe

Crossing the Border: Encounters Between Homeless People and Outreach Workers

The Book of

Jesse

A Story of Youth, Illness, and Medicine

Michael Rowe

The Francis Press
Washington, D.C.

Printed in the United States of America

FIRST EDITION

LIBRARY OF CONGRESS CATALOGING-IN-PUBLICATION DATA

Rowe, Michael, date.
The book of Jesse : a story of youth, illness, and medicine / Michael Rowe.-- 1st ed.
p. ; cm.
ISBN 0-9665051-6-6 (hdc.)
1. Harlan-Rowe, Jesse, 1975-1995--Health. 2. Liver--Transplantation--Patients--Connecticut--Biography.
[DNLM: 1. Harlan-Rowe, Jesse, 1975-1995. 2. Liver Cirrhosis--surgery--Adolescence--Personal Narratives. 3. Liver Transplantation--adverse effects--Adolescence--Personal Narratives. 4. Multiple Organ Failure--complications--Adolescence--Personal Narratives. WI 725 R879b 2002] I. Title.

RD546.H325 R69 2002
362.1'975562'0092--dc21

2002010484

Photo of Jesse on the jacket and the frontispiece by Julie Rowe Cooke

Jacket and interior design by Dawn Christopher

Published by The Francis Press
Washington, D.C.
www.francispress.com

I must lie down where all the ladders start,
In the foul rag-and-bone shop of the heart.

W.B. Yeats
"The Circus Animal's Desertion"

for Jesse, and for Gail, Daniel, and Cassandra

Introduction

The obituary from the August 10, 1995 *Waterbury Republican-American* is tucked in between the oak frame and glass of an antique mirror decorated with photos, necklaces draped over the top corners, and an oriental fan wedged between the frame and the wall. The clipping is set on a piece of white cardboard with a pink and blue border, and clipping and cardboard together are laminated in heavy plastic. When it arrived in the mail from Ciarlo Monumental Works, I was surprised at the yellowness of the paper and I wondered, if newspapers yellow so quickly, why the monument company had not bleached the paper before laminating it. It has occurred to me since that the clipping may have been antiqued to give it a more sobering look. Much as I could hold up this obituary embalmed in plastic and sent to the grieving family by the local monument works as a humorous artifact of America's way with death, I'm happy to have it on my wife's mirror by our bedroom door and I wasn't offended by the commercial interest that brought it to us. It reads*:

In Memoriam

Jesse Harlan-Rowe

NAUGATUCK–Jesse Harlan-Rowe, 19, of 222 Quinn St., died Tuesday at __________ Hospital in New York City.

Mr. Harlan-Rowe was born in New Haven, Oct. 12, 1975. He lived in Naugatuck for the past six years and until his illness had been a student at Naugatuck High School.

He leaves his father and stepmother, Michael Rowe and Gail (Evans) Rowe of Naugatuck; his mother and stepfather, Rachel (Harlan) McLaughlin and Will McLaughlin of Stamford; a brother, Daniel Rowe of Naugatuck; a sister, Cassandra Rowe of Naugatuck; a paternal grandmother, Elizabeth Rowe of Rochester, N.Y.; maternal grandparents, Allan and Kelly Harlan of Jacksonville, Fla.; and three stepbrothers, Richard McLaughlin, Peter McLaughlin, and John Mc-

*Here and in the narrative that follows, I have not used the name of the hospital in which Jesse died, and have changed, in whole or in part, the names of all individuals other than those on my side of his family.

Laughlin, all of Stamford.

Arrangements: Memorial service Saturday, 1 p.m. at Congregational Church of Naugatuck. Burial: at family's convenience. No calling hours. Arrangements by Alderson Funeral Home of Naugatuck, 201 Meadow St.

Contributions: Jesse Harlan-Rowe Memorial Fund, care of Naugatuck High School Art Department, 543 Rubber Ave., Naugatuck, CT 06770.

I suppose we gave this information to our funeral director and he gave it to the newspaper. Technically speaking, Daniel and Cassandra are half-siblings to Jesse by my second marriage, to Gail, but we never thought of them, or him, that way.

Daniel, eleven at the time, stood before our front steps talking to Cassandra, eight, and their friend Jamie, whose father had died of cancer the year before. I heard Jesse's name and crept up behind the front door. They talked about how awkward and insensitive other kids could be around the subject of the deaths that now marked the three of them as being different. Cassie said that her friend Alice had told her, "Now you only have one brother." Jamie nodded in agreement. Some of his schoolmates still broke the news to him of his father's death. Daniel brought up Jesse's obituary. "It makes him sound so boring," he said.

Daniel was right, of course. There was nothing of Jesse's dry and quick wit in that report. There was no mention of his artistic talent, including his flair for outrageous caricature and for comic-mythic creations such as the planet Eggnog III and its most renowned citizen, George 10, in drawings and stories. Daniel could not have known that most of us who make our exit at four or five times Jesse's age won't get much more than that—a few lines about what we did for work or community service and a survivors' list with a higher percentage of family members who are younger, not older, than us. If Jesse or his parents had been better known or been at the center of some notable event, his obituary might have given Daniel some satisfaction with references to his brother's wit and imagination and artistic talent. It might have answered the question implied by the statement, "He lived in Naugatuck for the past six years," to say that, with a brief detour to its neighboring town of Branford, Jesse had spent the first thirteen years of his life in New Haven. It might have noted that his parents separated when he was three years old and later divorced; that his father was a sociologist who wrote about homeless people; that his stepmother was a children's librarian; that his mother worked in medical sales; and that his stepfather was a manager for Amtrak's Boston-New York City line. Depending on the reason for Jesse's notoriety, it might have reported on certain aspects of his personality: his wit and creativity, yes, but also his isolation from peers and near-impenetrable defenses against disclosing himself to prying adults, and the lingering questions about whether such traits were related to the residual effects of hydrocephalus, a condition in which the spaces in the brain, called ventricles, that produce cerebrospinal fluid, do not drain properly, resulting in an enlarged head and pressure on the brain. Taking off from this cue, it might have gone into some detail about his medical troubles: Three operations for hydrocephalus in the first year and a half of his life (in remission for the rest of it). Diagnosis of ulcerative colitis in 1991 and an operation in 1993 to correct it. Diagnosis of cirrhosis of the liver during that same year. Finally, liver transplantation at __________ hospital in early May 1995, with complications from the transplant that led to massive infection and multi-organ failure, followed by a rally and a second liver transplant, followed by further complications and surgery before his death on August 8.

I first thought of writing this book about midway through Jesse's hospitalization. Then, I hoped to write the story of his battle for survival and miraculous recovery. Standing by his bed, I told him about my idea and said I needed someone to illustrate the book. He gave a little smile. Later, the idea of "witnessing" Jesse's struggle impressed itself upon me. Now, it's easy to see that the notion of witnessing carries with it a weighty responsibility and the dangers of arrogance and error, especially when one's subject has not asked to be spoken for. A rule of thumb might be to take on this mission only when you think that the possible benefits of doing so—in this case, telling the story of how one young man and his family confronted serious illness and the underside of modern, high-technology medicine—outweigh the possible harm of going ahead.

As time passed the story became for me, in part, a search for who Jesse was and how he saw himself in the world. This search then ran parallel to what I came to see as his quest for the safe harbor of healthy body, love, and acceptance for who he was with the help of those very elements—his obsessive love for mythic heroes and legends—that we feared he was using to retreat from the world. To tell the story these ideas shaped for me, I felt I had to get under the skin of the experience: to start in the present, which for this book is late winter 1999, and go back and forth to and from the near and more distant past, to go close up, circle and drop down, draw away and return, as one draws away from and returns to the site of a trauma. Thus the skin I am getting under is mine, too.

As for the medical aspects of this narrative, Jesse's struggle to earn an identity that fit his skin was, I think, inseparable from his struggle with physical illness. Seen this way, his last hospitalization casts a long shadow before and behind it. If taste and judgment and the economies of storytelling demand that the writer spare the reader many unpleasant details, those same qualities, and a regard for the truth as one can tell it, demand that he leave many of them in.

This is a book about real people and events. It is based on memory, my notes, and my conversations with others, especially my wife, Gail. I created no events (other than the structural motif of walking through my house on a given day) or characters, composite or otherwise. Still, a writer has to pick and choose from among a mass of events and their details. He has to summarize or expand and then juxtapose those events, and each event, and all together, can be written about in any number of ways. Finally, he must breathe life into those events or he writes falsely. The facts alone are stale, flat, and dead.

The writing of a memoir, then, is a creative act. "Act of re-creation" is too ambiguous—it lets the writer have it both ways, donning the mantle of creative artist while dealing in the coin of true story. Best for him to lay claim to both, I think, but separately, without allowing the strictures of either one to excuse his failings in the other, and let his readers decide whether he has written a good story, and a true story.

one

Looking toward Chestnut Street, not in this near-dusk light a few days shy of the vernal equinox but at noon in summer's full tide, I see him coming this way, backpack slung over his right shoulder and an enormous Bugs Bunny T-shirt hanging loose over his hips to disguise the outline of his ostomy bag. He has walked almost a mile, even with the short cut behind school up three flights of steps dug into the hillside.

Everything is wrong with this fantasy, spun in 1999 of a time in 1995 when Jesse was fighting for his life a hundred miles away. It couldn't be summer, and him with his backpack slung over his right shoulder, because school was out by then. It could be mid-spring, early May, he kept going that long rather than sit at home waiting for Friday the 5th when we would take him to the hospital in New York City to wait for his liver transplant. But the sun would not shine this high overhead in mid-spring, and he wouldn't be walking home at noon anyway unless he was ill or this was a half day, and then Gail would pick him up or he would get a ride home in the school minivan. Still, instinct tells me to go with this image of him walking down Quinn Street from Chestnut and the associations that go with it.

On the morning of this day I imagine for Jesse he is not taking the minivan, no, he is not yet so fatigued from the effects of slowly advancing cirrhosis that he cannot walk home from school. Still, his grandmother has offered to pick him up, Gail and I both at work, unless this is a Friday and she's having her hair washed and set or visiting a friend in Southbury.

No, that's all right, he says, I like to walk home.

What he likes to do is stop at Marty's Corner at Chestnut and Quinn for the candy we'd warned him not to eat so much of when he still had a large intestine. Then, we hoped cutting down on junk food would save him an operation. We felt guilty afterwards, as though we'd been telling him in advance that removal of his colon and placement of a plastic bag on his side would be just punishment for his love of sweets.

So he has stuffed candy wrappers in his pockets. We will find them when we do the wash. He is devious but not a professional or he would lose them in the trash. If he has been reading a paperback science fiction novel he has put it away. He is tired but doesn't stop to rest. He turns at the driveway, not looking toward the front porch where I stand, and walks up the steps to the back deck. No one is home in our part of the house. He pretends to look in his backpack for his key to the glass doors to the kitchen, which he has lost again. If it were raining and Gail's mother were not at home, he'd walk to the far end of the deck and sit under the umbrella at the metal table dripping rainwater onto the planks. But he's in luck. The sun is shining, this is some weekday other than Friday, and his grandmother is home in the in-law apartment that runs along the deck at a right angle to our kitchen. From the easy chair in her bedroom she has watched him wave his hand over his backpack. She lets him in, scolding him for not knocking at her door.

He turns a half smile away from her, for this is a ritual they both enjoy. They talk for a minute, then he goes into the main house through her kitchen, his bedroom before we built the addition after her husband died.

Later he comes back to visit. It's a story I love to hear and she always tells it the same way. Jesse knocks. She calls out to him from her bedroom. He stops to check his hair in the small mirror at the passageway to her living room. She sees him, at the small mirror, reflected in the large etched mirror over her couch, which he uses to check himself again on his way to her bedroom. They talk about mundane things. If she asks, he goes and gets a drawing he's working on. Typical teenager, she says about his grooming routine. It is my favorite part of the story.

Inside, in the living room. Everyone has gone out, Gail, her mother, Daniel, and Cassandra. To give me some time, Gail said. The car had barely cleared the end of the driveway before I made it down to my study in the basement, gathered my Jesse notebooks and folders and X-rays, too quiet to work down there now, came back up, and piled everything on the kitchen table.

I long for this solitude, but I wander. Upstairs, a breeze so faint it hardly lifts the curtains in Daniel's room to my left off the landing, hardly leans against the curtains in Cassandra's room to my right. I went through Jesse's belongings after the funeral service. Everyone got a shirt and got to choose a drawing. Daniel claimed the Skydiver for his room. We argued over it. I knew I had to lose, but I wanted to see the heat of his love draw Jesse from his shadows. I hung it over Daniel's bed next to the windows. Then one day it was gone. I found it behind the bed and used a longer nail and heavier picture hook. The next day it had fallen again. I put it back up. The next day it had fallen again. I waited until Daniel came up.

Shall I take the Skydiver downstairs? I could put it in my study.

No.

Are you sure?

Yes.

How about over here, on the floor?

Maybe.

Jesse drew the figure of the skydiver backwards with colored markers on the inner side of a sheet of plastic laid over a heavy paper mat on which he drew a landscape in crayon. The skydiver is a young man. His suit is military brown. Green straps across his shoulders hold an orange parachute bag on his back. There are no pull strings for the parachute. His right arm is stretched out and down, his left arm is bent. Both hands are clenched. His right leg is stretched out behind him and a purple shoe points forward. His left leg is bent forward. There are short black action lines above his left hand and right leg. Behind him is a pale turquoise sky, below, an unfamiliar rocky terrain too close for parachuting or too far away. The goggle straps of his red aviator's cap fly upward but to the rear, showing a downward maneuver, planned, or a free fall, unplanned. Black dots for eyes, cartoon eyebrows, and mouth wide open give him a look intent, surprised, inscrutable.

We studied the drawing where it sat propped up against the wall under the windows.

What's he saying, Daniel?

I don't know. He's shouting something.

What?

Maybe not words. Maybe he's just shouting.

With fear? Or excitement?

Excitement. He knows what he's doing. He's a professional.

People come up sometimes to look at the drawing, and everyone sees something different.

He's flying. He's the first man to fly on his own.

He's shouting for joy. To himself or his audience.

He's falling. His parachute won't open. He didn't check for pull strings before jumping.

He's holding a pair of invisible pull strings.

He's turning the steering wheel of an invisible ship.

He's not flying or falling, it's not about that. He sees something outside the picture frame. The drawing is about what's not in it.

The Skydiver lifts these people up one moment and drops them the next, and then they walk away. But I drift, out the window, rise up fifty feet above the ground, and drift south on Route 8 then southwest along the Merritt Parkway to the Saw Mill, the Hutchinson, and the Henry Hudson Parkway. Down to my right on the sheet metal surface of the Hudson River, the last-held images of the day tremble in its last light and sink from view. Clouds of trees of Central Park divide the West Side of Manhattan from the East Side. I make my descent and then approach, right leg leading left leg bent, and brake to a slow-motion landing on the sidewalk outside the hospital. I walk through the revolving doors that talk, past the guards and up the stairs to the main pavilion with its mighty glass rafters overhead. I walk diagonally to the left through another set of revolving glass doors to the escalator down to the basement. I turn right at the vending machines and follow the yellow-striped corridor to the elevators and up. The neonatal lounge sits empty in its alcove. I turn left, then right, then walk down the hall and through the double metal doors to the pediatric intensive care unit.

At the other end of the unit I see Terri, Jesse's nurse this 7 a.m. to 7 p.m. shift, grab the handle of a device, called the Scale-Tronix 2001 by its makers and the Tuna Scale by the nurses, and pull it out from its cubbyhole next to the linen cart.

It is evening, mid-May, and it is time to weigh Jesse. I go into

Room D next to the double doors. Gail, Rachel, Jesse's mother, and Will, his stepfather, are here. I go up to Jesse. He lies on his back inert, waterlogged, critically ill. And all because of a tiny hole in his intestine!

One of the surgeons had made a nick in his bowel, too small to see at the time, cutting through scar tissue from old surgery during his liver transplant on May 6th. Four days later they scooped two liters of watery feces from his abdominal cavity. Then sepsis, severe infection, set in. Sepsis, an exotic word then, as if a new and terrible enemy had been set loose when we gambled on the giving and taking of the body's organs.

Within days his body was falling like dominoes. His antibodies attacked the bacteria that caused and carried the infection but poked tiny holes in his blood vessels and capillaries, too. The blood cells, big, stayed put, but water and protein and electrolytes leaked into his tissues, his abdomen, and into his lungs, his hands, and his feet. Fluid in his belly pushed up and crowded his lungs. His lungs pushed up on his heart. Fluid and blood seeped inside his lungs. The doctors worried that his left lung might collapse or hemorrhage and that he might come down with pneumonia. They cut a hole in his side and pushed a rubber tube through his ribs. Bloody fluid rushed out and down the tube along the side of the bed to a thin aquarium, divided into vertical cells of equal size, that sat on the floor. We watched the clear cells turn red one by one in columns before our eyes. Dr. Atella, the gastrointestinal, or liver, fellow, took us into the conference room to show us the X-rays. The Before X-ray was white from fluid, the After X-ray was pitch black. Jesse had been breathing on a quarter of one lung, she said.

A respirator wheezes nonstop by the windows pushing oxygen

into Jesse's lungs through a breathing tube in his mouth. Several times during her shift, Terri will suction blood and fluid from his lungs, making a vacuum with her thumb on a piece of plastic tube that goes to the respirator and snaking a second connected piece down his breathing tube. She will pull up blood clots in stops and starts with her thumb, probing as deep as she can without damaging his lungs or stirring up blood and bacteria. The clots will smother him if she doesn't do this, and they are breeding grounds for bacteria. But suctioning is a balancing act because pulling up old clots causes fresh bleeding, like picking a scab on your arm instead of waiting for it to fall off. We had to leave the room the first time we saw Jesse gag and fight against the suctioning. Now we stand by his bed watching numbers on the oxygen monitor drift down, rooting for a thick dark clot to be sucked through the curve in the tube on a successful probe and send his numbers climbing back up into safe territory.

He has IV lines wherever they can find places to put them, for antibiotics, for pain meds, and for giving blood and blood products. He has a big line to a vein in his groin for dialysis. Meds and blood hang from poles at the corners of his bed. Medical residents and lab technicians stick him several times a day to measure the antibiotics and immunosuppressants in his blood and to measure his hemoglobin and hematocrit and red blood cells. A red light clipped to his index finger is attached to the oxygen monitor. Electrodes on his chest send signals to another monitor, above the oximeter, for heart rate and blood pressure.

I squeeze his hand and wonder whether I feel the hint of a squeeze in return. We have taped up pictures of him around the room and next to the liver chart on his door where the doctors gather on their rounds. We want to show them who Jesse is, and remind ourselves.

Dr. Lanier, the chief of gastroenterology, came in, was it earlier today, and waved his hand around the bed.

Never add anything, never give anything, never treat anything unless you have to. The more lines and poles and machines you see, the sicker the patient is.

But their standards are dropping to accommodate hope. Or at least Dr. Dorand's, his attending surgeon's, are. If Jesse is in pain and needs lots of medication for it, then his new liver, damaged by sepsis, must be metabolizing that medication and therefore must be working a little bit. If he is running a fever, at least his body can mount one. Common sense, which we cannot afford, would tell us that when everything is bad but some of that is good, things are bad indeed. We have heard the message only the stricken can hear in the Negro spiritual about the dry bones of the grave coming together at the resurrection, the shinbone connected to the knee bone connected to the thighbone connected to the hipbone. The word of the Lord, the singer whispers beneath the jubilation of the choir, is the miracle of the body, its million parts giving breath to each other from moment to moment with impossible luck until the miracle of illness turns each part against itself and every part against the other and takes your breath away.

And we have shut our ears to the singer.

Terri wheels in the Tuna Scale. An upright metal stand with a digital monitor rises from the back of a three-sided steel frame, open in front like a forklift on rollers to fit under the bed. Attached at the top, perpendicular to the metal stand, is an aluminum rod that runs parallel to the floor. Attached perpendicular to the rod is a six-foot aluminum crossbar. Two curved metal arms hang at either end of the crossbar, each ending in a steel claw.

Terri pulls out a six-by-three-foot green plastic sling rolled up and leaning against a claw. Metal bars are hemmed into the long sides of the sling. She lays the sling on the bed to Jesse's left. We take positions, three parents and one nurse, two on each side of the bed. The other parent takes a turn at getting in the way. We roll Jesse onto his right side, push the sling snug against his back, and partially unroll it behind him. We roll him over the hump of the sling onto his left side and hold him steady. We unroll the rest of the sling behind him and roll him onto his back. We hook the claws into metal rings at the four corners of the sling and check him for balance. Terri turns the crank on the metal stand, Jesse clears the bed, and we check him for balance again. Once when we hoisted him, he tipped back. I was afraid he'd fall head first off the end of the sling. Terri cranks and stops when the sling is a foot above the bed. We steady it and release. Terri pushes the monitor and calls out a weight for one of us to remember. She lowers the sling onto the bed, we roll Jesse in reverse to retrieve the sling, and she rolls the Tuna Scale out of the room.

This scene begins to fade away as concentration fades. Soon I will drift back over Central Park to the Henry Hudson, the Hutchinson, the Saw Mill, and the Merritt Parkways. But I must hold on and look for other days and scenes and gestures, I must see Jesse awake and aware before I leave. Even a hand squeeze I don't have to pretend to feel, I will settle for that.

I stand outside Room B, the larger room we lobbied for two doors down from Room D and behind the nurse's station. It is early August 1995, a second transplant for Jesse, several more operations, and a tracheotomy to place the breathing tube directly into his windpipe, later. It's the middle of the night. The little Orthodox Jewish girl across the hall has died. They wrap her in a white sheet from head to toe. The rabbi leads the procession down the hall to bury her before the next sundown. I go into Room B. Jesse is awake. He motions for me to come over.

Will you take me home, he mouths.

Yes, Jesse, I'll take you home.

And I still want to lift him up and take him home, although he's long since gone up in flames. I will come back into Room B just a few days later in August and remove the extension tube they added to his tracheotomy after his last surgery on August 6th, that stuck up eight inches in the air. It will make it easier to suction him, Dr. Kostos the surgeon told us, but it made it almost impossible. Anyone who'd ever sucked on a straw could tell at a glance it was good for nothing but a flagstaff for a skull and crossbones. I will pull out the tube slowly, and pull out the inner cannula from his windpipe and put a bandage over the hole in his throat. I will remove all his IV lines one by one, those in his arms, in his neck, and in his legs. I will put lotion on his wounds and cover them with bandages. I will draw the catheter from his penis and cover him up. He had little enough privacy here, poked and cut and probed with needle and scalpel and tube, surrounded by love and vain prayers. I will remove from his finger the red light that frightened and oppressed him. Then I will turn off the respirator that bubbled night and day and we will sit here for a moment alone in the blessed silence. And then let all his mothers come in and stand around his bed wearing black veils and black dresses and wailing softly. Or let them grieve in their own ways as long as their grief is filled with time so he can see his ancestors standing behind them and so we don't have to believe that all this was nothing more than a surgical accident. And then I will lift him up and carry him out of his room. Going down the hall he will shed the heaviness of disease as the bile- and blood-tinged water that engorged him falls in our wake. We will take the elevator down to the basement and wind our way through the dirty intestines of the hospital to the escalator and up. His open gut wound will close and his true face will emerge from his bloated Sumo wrestler mask, and his crooked smile. He is so light now I have to hold on to keep him from floating up to the mighty glass rafters of the pavilion. We come to a flight of steps and go down past the guards. We come to the revolving glass doors that talk, that beckoned us to enter then but now turn slickly on their hinges. We pause at the threshold and then walk out and I have to close my eyes, like him, in the sun's stone-oven-shattering light.

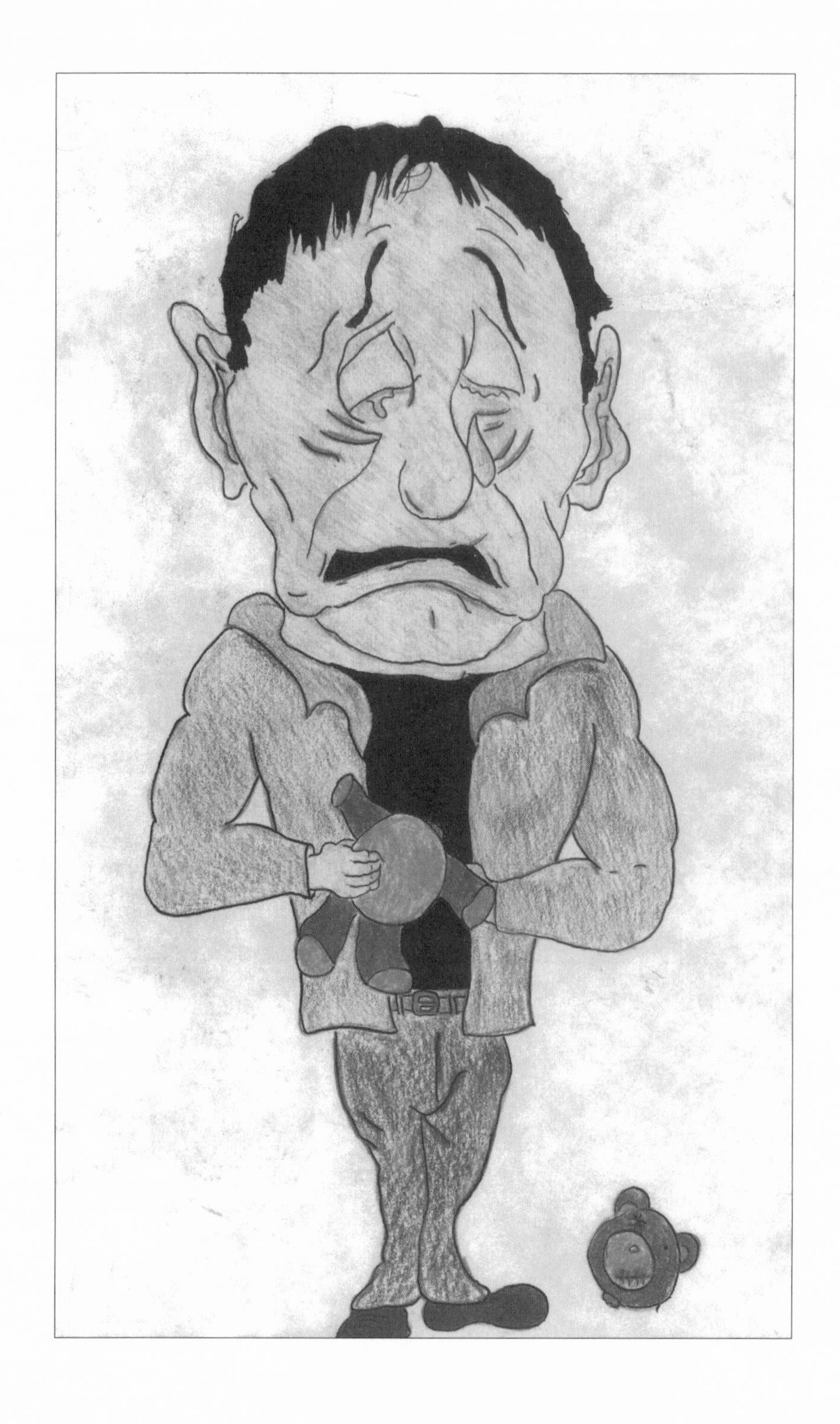

two

Sticking out from a pile of clothes and drawings and audiotapes in the corner of Daniel's room is a small cloth-covered notebook labeled *The Old Jestament and the New Jestament* in Daniel's handwriting. The title is Daniel's tribute to his brother's genius for puns, but his purpose is a solemn one, to tell Jesse's deep secrets to his own children one day. He got the idea for it three years ago. I would dictate the Old Jestament to him and he would write the New Jestament himself. The Old and the New, he said, separate the time before and after he and Jesse bonded. Only the first few pages of the Old are filled, with my recollections.

The doctor brought him out to me... Jesse was a Caesarian, like you and Cassie. You know what a Caesarian is?

Yes, Mom told me.

So I couldn't be in the operating room with Rachel. I had to wait outside.....

OK.

The doctor brought him out all wrapped up in a blanket.

Like a papoose.

Or like a bottle of champagne.

What?!

He held out Jesse on his arm, like this, to show me. Like a waiter in a fancy restaurant with a bottle of champagne wrapped up in a cloth. That's what they do in expensive restaurants. Someone told me.

OK, Dad.

Jesse's eyes were wide open and he looked right up at me. His eyes were black, like big black pools looking right into me....

OK.

I probably looked like a blob to him. With a halo around it.

Like an angel.

Or a big blob. A halo from the fluorescent lights on the ceiling. With a big blob in the middle.

Jesse was almost nine when Daniel was born. It had been hard enough for him, shuttling back and forth between Rachel's home and mine and now, a baby brother to compete with. Once when he thought I was out of sight I watched him looking down at Daniel on his back on the living room floor. He wants to step on his head, I thought. I called out or came in and changed the subject, thankful that Gail hadn't seen. And yet the photos from that time show Jesse looking at his baby brother with friendly curiosity, even joy. Do they lie? Or did we miss something essential? But Daniel knows the difference. We hated each other back then, he told me. Thus the two books. We talk about getting back to this project, but we don't.

I dig around in the pile and find one of my favorite audiotapes and put it in Daniel's tape player. This one takes place on planet Neptune, and Jesse is the King of Neptune. I listen, enthralled, as the two of them maintain a rapid-fire dialogue yet stay with the terminology the setting dictates, Jesse's king ordering Daniel's earthling to bring him a glass of intergalactic milk and a space pizza with no space anchovies in two point nine space minutes, when the Abbot-and-Costello structure of the bit could put them at any street corner on planet Earth. Daniel engineered all of these tapes, begging Jesse to record with him until he gave in, then supplying the story line that Jesse fractured with nonsense and non sequiturs and Daniel with squawks of news reports and music in between their dialogue, switching radio stations dead in the ear of the tape recorder.

The winter after August 1995, Daniel was sunk in his own grief. He threw down the Nintendo controller at an impasse in one of the Mario Brothers games that Jesse would have rescued him from and that I couldn't help him with.

Jesse was the greatest escape artist of all time.

Yes, I said. Almost, I said to myself.

I brought up a folder full of Jesse's drawings. We sat in Daniel's room and looked through them. Then he closed the folder.

No more recording.

You'll record again, Daniel.

No, I don't want to.

I could record with you.

No.

But he relented. I would play Jesse and he would be himself. The story line was that he, Daniel, and I, Jesse, would wake up two days after we fell asleep and would have to find our way back to the day before with Gail, Cassandra, and me, Michael. I surprised myself with my imitation of Jesse's voice and sly wit. We played back the first side. He was quiet. Suddenly he looked like a little adult.

Are you upset because I don't sound like Jesse?

No. You sound too much like him. It grieves me.

Because it reminds you of Jesse?

No. It's like paper, when you burn it and there's nothing but carbon left.

You mean that's what I've done with Jesse?

No, with me. You get my meaning indirectly.

I had failed to be me and failed to be Jesse at the same time. Or did he grieve because I'd caught something in my performance that he was too young to hear in Jesse's voice or manner back when they made their tapes, or was too devoted to fault Jesse for, but now, older, could not ignore when I acted it out for him? I grieved, too, over a hundred possibilities. That Jesse was poking fun at Daniel, working him up to a pitch of excitement because he could do it, adding lines that were either a sincere contribution to the story line or a sardonic commentary on its inanity. And if the latter, because of a cruel streak in Jesse, or a garden-variety big brother cruelty, or bitterness that his best friend Nicholas had moved south and he was playing with a child eight years his junior? I grieved for Daniel, that all this might be true and I had made him face it in my too-accurate parody. I grieved for Jesse over what I had exposed in him, then grieved that I might have misjudged him but that the damage was done for Daniel. And I grieved that Jesse would no longer have the chance to test his possibilities against the hard rock of unrepeatable events that is softened, rounded, finally worn down, and must give way to the next event because one is still alive.

On the other side of the tape I played myself pretending to be Jesse. Daniel seemed satisfied, but he never asked me to record with him again.

They were eighteen and ten, perhaps, when they made this King of Neptune tape with the rudest of equipment and Daniel's technical wizardry. Listening to Jesse's voice now, still deepening at the call of manhood, he could be sitting here next to me. I think about his silences and his secretiveness. It's true that he hid himself away. He worked so hard to defend himself against others' inquiries that he must have felt at times like a laborer outside the gates looking up at the fortifications he has built around his imperial self. So vast was this undertaking, it left him spent for the petty details of social life. Daniel had figured all this out.

Jesse had his own world, you know. He could go to it anytime he wanted.

Was he so much at home in that world and so eager to escape from this one, I wonder, that it was nothing for him to switch from minutes to space minutes? And yet the videotape of my father's exhibit at the Genesee County Museum outside Rochester, his carved shore birds and bass and trout conjuring streams and oceans while he lay dying a few miles away at the hospice, show Jesse, at age fourteen, animated and sociable, talking to my father's friends with me. Does it lie, or did we miss that too?

Daniel carries the burden of being the one who knows him best, the keeper and chronicler of the image of Jesse's shining self. You are the sun of the first day's light, he wrote, which shines on the sparkling waters on a bright day called Paradise. But who am I? Let him miss his brother then, without having to become him. This notebook of the Old and the New will make its way back down to the bottom of the pile. It's up to me to tell the tale.

Across the hall, Cassandra's room. She wouldn't talk about Jesse for a long time. She pretended not to hear when his name came up or gave a nervous laugh when it was about the two of them. Daniel shields her, standing between the two of them in age. But she has her own sorrows, Cassandra. And it was she who first spoke the dread words.

The grandmothers brought them to the hospital in late May. We met them at the lounge for the neonatal intensive care unit, the NICU. We preferred it to the pediatric intensive care unit, the PICU, lounge. It had more comfortable sofas, if none too clean, and no locked door between it and the pediatric unit. We had decided not to let them see Jesse. He was too sick, swollen and stuffed with tubes and IVs. Daniel did not protest and Cassandra, a few days from her eighth birthday, was afraid.

We went down to the noisy cafeteria at noon and found a four-person table. The grandmothers sat a few tables away and pretended not to watch us. The children skipped from subject to subject amid the din of medical chatter. I told them we needed to talk about Jesse. He was very ill, I said. His doctors were worried about him. Cassie's eyes opened wide.

You mean Jesse could die?

Yes, Jesse could die.

Gail told me later she was shocked that I had answered so plainly. She didn't believe it herself in spite of what she'd seen and heard. She had made a deal with God, who was going to watch over Jesse but would tell her if his time was up.

She was going back to be with the children for a couple of days. Cassie didn't want to leave without me. I took her into the gift shop under the eaves of the mighty glass rafters and bought her a beanbag dog to match the one we put in Jesse's hand for something soft to hold and to straighten his wrist, cocked toward the inside of his forearm like a pitcher hiding a knuckleball from the batter. I checked my billfold, worrying, always worrying about money, although it was starting to come in from family and friends. We walked to the hospital parking garage. My beeper went off as they were all getting into the car. I ran and they left. If we changed our plans for every downturn Jesse had, or might have, the children would never get home. Still, the five of them, grandmothers, Gail, and kids, had two hours on the Henry Hudson, the

Hutchinson, the Saw Mill, and the Merritt Parkways and north on Route 8 to Naugatuck to wonder whether Jesse was alive or dead when I had mistaken a routine beep from his mother, no 911 tag, for catastrophe.

Cassie chose one of his ink and crayon drawings for her wall, a Dickensian office clerk with the craggy face and dyed-black hair of an old man. The man's mouth is a black trapezoid. One big tear runs down his face and others well up at his eyelids. Above the upper lids, two black worms of eyebrows rear up to salute each other. The irregular shape of the ears, the droop of the jowls, and the chin that suggests its own double betray his age, as do the lines below his eyes and those around his jowls. It is the old refrain of skin that has lost its bounce and is now draped over bone like an unmade bed. The man's head and football lineman's neck are huge compared to his muscular upper torso squeezed into a brown jacket, as for a child's Sunday confirmation, over a skintight black sweater. His legs are as small in proportion to his torso as his torso is in proportion to his head. His belt is tight at the hips. His blue pants are crumpled and loose with the impossible fit of an older man who, rather than blossoming at the stern, has lost in time what little he had of the buttocks of youth. He is holding a headless Teddy Bear. The head lies on the ground with one X'd eye, one button eye, and an X'd mouth. The man's face is distorted in tragicomic grief that pokes fun at loss but pays homage to it, that scorns vulnerability but embodies it. It is the only drawing we have of Jesse's in which the figure is crying, an act he rarely committed, except when he was younger at a word of criticism from an adult, and later, shaking his head and saying No! when I sat with him on our front steps and told him that his grandfather, my father, had died.

Looking at the Teddy Bear Man, I think of my father's ceramic head of Jesus fastened to a cross made of weathered fence post. He made it in his early 50s, unhappy with his work in sales of clothing and buttons but stuck in it. The head is stylized, an inverted teardrop rounded at the top, then elongated and narrowing to the bearded chin. The crown of thorns is snakelets of kiln-fired clay. The beard is ten delicate fingers of clay. The mouth, an O laid on its side, moans one drawn-out syllable. The eyes are two sockets with heavy lids. It is an image of suffering untainted by redemption. I see their suffering, my fathers and Jesse's, in the Teddy Bear Man, but today I see something else, too. The man's face could be an expensive Halloween mask, the kind you pull over your head, with the floppy neck hanging over the collar of the brown jacket rather than being covered by it. Yes, it could be hanging over the collar, you can see that in the line where neck and collar meet. If so, the man may be a child dressed up for Halloween with newspaper muscles bulging under his sports jacket. He has just found his broken Teddy Bear, a trick instead of a treat. And there is a darker, more dangerous possibility. Who, after all, knocked off the Teddy Bear's head?

My mother gave Jesse a Teddy Bear before his first surgery in New York in 1993. We encouraged him to bring it with him two years later for his transplant. If adults can get away with one in the hospital, why not a young adult on a pediatric unit? The Teddy Bear sat, most times, on the window ledge, then one day at the end of the second month it disappeared. Perhaps it had fallen in the flurry of blood-soaked towels and pads tossed away over the Fourth of July weekend. The ledge it perched on was narrow and there was plenty of traffic to give it a nudge into a wastebasket below. But when the pillow that Rachel was sewing for him disappeared as well just after she finished embroidering his name on it, we knew the Teddy Bear's disappearance was no accident. To think that one of the nurses had taken it was horrible, but it left room for the idea she took it out of love, for surely these women, and one man, loved him. More horrible still was the thought that someone else walked in when there was no immediate crisis to keep us on the unit and we'd gone back to the transplant shelter for the night. Some Good Samaritan, maybe, who thought he'd put Jesse out of his misery but lost his nerve or heard someone coming and took the Teddy Bear for a souvenir. And who? The Orthodox Jewish man, not the father of the little girl in August but the father of another child, in July? He stood staring at the end of the hall in his long beard and prayer sash and black pants with green hospital slippers. One evening when the lights were out in Room B and we were trying to get Jesse to sleep, he crossed the threshold and asked for directions. It was the first time he had spoken to us. Or the toothless grandmother who walked in one afternoon around the same time and asked for the bag of pretzels I was holding? I gave it to her and cursed my stupidity for allowing the violation. She left the room and told the nurse, I can't eat these, I have no teeth. No matter that the man was numb with his own horror and the old lady took the pretzels for her grandson, they had crossed a border and it would be easier to cross it again.

Or the respiratory technician who worked the unit one night in August just before the end? We thought it was his first time on the unit since we'd been here, but he might have worked a shift or two in June or July and now, this night, saw what Jesse had become. He looked at Jesse with disgust and us with reproof for not putting our child out of his misery when he was ballooning up like a parody of the freak show characters he used to draw. I still think of ripping the technician's heart out, sticking it in his face, and whispering the last words he will ever hear, But Jesse has a heart! And what else could have happened at any time, night or day, with nurse or doctor or interloper when we weren't there to watch over him?

The huge head of the Teddy Bear man is a convention of caricature drawing, but, like the thousands of other huge-headed characters Jesse drew, I've always thought it must be connected to his infant hydrocephalus. In hydrocephalus, the ventricles, spaces in the brain that produce cerebraspinal fluid and help to cushion the brain from the jackhammer blows of running, walking, and standing, fail to drain their excess fluid into the abdominal cavity, and become engorged. Left alone, these sacs squeeze the brain and tip the child's head onto his pillow to wait for death at an early age. Hydrocephalus, I think, made Jesse's body a strange and fearsome object to him, less fearsome only than the doctors who attacked it with scalpels and the alien cameras called CAT Scans that swiveled around his head.

When he was four or five he drew a series of monsters in crayon on a cheap pad of paper. They are simple, sometimes comical, often sad or frightening, and I have lost most of them. What I do have I found going through boxes in the basement, a Sun Monster, a Letter D Monster, a Cheese Monster, a Rock Monster that Ate a Fish Monster, a Snowman Monster, and the heartbreaking Sad Monster with Sad Shoes, round head with eyes and tears, short stick legs with clown shoes, and a stalk-like growth that shoots up from his head and ends in a blossom of flowers or antennae. But I have lost the most fearsome monster of all, the mighty Squash, all red crayon and razor-sharp teeth and wild eyes.

He drew these monsters around the time when everything was Bwoken. Walking down the street with his hand in mine, he had an uncanny eye for a car on blocks, a lame dog, an almost undetectable crack in a board on a picket fence, a dead bird in the street, all things broken. The three of us, Rachel, Jesse, and I took a walk to the playground at Edgewood Park in New Haven. It was fall, my favorite season, but not this year. Our marriage was ending barely three years after it had begun. Gail and I had been meeting secretly for months. We walked inside the fenced enclosure of the playground. We encouraged Jesse to try the small tree that other kids his age climbed and he had avoided. He climbed up and went down the slide and on the monkey bars. As we were leaving the playground, he took three action figures from his pocket and buried them in the sand.

I saw these monsters as emblems both of Jesse's terror and his attempts to tame it, but with time I've become less smug. I see him now as a child general mapping out his strategy on a battlefield overrun with enemies he would have to face one day in hand-to-hand combat, and his monster drawings as early skirmishes on that battlefield, with ulcerative colitis, the angry inflammation of the colon, foreshadowed by the Rock Monster that Ate a Fish Monster, and sclerosing cholangitis, the scarring and narrowing of the biliary tree going into the bile ducts in the liver, foreshadowed by the Sad Monster with Sad Shoes, and cirrhosis, the leathering and hardening of the liver, foreshadowed by the wedge-shaped Cheese Monster with Swiss holes pocking the surface of his body. And the great, the terrible Squash? He foreshadows the great and terrible Sepsis, Jesse's final enemy. His vision was narrow, but keen as the eagle's. It had to be. He was bidden, he did not ask, to witness the secret terror of the universe.

three

Downstairs in a wicker basket in the living room is a scrapbook with thick front and back sandwich covers for adding extra pages. Slipped inside a frame on the front cover is a photo of Jesse from the fall of 1994, a handsome young man with a crooked smile sitting on the steps leading up to our front door. A Buffalo Bills logo is visible on his sweatshirt and sweatpants. He looks to the left at something outside the frame of the photograph. How pale he is, how thin! His shoulders are narrow, his hands bony like a pianist's, or a surgeon's. I look at his image and think of his secrets and little revelations.

He lived here, but this borough was never home to him. Home was always the next place, or the place before. He had New Haven, and the knowledge that his father still worked there after both households had moved out, to compare it to. He missed walking downtown from his mother's apartment on the Whitney Avenue side, an image I treasure, of Jesse navigating downtown New Haven dreaming his life while we worried about how he would ever make it on his own without us to remind him to take his medications, let him in when he lost his key, take him to doctor's appointments, or get him to do or not do what we routinely let his brother and sister get away with now. Here in Naugatuck on a Saturday if he hadn't gone to his mother's in Norwalk, I might give him a five and encourage him to walk downtown to the library, the town green, the baseball card store, the Subway for lunch. That was about it, unless he was hanging out with someone, and by this time Nicholas, another outsider, more flamboyant with a long black coat on his skinny six-foot-two frame in the hottest summer weather, had moved to Louisiana. Jen DaSilva, Jesse's high school tutor, told me he was devastated when Nicholas left. Then, after a while, he didn't want to talk about Nicholas anymore.

It's the little things that weigh on my conscience today. Walking down Elm Street in New Haven where it turns into Broadway, a sharp twinge of regret that I never blew off work, called Jesse out sick, and drove us in for lunch, a walk down Elm Street to the Green and then up Chapel to the Yale Art Gallery or maybe the British Art Museum across the street, which had a William Blake exhibit not long ago. I studied the watercolors and etchings of angels and demons and radiant light, happy to take credit for Jesse's love of Blake, who, I told him, was the father of superhero comic book illustrators.

Or scolding him about turning up his thermostat to ninety when I understand, now, that he was cold, skinny from colitis and liver disease. And heat, I've learned from sitting down there, is different in a basement room, warm in the air but cool on the floor.

Or insisting that he go back to high school after his transplant to finish the couple of credits he needed to graduate. They'd have listed him as a full-time student so he could stay on my health insurance, and that would have been easier on him than going to college full-time where no one knew him or cared what he was recuperating from. But he was older than his peers and hated the

Mickey Mouse courses he was taking. He wanted to get his high school equivalency degree and be done with it. Late July 1995 in the hospital, Gail brought me a form letter from our health plan. They needed proof that Jesse was a full-time student, the letter said, or if not they could switch him over to an individual plan. If I had a minute to talk to him, assuming only a high wall separates us, it would come unexpectedly, a sudden breach that neither of us would be prepared for, and I'd squander the chance, taking him by the ghost of his shoulders and telling him he doesn't have to go back to high school after all.

Or the time Rich Barone, his high school social worker, called and said the janitors had to clean up a feces-stained stall in the men's room. They knew it was Jesse because he was the only student with a key to that bathroom, a privilege they allowed him because he might have to leave class at a moment's notice to empty his ostomy bag. Receiver to my ear, I heard the exasperation in Rich's voice. The politics of the situation demanded his righteous anger. It wasn't he, after all, who had to clean up the bathroom stall. But he, too, must have felt betrayed, watching out for Jesse for years and getting so little in return. This was an angry statement that Jesse had made, Rich said, and I, too, worked up a righteous passion as he spoke. It was an angry statement, I agreed, and when Jesse came home I so interpreted the incident to him. He acknowledged the incident but denied the statement.

And it wasn't that much of a mess.

But why did you leave it that way, Jesse?

Ow no.

I must have asked the same question five different ways. It was a miserable nonconversation, and something about the angry statement theory didn't sit right with me even then. Jesse showed his anger mostly passively, silently. Today I have a different interpretation. He needs to empty his bag. He goes to the locked bathroom during class so there's little chance a teacher will come in. He kneels or half-kneels beside the toilet and holds the end of the bag over the bowl like the mouth of a small hot water bottle over a sink. The feces are watery. They splatter because he has no large intestine to absorb water and form logs of hot stool out of the soupy mix of food particles and enzymes and liquid delivered to it from the small intestine. But his aim is off. He gets some on the edge of the toilet seat and some on his hand. Reaching for the toilet paper, he gets some on the stall. Trying to clean up the seat and the stall with the crisp institutional sandpaper they use for toilet tissue, he succeeds only in spreading it around. Perhaps he wets some toilet paper with water from the bowl after a first flush. If so, he rushes and spreads the brown stain even more. He could wet some paper towels, a softer and thicker grade of sandpaper, at the sink, but everything is going too fast. He tries more toilet paper but by now the stain is drying on the stall. He knows he should tell someone but he can't. They'll be furious, disgusted, scornful. If he thought about it he'd know that leaving the scene of the crime will make things worse for him, but he has to escape. He walks out, casually, and goes back to class.

Or maybe the bag exploded, accumulated gas popping the plastic clasp just as he was about to empty it. It wouldn't have been the first time. Once, outside his therapist's office, his bag exploded and we had to drive home with the windows open and no clothes for him to change into. At home his stoma would fart without warning and he'd jam his elbow over it, too late. I assumed this happened at school as well, but couldn't bring myself to ask him. And yes, I believe it wasn't as bad as Rich and the janitors said. It was their reading of his intentions that smeared the shit so badly on that stall.

If I'm right, it would have been characteristic of Jesse not to explain or defend himself against the accusation. And I can imagine myself doing the sensitive routine to get to the bottom of things with the boy who knew every psychotherapeutic trick in the book.

Jess, I got a call from Mr. Barone today.

No response.

He said the janitors were upset because they had to clean up after you in the bathroom.

A look from him as though he's just been accosted by a rare species of carpet bug.

What happened, Jess?

Ow no. Just got some on the stall.

They were kind of upset about it, you know.

Shrug.

Was it an accident?

Well, yeah.

One of those damned-if-you-do-and-damned-if-you-don't kind of things, huh? You can't leave a mess but can't clean it up yourself and don't want to tell anyone?

Ow no.

I wonder how we can deal with this now.

Shrug.

Do you think you should say something to Mr. Barone tomorrow?

Shrug.

Can I help you figure it out?

Ow no.

And when he did engage in verbal sparring with adults he was just as formidable as he was in his silences, catching up his opponent in a battle that he, Jesse, had committed himself to win before his opponent realized how high the stakes were. It would start innocently enough, like an outtake from one of his comic routines with Daniel.

Jesse, remember we asked you not to eat in your bedroom?

I'm not.

Jess, I found taco shells in your wastebasket when I emptied it.

I know.

That's what I'm saying, you're not supposed to eat in your bedroom.

I'm not eating in my bedroom.

Then what was the food doing in your wastebasket?

I threw it away.

Right, after eating in your room.

No.

Jesse, the food wouldn't be in your wastebasket if you weren't eating in your bedroom.

How can I eat it if it's in the wastebasket?

Cute, if you stop there, figuring she gets the point and is saving face. But by now the attitude has got you pissed off and you must prove you are right. Before long you have crossed a border into a world of opposition where language is so contradictory you can't recite any part of it to an outsider five minutes after it's over.

Does the passage of time bring me back to our lives away from doctors and hospitals while my rage against them fades? Or has my rage faded because I've been defeated and have no choice but to dwell on petty regrets? The rage is there but I force it down, then watch it flare up like clockwork with the children or Gail after I look through my Jesse notebooks. Or I turn it against a lowly respiratory technician whom we had to endure for only one night. Or if against doctors, then against a bit player like Dr. Herman, the osteopathic surgeon who strutted and exited before colitis surgery in 1993.

Jesse had been diagnosed with sclerosing cholangitis, an ominous sign for his liver, in the summer of 1992. A tube with a tiny camera, snaked down his throat to look at the tree of ducts going into his liver to carry bile for digesting fats, revealed that the branches of the tree were narrowing, not severely, but enough to make the diagnosis. And his colitis was getting worse. He had loose bowel movements and bad gas even on large doses of prednisone. The prednisone gave him acne and a moon-shaped face and dreams of being shot into the outer darkness of space. His gastroenterologist in New Haven, Dr. Gardner, prescribed a special enema. It helped for a while and then it did not. She added a drug for leukemia patients, 6-mercaptopurine, discovered by accident to help with ulcerative colitis. It didn't work. His hands started shaking and then stopped. And then, miraculously, his bowel movements became less frequent, his stools more formed, and he felt good. He smiled when Dr. Gardner walked into the room, a first for him with her.

How's my favorite patient today?

Great. I'm all better.

She did a rectal exam and found no blood. She came out of the examining room and looked pleased.

Maybe we've finally got this under control.

But Jesse's frequent bowel movements and near accidents started again. Then his right leg gave out on him walking home from school early in the fall. Steroids can weaken the bones, a reason to worry about keeping him on prednisone. We kept him home for a couple of days at a time and got him a pair of crutches for when the pain flared up. Dr. Gardner sent us to an osteopathic surgeon.

Dr. Herman, tall, with the trim good looks of Virginia neo-aristocracy, stood at that time of life when dissolution lends character to beauty yet whispers that one has reached one's physical peak and is looking down those rolling hills toward the Shenandoah. His silk suit, burnt umber, fit him perfectly. He sent Jesse for a series of X-rays and then a bone scan. They showed a soft spot in the ball joint of his right hip, a harmless growth, Dr. Herman said, that had been there for years. And he had a stress fracture in his hip. It might or might not have been caused by the prednisone, but prednisone made him vulnerable to a true fracture where the bone breaks through the skin or the fracture cuts off the blood supply to the hip socket, forcing hip replacement. All highly unlikely, Dr. Herman added, in a manner that was calm but studied, that was light but humorless. My note taking, I sensed, was faintly amusing to him in order that it not be offensive. Jesse should avoid contact sports, he said. Jesse had been doing so religiously for years. Dr. Herman had performed competently, but with no opportunity for clear etiology or cure. His tone as we parted, rather than his words, said to Jesse, There are things in life we must endure, and to me, Your son is malingering. Unjust, untrue. Jesse went to school when he could hardly drag himself out of bed and, with patience worthy of Job, endured pain and disappointment that would have laid out one obese with success.

Or I turn my rage against myself for not making a bigger scene the night of May 9th, three days after the first transplant, not insisting on talking to Dr. Dorand when Jesse was writhing in pain and a tiny hole was opening up in his intestine, the result of a surgical accident, Dr. Dorand told us later, from cutting through scar tissue that had built up after colitis surgery two years earlier. Cutting through intestinal adhesions, my friend the nurse told me, is extremely difficult, like peeling the skin from a grape without pulling off any of the meat.

Or I go back before May 9th and regret that I pushed so hard for Jesse to get his transplant once the hospital knew our insurance would pay. Nine months earlier Cindy, the transplant coordinator, had called me and told us to pack our bags. Jesse was at the top of the list, she said, and would be called within six weeks. We went to bed each night half expecting the phone to ring or my beeper to go off before the alarm clock. Six weeks came and went, then seven. I called Cindy. There had been a miscommunication between her and the surgeons. Jesse was at the top of the list for children, but at a hundred twenty-five pounds he was competing with adults. And he had type O-positive blood, which can donate to anyone but accepts only itself. But by April 1995 they were ready to schedule a day to admit Jesse to wait for his new liver. I came home from work.

Hey Jesse. I talked to Cindy today. The transplant coordinator from the hospital?

Oh. Yeah.

She said they want to admit you soon to wait for your transplant.

When?

Soon. Within the next few weeks. We have to set a date.

Cool.

You've been waiting a long time.

I'll say.

You got bumped by people who were sicker than you. But you're coming to the top of the list now.

He looked down. His face was pale.

I don't want to take someone else's place.

I knew he was frightened, but I knew he was thinking of the others standing in line, too. I was filled with admiration for him.

No, Jesse, you're not taking anyone else's place. You've been waiting a long time, longer than most people wait. It's your turn now.

Of course he was right, he was taking someone else's place.

Jen DaSilva called me after it was all over. She said she had talked with Jesse at school as the time was approaching for his transplant.

He told me, I'm afraid to die and I'll do anything to stay alive.

John Riccio, Jesse's therapist, whom he'd been seeing for a few years for, for what?... there never was an easy explanation for Jesse's distancings and defenses, told me he had asked Jesse how he was feeling about his upcoming liver transplant. This was probably around the same time that Jen DaSilva had talked with him.

He looked at me, John said, with this look of, Shall I fuck with him or shall I tell him the truth? I shot him back a look that said, Don't you dare fuck with me now! We're talking about your life. He shot back a look that said, Screw you pal! It's my life, I'll fuck with you until the day I die if I want to! Then we both backed down. Jesse said, I want to get it over with. I'll either make it or I won't. If I live, I'll get better. If I don't, I'll die in my sleep. I won't even know about it. I think he believed that, or he made himself believe it, but there was still some bravado. And then it was as if all the antics stopped and he spoke in the voice of someone older, who knew exactly what he was up against. He said, If I don't make it, will you look after my family for me?

Sometimes the good and bad times change places and look only rich, as if memory had built a cathedral from the stones of all those moments while we weren't looking. Outside the cathedral, the flying buttresses of the Star Wars myth that fired his imagination, and mine. Jesse and I drove away from the theatre on I-95 and my wheels didn't touch the road for ten minutes. Inside, the vestibule with its domed ceiling and the images that he created in stories and drawings. On the eastern quadrant, planet Eggnog III, native land of George 10. Eggnog III, with its five moons, Loki, Seth, Thanos, Mephistophese, and Xanon making elliptical orbits around it, is eighth in line from the starsun Amonhetep II in the Snegian dimension. On the western quadrant, portraits of the Major Ruling Powers of Eggnog, among them Her Majesty Ghardrex, ruler of the Duatian Empire, and the Great Gar, ruler of all former lands of the Thangorian Empire south of Duatia and the former lands of Ronanin on the dimensional planes of Tyjurym. On the southern quadrant, the capital of Eggnog with depictions of the major Eggnogian industries, cattle dragon raising, Duatian cigars, asparagus and plutonium harvesting, and the production of rubber nipples. On the northern quadrant, representative portraits of the major Eggnogian races, the Highbrows, the Mindless Morganians, the Fugitive Duatians, the Mutual Renegades, and the Exiles. At the center of the dome, portraits of George 10's heroes and friends, Comet, Whiteout, Plaid Lad, Shali-Dazire, and his archenemies Maelstrom, Ronanin, Abattoir, and the Ancients of Eggnog. Behind them all, George's ambiguous guru, Egghead of the Highbrow, a thin, El Greco-like figure with a bulging forehead, looks down on the visitor.

George 10 himself, a hero in some dimensions and a wanted man in others although most look the other way, George 10 who suffers from chronic tomatoed eggnog disease, an illness common to all Eggnogians, and must take specialized pills ten times a day to avoid turning into tomatoed eggnog substitute, George 10 who believes that smoking a cigar before every meal will prevent food poisoning, George 10 whose c.v. includes positions as Commander of Her Majesty Ghardrex's Army, professional whistler, and rubber nipple salesman, George 10 who believes in no God because whatever put us here no longer cares and therefore deserves no worship, George 10 is not shown here, perhaps because, like Superman, he lives in exile on planet Earth.

The center aisle of this vast and mighty cathedral. I count the ribs of the nave. Of first grandchild on my parent's block in 1975, the neighbors standing in a semicircle around the couch like envious and dreaming Magi. Of coaxing him all his life to walk beside me and finally he did, an inch and a quarter behind my left shoulder but close enough. Of all the childhood sports he did play, baseball, tennis, and soccer. The ball rolled right up to hit his eight-year-old foot and he didn't flinch, but he was out on the field. Of endless car rides in silence on the way to something unpleasant.

The chancel with its latticework criss-crossing the choir of adults and teachers and therapists who worried over him and the medical priests who ministered to his body. The font of his baptism at age eight with his baby brother in an Episcopal church. The rose window with the multicolored helicopter he drew in kindergarten, the first time he astonished me, a wondrous helicopter, a perfectly proportioned helicopter drawn by the boy who never ever raised his hand in class, a visionary helicopter, now lost, that shines in the center of my mind.

The chapel of his courage and tolerance for pain. The chapel of the cruelty of his silences. The chapel of his mysteries, where he didn't know how to ask for what he needed. And the chapel where he made his wishes known in silence, where lights and shadows seep into each other and become one.

Over here in an unfinished section, stones of moments not yet set in place that could not look and feel so and have such heft unless those times were real. Or did we dream them, and they are dreamstones, weighing nothing? Looking up, the ceiling blown away, the walls. A vulture circles its own carcass where a cathedral once stood.

Inside the scrapbook, letters, cards, stories, and photos. A letter from Cassie from May 1995 offering a trillion dollars to spring Jesse from the hospital. A typed copy of a letter from Daniel. I filed away the original, blurred from a failed attempt to clean it up after Jesse vomited blood onto the wall where it was taped.

A photo of Jesse at age three as Superman. Precious, anyone looking at it would say. They could not know how we worried over his superhero obsession, feared that he would retreat to an inner world where he could not be wrong. A Superman comic book parody about Hilario from the planet Ha, so named for the laughter that greeted Hilario's father when he warned of the planet's impending demise. Another comic book parody, Normal Man. The hero tells of his heartbreak when his true love marries another man. One time a girl called the house asking for Jesse. I left the kitchen but stood around the corner in the living room, hoping the conversation would produce more than a couple of grunts from him. It didn't. Because I was close by?

Daniel's memories. The time we stopped for gas and Jesse asked me to pump exactly two gallon's worth. He pumped his fist, Yes! when the pump stopped at two point zero zero. Daniel and Cassie looked on in awe, knowing they had just witnessed an event of cosmic significance.

The time a fellow student told Jesse he had the brains of a paramecium and Jesse responded that his fellow student had the brains of one mecium. It sounds calculated, reading it in here, as though Jesse was telling Daniel what he wished he had said, but I'm sure that he, coming to earth with strange powers from another planet, parsed the student's insult in a millisecond to come back with his own.

Jesse and Daniel's Socratic dialogue on tangibility and intangibility.

One time after school, I started to tell Jesse what we were learning about figures of speech. I told him all the figures of speech I knew. He told me another figure of speech I had never heard of: tangible and intangible. He said that in order to be tangible you have to move, see, be seen, hear, be heard, taste, be tasted, swim, feel, or be felt.

I said, Air is tangible.

He said, No it isn't.

I said, Yes it is.

He said, Can it run?
No.
Can it see?
No.
Can it be seen?
No.
Can it hear?
No.
Can it be heard?
No.
Can it taste?
No.
Can it be tasted?
No.
Can it swim?
No.
Can it feel?
No.
Can it be felt?
No.
So therefore it isn't tangible, he explained.

If there's a joke here, I don't get it, I just like the fact that they had such conversations and that Daniel remembers them.

Daniel's instruction in the subtleties of Wolf Language.

One day Jesse and I were taking a walk. I was talking about different languages when Jesse told me about a new language, Wolf Language.

He said, You know what pool is in Wolf Language?
What?
Wolf. You know what house is?

What?
Wolf. You know what tiger is?
What?
Wolf. You know what wolf is?
What?
Dog.

Here in the middle of the scrapbook, two of the hundreds of mazes Jesse drew after his mother and I had separated and Gail and I were guiltily together. He knew of the maze with no exit, for in one the Start and End are contiguous, separated by a common wall in the middle of the maze. They remind me of the science fiction epics we created together, destroying and rebuilding galaxies under siege from the forces of evil, I solving the endless crises he concocted, he undoing my solutions and putting our hero back in peril of his life. He understood that the hero must face the same dilemma over and over again in different guises, with different names, and on different battlefields, for it is his dilemma, no one else's, and he must gamble everything on the outcome of each battle. Also, there is a mandala-like appearance to these mazes. And it has occurred to me that they resemble intestines.

On the last page, a copy of a drawing that hangs by the window facing the street. He was nine or ten when he drew it. An Eskimo child bundled up in a heavy coat with gloves and a fur cap looks down at a semicircular globe with continents floating on their oceans. Two mountains meet in a narrow valley behind him. There is a dignity and vast loneliness about the child. He is too shy and polite to look at the viewer. I wonder if he is searching for his reflection in the ice and I too feel the impulse to lean forward and ponder the mystery that water must be loose to give the reflection we see in glass. Years later Gail and I were admiring the drawing. We tried to engage Jesse in conversation.

What's that at the Eskimo's feet, Jess?

Cracked ice, he said.

The small dark look in the Eskimo child's face. His bundled shyness. The same qualities that made adults, and especially women, want to protect Jesse, like Marion, the nurse, with her long red hair and the Irish lilt of her voice coming in on the 7 p.m. to 7 a.m. shift.

Jesse, it's me, Marion, hmm?

Marion in July after she hadn't been assigned to Jesse for several shifts, asking me if we didn't want her to take care of him anymore. Marion the night of the first one-to-two-days-to-live speech, washing and brushing his hair, giving him a sponge bath, making his bed with clean sheets like a good Irish mother with another son brought home from the sea, dressing him for his burial.

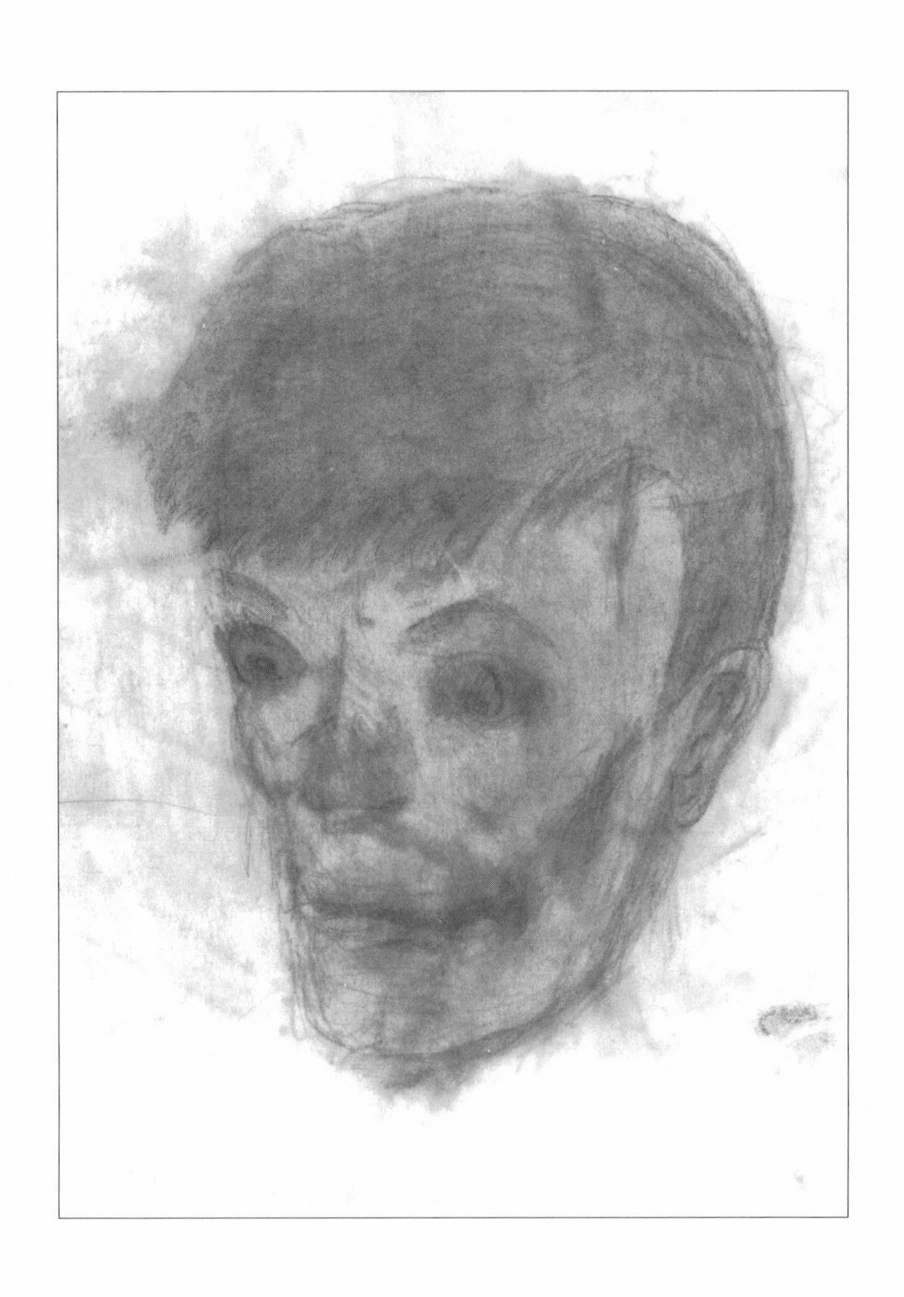

four

This midway light hangs fire between daytime and nighttime. It starts behind the trees out back, leaves a pink tint on the grass, the windows, the plastic bags and wood scraps off the deck, this shirt, even the shadows in here. The smell of metal will hang in the air after it's gone. Notebooks and folders, X-rays on the kitchen table. I hold them up to the glass doors, make new piles.

Sitting here arm outstretched, my hand would have brushed his arm on the path he took from the shower to his bedroom. Jesse the most private of persons, hernia bulging over his towel, scarred belly on nineteen-year old body, mock dancing past our green and rose and cream wallpaper and the images it evokes, a young ram at the water's edge, beard dripping into the lake, a wheat field in winter, a rose garden covered in gauze, a forest opening into a clearing with a barbed wire fence at the far edge. But no, the table was at the other end of the kitchen, by the glass doors, when Jesse was here. We moved it only a few months ago. Coming through the archway he would have walked straight through where the table stands now and I would have been sitting eight feet away from him where the table was then. And here, close up, the wallpaper is merely a pattern, soothing to the eye, with no hidden images but the ones that memory pastes over it.

My hospital memories come back at odd moments. Watching the nurses eat ice cream bars in late July and remembering early May when the chief resident brought in ice cream bars for all and we ate at the nurse's station, guilty that Jesse could not join us. And did I go out for croissants the morning of May 5th before we left for the hospital, a matter of no small importance to me now, or do I only think I did because I would do such a thing on such an occasion? I can't ask the children, and Gail only so much and at certain times. She lacks the buffers I have built up from reading these notes over and over again like Mithridates sipping a little more poison each day against the Day of Much Poison, and from plotting my revenge. Rachel and I don't speak anymore. I've been back to the hospital several times, of course. Once, I walked into the admissions department where we had waited for the attendant to take Jesse up to the floor, but this time from the back end. I went around to the cubbyhole where we signed the papers and wondered if the lady with the frosted blue hair still worked here, and if that was the color of her hair. I turned back at the waiting room, not because I couldn't bear to see it again but because I lacked the imagination or the courage to play-act, if the receptionist were to ask, Can I help you? And effort stops somewhere, even with one's child. I wonder how much I'd remember if I didn't have these notebooks. No matter. Notes to memory, memory to notes.

It was May 5th. We drove along the Henry Hudson Parkway where it approaches the George Washington Bridge. The river outside the passenger's window looked too close, too high, too level with the road, as though a heavy rain might flood its banks.

We got off the parkway and crossed through Central Park to the East Side and up. I tried to appear confident, aggressive in traffic to impress the kids and counter Gail's loathing for the noise and congestion of New York City. We got to Second Avenue and doubled back on a one-way street to the Transplant Respite Center, an elegant shelter in a high-rise building that caters to medical students and young professionals. I hated to pay for parking for a car we wouldn't use in Manhattan, but Gail would be going back with the children on Monday. I would stay for a few days, then Rachel and I would trade off a few days at a time and Gail and the kids would visit on weekends for the couple of weeks it would probably take until they had a liver for Jesse.

The ladies showed us around and fussed over Jesse. The director, a volunteer like all the other women here, hadn't been pleased when I called to reserve a room and told her I'd have young children with us. What's more, I wanted to squeeze four of us, two adults and two children, into one room. But she was gracious now. She told Jesse she'd had a liver transplant fifteen years ago at Pittsburgh. She had bumped into Dr. Starzl, the father of modern organ transplantation, years later, she said, and he had remembered her. She was in her early sixties and looked healthy, with a little discoloration on her hands that I've always known as age or liver spots.

Jesse was pale, frightened, like the young man whose head he had drawn on tracing paper and superimposed on the skull, drawn on heavy paper. The style puts it in the last two years before transplant when mortality had to be more real for him each day. The young man's hair is medium length and straight. A dark line for the hollow between jaw and cheekbone extends to the left side of his mouth like a gash from mouth to ear or a shadow grin. His eyes show both fear and surprise. I move the tracing paper to see if their feverish cast goes away. No. All the expression is in the transparency, but bones add weight and depth to all. The mouth opening on the skull is tight and wide and supports the young man's shadow grin.

We walked four blocks to the hospital and looked for a restaurant. That was the plan, to have a decent lunch outside before Jesse began his confinement. There were delis, newspaper stands, a grocery store, a bagel shop, noise and traffic and sidewalks but no restaurants. It was a longer walk than I expected and harder on Gail and Daniel, I think, than on Jesse. I was annoyed with Gail for her irritation with New York and for not pretending we could make this trip enjoyable. She was annoyed with me for using the hunt for a restaurant to save a few bucks on a taxi. Daniel wanted to get inside. Cassie wanted to eat. Jesse was silent, dodging the buckshot of tension flying around him. We ate at the crowded hospital cafeteria, quickly, and were pleased to get it over with.

We sat on the couches at the back of the admissions office. Rachel and Will arrived. Rachel had got her Irishman and I my dark Italian girl. We extended to each other the politeness of ex-spouses and their spouses who will need to get along with each other at close quarters around a shared child whose life is on the line. I wondered why we hadn't heard from anyone at the liver clinic, connected to the pavilion, where we were, by a tangle of underground passages gerrymandered over the years as the hospital grew to occupy a large city block. Cindy, the transplant coordinator, had told me she would call Admissions to make arrangements and Admissions would call the clinic when we came in. And I, filled with the vanity of a revolution that was overthrowing only us, thought the liver clinic would send someone over to meet us, although I don't recall that such a promise was ever made.

The liver team wanted to admit Jesse so they could bump him

from status three to status two on the transplant waiting list. At status four you have liver disease and may need a transplant some day. At status three you need a transplant but are not in immediate danger without one. At status two your condition has deteriorated and you need to be hospitalized. At status one you are in full-blown liver failure and will die within days without a transplant. At status two you could get a liver within a week or two, maybe longer. Part of me was ready to cut the throat of anyone who got between Jesse and an available liver, to crawl over dead bodies at the car wreck to get to a card-carrying donor. Another part of me acknowledged the injustice of this waiting game played by desperate people and their surgeons, where people who did not need to be hospitalized got hospitalized in order to beat the odds.

Dr. Gardner, Jesse's gastroenterologist, did not approve of the system. I cancelled Jesse's last appointment with her. He knew he was going to be admitted but didn't know all the details, and I didn't want to put another burden on his conscience or risk that he'd say something to Dr. Gardner. After three years of pulling every trick she had out of her bag, Jesse's case was about to pass from her hands. I was doing her a favor, I told myself, by not forcing her to choose between her scruples and her favorite patient. But I almost blew it when I told the benefits coordinator at my health plan that the liver team wanted to admit Jesse.

We don't want to pay for Jesse to sit around in the hospital, she said.

I relayed this message to the administrator for the liver team, who sighed as I tried to fill in the details of my conversation with the benefits coordinator.

You need to let us deal with your health plan, she said.

Gail agreed.

Let the doctors decide. They can argue with our insurance company if they have to.

She was right. I had grown too accustomed to being in the middle of anything that had to do with Jesse and his health care.

A woman with blue frosted hair and pale white skin took us into an office. She was friendly enough to play grandmother but a pile of documents, redolent of the thick ink of carbon paper, stood between us. She turned them toward us one after the other. She had handled too much paper on too many shifts to have any insight left about what this scene meant to Jesse. She explained the forms. I scanned them, Jesse glanced at them.

Do you have questions, Jesse?

I guess not.

It's just giving them permission to do the surgery.

OK.

I signed for complete financial responsibility if the insurance refused to pay. He signed for permission to treat. Now he, and I, had passed a checkpoint that separates private citizens from hospital citizens, and now we could move to a backstage waiting area without the benefit of bad paintings, and wait again. Half an hour later an attendant came with a wheelchair. We took an elevator up and turned long corridors joking about the wheelchair ritual under the watchful eye of a spirit of obedience whose presence appealed to the good child in us. We defied this spirit with a conscious effort that made us feel childish. We came to the pediatric unit on the sixth floor of one of the hospital's many wings. It was late afternoon. Jesse sat on a bed near the window. We had walked past this same room many times after his colitis operation in 1993, shuffling at first, my arm under his arm on his IV pole, and then, over the next few days, quicker and more confident until finally we made it all the way to the lounge at this end of the unit and back to his single room at the other end.

But now he had a double room and wasn't happy about it,

although he didn't have a roommate yet. A nurse came in and took a history and admission note. Jesse gave mostly monosyllabic answers. Rachel and I competed to fill in the gaps that he left. Gail filled in ours. Tightness at the corners of the nurse's mouth gave her the chiding smile of one who took Jesse's silence to mean sullen uncooperativeness. It was that, but only in part. Rachel asked him if he wanted someone to stay with him for the first night. They could bring in a cot. Maybe, he said, just for the first night. She told me she would stay with him. Which irritated me. Gail and the children and I took a taxi back to the transplant shelter.

We squeezed through narrow aisles at a grocery store near the high-rise and cooked a meal at the shelter that Jesse would have hated, something with asparagus. We weren't in the mood for socializing with the other guests in the spacious living room the surgeons' wives had tastefully decorated. We retreated to our long narrow bedroom with twin beds, folding bed, and an air mattress. I wanted to unpack everything, Gail wanted to leave things in their suitcases and bags. The children fought over folding bed and air mattress, bouncing back and forth to test their softness and line of sight to the little black and white TV we'd brought. I tried to read. The TV droned Jeopardy and other Friday-night shows.

Then the children were quiet. I shut off the television. The sounds of the day were gone. We were amazed at the sounds of night in New York City, horns and engines and brakes on Second Avenue, boom boxes and passersby on the sidewalk eighty feet away from our bedroom window across a plaza with a water fountain. The sounds of night became a steady sizzle, a tune played low on a frying pan, then a tolling of bells. Worshippers walked single file on a broad avenue that pitched and rolled and, on closer inspection, turned out to be a bronze river. The phone was ringing, outside, near the kitchen. I didn't mind taking my turn, but at two o'clock in the morning by the clock next to my bed, whoever knows he might get a call ought to have the decency to wake up like a shot off a shovel and grab it. I got up, wobbled around the mattress, felt for the doorknob, and made it halfway across the dining room. The phone stopped ringing, like a dull joke.

Now I wondered if the call had been for us. Gail came out. My beeper went off in the bedroom. I ran back in and climbed over the air mattress and around the folding bed to get to the nightstand. I came back out and dialed the glowing green number on the display.

Pediatric Unit.

I gave my name. The nurse said to hold on. Rachel came on the line.

Michael? I called you before but no one answered.

I know. I didn't get to the phone in time.

Well, I've got news. There's a possible transplant for Jesse tomorrow morning.

I waited. You mean this morning?

Yes. Around 7:00 a.m.

Today? Jesse might have a transplant?

Yes.

How's he doing?

He's OK. A little shocked. And nervous. They're starting to get him ready.

How did this happen?

I don't know. They just told me a few minutes ago.

So we don't know for sure?

No. But it sounds likely. They're getting him ready.

All right, tell him we'll be right over.

Gail and I sat in the dark dining room and talked. Twenty minutes might have gone by before we had our plan made. Gail called her sister to meet us at the hospital and we woke the children. They had slept through all of it, the ringing and beeping and loud whispering, the climbing over folding bed and air mattress. Now I was anxious to see Jesse and get the details from Rachel. We dragged the kids and their bags and whatever we could find that might come in handy for a long day at the hospital and flagged down a taxi on Third Avenue.

Jesse was shaken, paler than usual. They took his blood pressure and started an IV and gave him something to keep him calm. His room was cramped with beds and chairs and family members. Nurses and doctors came in and walked out. I sat on the other bed with Gail. An aide came in.

You can't sit there. Another patient is coming in.

It was four o' clock in the morning on a medical floor. No one was coming in, but we might need this guy later on. Gail's sister and her husband arrived and stood around with the rest of us. Daniel and Cassandra wandered back and forth between Jesse's room and the lounge. We wandered back and forth to check on them. There was only so much small talk to be made, and nothing but small talk was worth making now.

Then we said goodbye to Daniel and Cassie and they left with their aunt and uncle. We stood next to Jesse.

I just want to get it over with, right?

Right!

The anesthesiologist and attendants came in. We walked Jesse to the elevator, then packed his things in his suitcase and blue plastic hospital bags and put them in the L-shaped utility room. Rachel went through his pants pockets. She handed a couple of chocolate-encrusted spoons to Gail.

I think these are yours.

We had always threatened Jesse with a utensil hunt in his bedroom. We figured he must have been afraid to bring them upstairs before we left the house, and stuffed them in his pockets so he could lose them on his hospital tray.

The surgical waiting room is a second-floor half-island open at both sides to the pavilion and its mighty glass rafters twenty stories high on the northwest side and four stories high on the east. At the eastern end, a couch with its back to the rest of the room sets off an area with easy chairs and a second couch placed around a large square wooden table. It was an open-air hideaway in plain sight for Dr. Dorand when he came looking for us, although on a Saturday afternoon with only emergency surgery being performed we all but had the place to ourselves. We talked and got coffee for each other, then retreated to books and phone calls and sidebars with spouses. After a few hours Gail and I began walking from one end of the now-deserted waiting room to the other. Using my stride as a yard we estimated that twenty-two round trips from rail to rail equaled a mile.

Dr. Dorand came out. Six hours. Is this early? I tried to read his expression but saw only that he noticed me reach for my notebook. I felt a quiver of shame, as though this moment should be sacred, not tainted by recording it while taking it in, then got out my pen. He sat down on one of the easy chairs. He was thin, small-boned. As he talked his right shoulder jerked slightly and suddenly and with no apparent connection to the rhythm or content of his speech or the movement of his left pinky finger, which dipped forward then back in a rhythm contrapuntal to that of both shoulder and speech.

We almost decided not to transplant him after we opened him up.

He mimicked, by the shake of his head and its inclination toward the wooden table in front of him, his amazement at Jesse's liver when he opened him up and, fingers extended toward the wooden table, the feel of Jesse's liver through his gloved hands.

His liver looked so good. A little firm, but not what we expected. We were puzzled.

What made you decide to go ahead?

His overall condition. We couldn't see any other reason for his symptoms. The fatigue, the portal hypertension, the enlarged spleen.

Did he get much blood?

He might have had a unit or two, I don't recall.

I had the impression he could have recalled quite well. His answer was a form of reassurance. The less blood given, the more routine the surgery. We were surprised to hear about the condition of Jesse's liver and even more surprised to hear Dr. Dorand talk so openly about their indecision. It was possible, then, that Jesse hadn't needed a new liver and the lifetime of drugs that went with it to hold his immune system at bay once it detected the intruder. Perhaps honesty was simply Dr. Dorand's style. He may have been treading on slippery ground two months earlier when we met him at the clinic and he told us, in so many words, that he would rather give a liver to Jesse than to a sick old man sitting at home watching TV with a beer belly from fluid leaking out of his blood vessels. But why be so forthright about the condition of Jesse's own liver when it might come back to haunt him? The question answered itself, of course. It wouldn't come back to haunt him. Here was an individual, good with his hands, who could appreciate the miter joint fit of absolute candor and legal strategy. Dr. Dorand was being straight with us about a judgment call he had made on the spot with a year and a half's worth of blood tests and X-rays and clinic visits to back him up. If calamity struck we would be devastated, but he had been honest about his doubts in a difficult situation that allowed for no easy answers.

We asked him about the donor. He hesitated.

A twenty-year-old male from Manhattan who died from a gunshot wound to the head.

The best organs, we learned, come from healthy people who die violent deaths, not those who die in the hospital loaded up with drugs that have made their way through the organs to be harvested.

Infection will be our biggest problem. We can deal with rejection. Hopefully, this will work for him.

He got up to leave and took our hands.

I'm happy. I hope you are too.

We were happy. Now we had to wait out the rest of the surgery, which involved hooking up the bile ducts of Jesse's new liver to his intestine and closing him up. We could see the night sky through the glass rafters overhead when Dr. Boyd, the assisting surgeon, came in. He was six-foot-six and trim but powerfully built. He rocked back and forth on his heels and tipped his head back when he talked or listened. I wondered if the faraway look in his eyes was a sign of fatigue or of compensation for having to look close up at Jesse's internal organs for half a day. He had cut through scar tissue, he said, built up from Jesse's colitis surgery two years earlier, in order to get to his intestine. Then he had cut the intestine in two, twisted the top part up, connected it to the new bile ducts, and sewed the bottom part of the intestine back to the top.

The scar tissue was dense. It was difficult to cut through. His white blood cell count is below a thousand. He could be losing the white blood cells because of his spleen, but platelets and red blood cells are usually the first to go with a bad spleen, and those are OK. We could remove his spleen, but the spleen helps to prevent infection. Or the cells could be draining from his blood vessels into his belly. It will be a miracle if he doesn't get an infection.

Because of the white blood cells?

Yes, and his stoma being near the incision. His intestines being moved around. The immunosuppressants he'll be on. Infection will be our biggest problem. We can treat rejection.

What about his hernia?

The hernia had appeared not long after Jesse's colitis surgery. The tendons they cut through to remove his diseased colon hadn't healed together properly and thus had left a space for his intestine to pop through. The hernia had swelled during the past year until it wouldn't flatten out when he lay down and pressed his hand against it. Dr. Boyd seemed amused that I would ask about his hernia when Jesse had just had a liver transplant. But he was nineteen years old. He still had to walk around in the world, didn't he?

We sewed it up from the inside. We can repair it again later if we need to.

He left to finish up. The contrast in words and tone between the two surgeons was unsettling. Different shticks, maybe. Dr. Dorand's is to calm you down, Dr. Boyd's is to shake you up. The surgery took thirteen hours in all.

It was May 7th. We sat in Room D after they brought Jesse back and got him settled. We watched him sleep and went out to make good news calls. We washed our hands at the sink in the room to keep our germs off him. One of the doctors said there was no need to, the danger of infection came from within, but we washed anyway. Dr. Atella, the liver fellow, told us that Jesse getting a liver so quickly had nothing to do with his being admitted the night before.

Patients can't be bumped up on the list until they've been hospitalized for five days. You would have been called at home if he hadn't already been here.

It was hard to believe that after a year and a half of waiting Jesse would get a liver within eight hours of being admitted, but there it was.

Walking back to the unit after a coffee run, Gail and I met a woman, Joan, taking a break in the PICU lounge. Joan's eleven-year-old daughter, Laura, had cancer. Her Broviac, a piece of hardware that delivered medication to a shunt surgically installed in her abdomen, had malfunctioned. The surgeons had to remove the Broviac and replace it, and then Laura had to be watched closely on the ICU for signs of infection.

Joan's husband wouldn't be here for hours and she wouldn't leave the unit. I went out again and bought her an espresso and a croissant. She tried to pay me. We were glad to make contact with someone outside of medical staff and family, but I grieved for Joan and Laura. Even Jesse's troubles seemed small compared to those of a child who had to carry around a box to pump medication into her that made her hair fall out. Joan said My Husband, not Laura's Father, but something in her tone made me wonder whether the two of them were pulling together or coming apart. Rachel and I had pulled together around Jesse's infant hydrocephalus, then come apart over my work and my theatre and being broke and her feeling trapped at home with a toddler. Near the end of our marriage, after Gail and I had started our affair but before I admitted it to Rachel, the three of us, Rachel, Jesse, and I, went to Lighthouse Point in New Haven. Out on the beach I saw a small rip on the front of her bathing suit.

Jesse was waking up, slowly, by mid-afternoon. They took the breathing tube out of his mouth. A gastrointestinal, or GI, fellow wrote in my notebook for my call to the benefits coordinator at my health plan.

Reasons for admission: Increased fatigue. Itching. Abdominal distension. Slow clotting time. Low white blood count.

Each of these was a sign of advancing, if not advanced, liver disease. It would feel more like a good news call now, since there had been no wait for my health plan to pay for.

Jesse was getting a powerful drug called Fentanyl for pain, and IV albumin, a protein, to help him urinate. They catheterized him. He had drainage tubes near his Mercedes incision, a large inverted Y cut into his abdomen, happy conjunction, for the surgeon who named it after the automobile logo, of an image of luxury superimposed on an image of pain, evocation of status equal to the status of liver transplants over Volkswagen kidney, Saab heart, and Lexus heart-lung transplants. Jesse's nurse, Tina, covered his incision, stapled shut and surprisingly tight and clean, with fresh layers of gauze every few hours.

That evening he was awake. We congratulated him. He was not yet ready to celebrate. At times he seemed confused.

So what are we going to do tonight, Mom?

He thought he was in Stamford, where he would normally be spending the weekend with his mother and Will. And this was Saturday night, after all.

Jesse pulled out his catheter on the night shift. The next morning he was still confused. His bedroom in Stamford was across the hall, he said. He sat up and tried to get out of bed.

I have more lines in me than I did last night.

No Jesse, it's the same number of lines.

No, there are more.

He told Rachel that Angela, his nurse last night, was a killer nurse. It was she who had added the extra lines. The chief resident tried to convince him it wasn't so. Jesse shook his head with the confidence of one who knows what he knows and sees no point in further argument.

Later he was in pain. They gave him more Fentanyl. He looked a little puffy from retaining fluid. He was thinking more clearly, though. Maybe the pain had driven away a fog of anesthesia.

Can I get something to drink? I'm thirsty.

Let me ask Dr. Meyer, Jess.

Dr. Meyer came in and asked him how he was feeling and whether he had any gas or stomach pains. No, he was feeling all right. She said he could have some apple juice. He drank it greedily.

Around noon an aide came in and left a full lunch on the portable table near the bed. I was surprised. Jesse must be doing really well.

Can I have some milk, Dad?

I went to get it for him, then stopped. Milk is so thick. True, he'd had juice earlier, and there was the tray just out of arm's reach, but Dr. Meyer hadn't said anything about milk.

Hold on for a minute, Jess.

I went out to the nurse's station. The nurse said he could only have clear liquids. I told her about the tray. She said they had ordered a parent tray for us.

Later, he was talking with Gail. Where are my things?

Upstairs, hon, for when you go back to the pediatric unit.

Oh. OK.

I can get things for you, though. Is there anything you'd like now?

I want the book.

Which book?

The red one.

It was a Bible she had given him and it was titled The Book in large white letters on its red paperback cover. She asked him if he wanted *The Hitchhiker's Guide to the Galaxy* as well. His guitar teacher had given it to him after his last lesson.

No, just the book.

I read to him from the psalms. Would you like a back rub, Jess?

I thought about how little we touched and how I would find excuses, goofing with him. Once when he was fourteen I came home from work and walked into the living room. He was sitting on the couch with Daniel. I opened my arms in mock astonishment as though the two of them were long lost children I'd had no hope of ever seeing again. He jumped up in mock astonishment of his own, cried Dad! and threw his arms around me. I was happy, and happy for him.

How does that feel?

Good.

Is that where it's sore?

Yes, and a little lower down.

His back felt warm. He had been lying on it for a while. He was so thin. His skin was so youthful, soft here compared to his poor scarred belly. I felt both sympathy and elation. I'd heard that a chronic sore back was one of the drawbacks of a liver transplant. So he was on the right trajectory, and so soon!

Later he was about to get sick. Rachel ran out to get a basin. Gail saw in his eyes that he couldn't wait. She held out her hands. He looked at her as if to say, Are you joking?

Go ahead, it's all right.

He vomited in her hands.

That afternoon he sat in an easy chair. Dr. Dorand came by on rounds.

How are you feeling, Jesse?

Pretty good.

Are you in any pain?

Not too much. Some.

Have you had anything to drink?

I had some apple juice.

Dr. Dorand turned to us and smiled.

He doesn't really need to be here now, but the nurses like to keep them for a few days.

Tina, Jesse's day nurse, was in her early twenties. She was pretty and often smiled, openly, without guile. She talked easily with us and with Jesse. She told us she was having problems with her boyfriend, who was away on business too often and didn't spend enough time with her when he was in town. Marriage? They'd been going together long enough for the subject to come up, but he avoided it.

She leaned over the bed in her white jeans showing her tight heart-shaped ass and talked to Jesse as she worked.

I'm checking your drainage tubes, Jesse. I'm going to pull up your bandage now to see whether it needs to be changed... Looks pretty good, but let's give you a new one, OK?

He nodded. Half awake as he was, I saw that he liked the attention.

I had a fantasy.

New liver, new health. New health, new hope. Jesse opens out to the world and Tina helps him do that. There's no rush to send him upstairs to the pediatric unit, that's just surgeon ego. They keep him here for a few more days. Tina isn't that much older than Jesse. She's getting to know his silences and wariness and he doesn't scare her off. Her big sister interest in him ripens into a touch of something else. Something ripens in Jesse, too.

He goes upstairs to the pediatric unit. She visits him, taking report from us and giving report on her shallow inattentive boyfriend. Jesse is doing well on the floor but his is a special case. Before his transplant he had portal hypertension, high pressure in the portal vein that carries blood from the intestine to the liver. It disappeared when they put in his new liver, but it had been abnormally high, especially considering the relatively benign condition of his own liver when they took it out. And his huge spleen is also unusual. They decide to keep him for a few more days, then another week just to be sure.

Tina visits more frequently. There is a subtle change in tone, a slightly forced cheerfulness in her greeting to us. We see ten degrees more of her back and none of her face when she turns from talking to us to talking with Jesse. The two of them, Tina and Jesse, Jesse and Tina, are creating a code from moment to moment in clear view of an illiterate world.

Finally the great day comes to take Jesse home, but not without balloons, a cake, and a large gathering of doctors and nurses. Tina is here, of course. Winks are exchanged around the room. The two of them write and call each other and we come by the PICU after his appointments at the liver clinic. One day he makes a phone call to his mother and then has something to tell us. We are happy for both of them, grateful to Tina for taking care of Jesse and, through a happy accident of timing and crisis, helping him through the treacherous passage from adolescence to manhood. We are proud to have her for a daughter-in-law.

Gail got ready to go home for a couple of days to be with the kids. She didn't think Jesse was doing as well as his doctors did. She kept notes on his heart rate, blood pressure, pulse, and his SATs, or oxygen saturation rate, which shows how well the lungs are moving oxygen through the blood. Jesse's heart rate, pulse, and blood pressure were going up and his SATs were down a bit. He was getting a lot of Fentanyl for pain. His hemoglobin, the protein that carries oxygen to the blood, and his hematocrit, the proportion of red blood cells to the whole blood, were down. He had a slight fever. Gail showed the numbers to the resident and the nurses. They weren't concerned. I looked at the numbers and worried with her, but thought they must be taking these things into account. And we weren't doctors. Maybe it's the actress in her. Everything must be dramatized. Oh well, that's how we fell in love. Would you like to be in one of my plays? She left for home.

The next morning, the 9th, Jesse had pain in his belly and needed a lot of Fentanyl to take the edge off it. He vomited and belched. Drainage the color of coffee grounds leaked into the tubes near his incision. A technician who looked a bit like Charles Laughton as Quasimodo in *The Hunchback of Notre Dame* wheeled in a portable X-ray machine. The X-rays showed what might be an ileus, where the intestinal wall stops making contractions to digest food. An ileus can come from a kink in the intestine or from an infection. They're not uncommon after intestinal surgery, but the doctors always watch them closely to make sure that what looks like an ileus isn't an obstruction, where the intestine above the part that's blocked keeps working like a fire hose when the water hits a tight kink and pressure builds until the hose springs a leak or, in this case, bores a hole in the intestinal wall and starts dumping its contents into the abdominal cavity. This can lead to peritonitis, an inflammation of the lining of the abdominal cavity, and that can lead to sepsis, severe infection.

But Jesse's belly was soft, not tender, a good sign. At eight-thirty in the evening he was given the first of a triple dose of three powerful antibiotics. Rachel and Will left to take their turn at the transplant shelter for the night. I was still trying to decide whether to go back to New Haven three days later for a presentation on homelessness I was supposed to give at the medical school with my boss. I could take the train to New Haven Friday morning and come back in the afternoon, but at this point I was looking for an excuse to pass, and I had history to back me up. Eleven years before, Gail started having contractions the night before my last performance with a touring theatre company. It was a small company that depended on bookings with schools and libraries. To cancel a performance less than a day in advance was, of course, unheard of. I called the artistic director several times that night. By morning the contractions had stopped and I was ten minutes away from leaving for the company bus when Gail started having sudden severe contractions. I rushed her to the hospital. The contractions got worse but she wasn't dilating. They strapped a fetal heart monitor to her belly and found a good heartbeat, then lost it.

The baby just turned away from the monitor, the nurse said.

Then the obstetrician came in and turned white as a sheet. Precious minutes went by as they searched frantically for a vein on small-veined Gail. They rushed her down the hall for an emergency C-section. The umbilical cord was wrapped around Daniel's neck. A few minutes later and he would have been stillborn.

The pain got worse. Where does it hurt, Jess?

Here.

He made a circling motion on the left side of his abdomen. He was writhing on the bed, rolling from side to side on his back.

It hurts! Can't they give me something?

OK Jesse, hang on, they're trying to figure out what's going on.

Carol the resident was holding off on pain medications until someone from the liver team could evaluate him. She was worried about peritonitis and didn't want to mask his symptoms with Fentanyl. I was pissed off at her, at the liver team, and at myself for not being able to do anything for Jesse. I wondered if I should ask Carol to page Dr. Dorand. Jesse rolled back and forth holding his belly. His face was twisted and creased in agony. Nine months before he had held the same area on the opposite side of his belly in a motel room in Rome, New York after a visit with my brother and his family. I called the emergency room of the local hospital. Within moments it was clear to me that I knew more about ulcerative colitis and subtotal colectomies than the doctor I was talking to. I was afraid they would do more harm than good. Finally the pain subsided. When we got back home I called Dr. Gardner. She said it sounded like a passing obstruction. But tonight was much worse.

At 11:30 p.m., three hours after Carol's first call, a surgical resident, Dr. Wolters, sauntered in, much as someone Jesse's height, five-foot-four in thick-soled orthopedic shoes, can saunter.

Why'd it take so long?

It's been very busy in the OR.

Jesse's in a lot of pain.

He's just had a transplant.

And he has a very high tolerance for pain.

Dr. Wolters examined him, feeling along his belly.

Where does it hurt, Jesse?

During the long wait I had encouraged him to give the surgeon as much detail as he could, knowing his way of giving scant information to his doctors. But he made the same circular motion over the left side of his belly. Dr. Wolters said he thought it was gas, or an ileus. Through the window of the vestibule that separated Jesse's room from the hall, I saw him at the nurse's station talking to someone, perhaps Dr. Dorand, on the phone. Jesse was moaning. Dr. Wolters prescribed a bolus, a big dose, of Fentanyl. It took a long time to kick in. Around two o'clock in the morning he got some sleep. They kept pumping him up with Fentanyl.

The next morning he felt fine. He watched two futuristic movies, Sylvester Stallone and Jean-Claude Van Damme. Across the hall, Laura, the little girl with cancer, was watching television. She wore a ski cap. Stuffed animals were piled up high on her bed and helium Get Well balloons stuck to the ceiling. Joan fussed over her. Laura ignored her. She wanted something to eat that she couldn't have. A recreation therapist tried to amuse her with Gameboy. She stared straight ahead.

Ellie, Jesse's day nurse, thought he might take a walk on her shift. She was stick-thin with short reddish hair, a roving eye, and a Brooklyn accent that could make you think the Dodgers hadn't taken a walk to L.A. to mix with the beautiful crowd. Jesse didn't like her bossy style, and iced her with silence. Ellie was blissfully unaware, or let him think so.

By early evening the pain was back. Jesse's breathing was shallow and fast. He was running a fever. He had tachycardia, rapid heart rate. There was bile and blood in his ostomy bag. His stomach was bloated. Dr. Rand, a young surgical fellow with a swipe of hair over a large bald spot, came in and examined him. He pushed down on Jesse's stomach. It hurt when he let go. Dr. Rand left the room. The technician wheeled in the machine and took another abdominal X-ray. A pattern of gas along the winding route of the intestine would be good. Free air at one point would be bad. The X-ray showed free air in the abdominal cavity. Dr. Rand came back in holding a clipboard.

Jesse, we want to take you down to have a look at you to make sure everything's OK. This probably won't hurt you afterwards.

Jesse signed the consent form. Dr. Rand left.

Yeah, right, it won't hurt.

His face showed restrained anger, an unwilling acceptance of new pain, and an absolute commitment to himself not to be bamboozled. I wanted to reach him but he was reaching down inside himself and any reassurance I could offer was as hollow as Dr. Rand's that he would feel no pain. Ellie buzzed in and out to get him ready to go down.

Don't wawwwry about it Jess. They do this all the time. They take you baaack. And baaack. And baaack.

And she buzzed out of the room. I was furious. Who could say what Jesse was feeling?

Rachel and Will were here. Gail was on her way back from Naugatuck. They carted Jesse off fully conscious for a second trip to the OR. We went to the surgical waiting room and took the same spot overlooking the gift store from the second-story railing.

Dr. Dorand came in. They had found a hole in Jesse's intestine, he said, caused by the electrical cauterization they had done four days earlier to cut through adhesions, scar tissue attached to his intestine.

You couldn't see it then?

If we had seen a hole during the transplant we would have sewn it up. It may have been so small we couldn't see it, or the cauterization may have caused a weak spot that opened up later.

He told us they had taken out two liters of intestinal contents from Jesse's belly. None of us knew exactly what that meant, but we knew it wasn't good.

The steroids masked the inflammation. We'll probably take him back for a re-exploration in a couple of days to clean him out and check for holes and abscesses.

What will happen now?

He will look bloated. His blood pressure will go down and his heart rate and pulse will go up. He will be intubated.

I had already cancelled my presentation. Someone else would

fill in for me. We split up to make phone calls.

Evening, the 11th. Jesse had slept, or been sedated, most of the day. Dr. Atella the liver fellow, was on the unit looking to play shunt games.

Nineteen years earlier, Jesse's pediatrician, Dr. Ritter, had measured his infant head each visit, charting it against his age and weight and scowling. Dr. Ritter was just out of residency and rarely had an answer to our questions, but always said he'd get one and always did. The chief of pediatrics at our health plan, Dr. Johnston, pooh-poohed Dr. Ritter's concerns about the size of Jesse's head, even giving him a condescending pat on the shoulder, but when Jesse began to have projectile vomiting, Dr. Ritter knew it was from hydrocephalus.

A few days later Dr. Lynd, a neurosurgeon at Yale-New Haven Hospital, drilled a hole through his skull at the back left side of his head and inserted a metal catheter through what she called a silent area of the brain and into his left ventricle. She attached the shunt, a long plastic tube, to the other end of the catheter and snaked it under his skin, alongside his neck, to his front and down. The catheter drained excess fluid from the left ventricle and from the right, which was connected to the left by a tributary between the two, and the shunt carried away the fluid to drip harmlessly into the peritoneal cavity.

After years of body growth and even with an extension added, the shunt's southern tip now lay at the approximate level of Jesse's diaphragm. His second neurosurgeon, Dr. Harrison, who took over when Dr. Lynd left for Texas A&M, had suspected for years that the shunt was no longer functioning, but that was good, it meant Jesse was in remission from hydrocephalus. He remained in that glorious limbo, but limbo nonetheless, for eighteen years, while a little parent inside us lived at the edge of panic wondering when the other shoe would drop on his head.

The catheter remained firmly in place. Dr. Harrison mused out loud, during check-ups, about removing the shunt, but decided against it. He couldn't be sure it wasn't working a little bit. We were happy to leave it where it was, clearly visible down Jesse's chest like a dividing line between infancy and adolescence, finally sinking under the growth of muscle and tissue he would need for his initiation into manhood. A little hernia, like a snub-nosed belly button at his diaphragm where Dr. Lynd had added an extension tube to accommodate his growth, was a visual reminder, slowly receding, of three early operations, for catheter and shunt at three months, replacement of malfunctioning catheter at seven months, and second shunt from the catheter into the right ventricle at seventeen months after a CAT scan showed that the tributary between the two ventricles had dried up and the left was no longer draining the right.

During the year-long process of getting Jesse listed for a liver transplant, the liver surgeons here had fretted over his shunt, since every foreign object in the body is a potential source of infection. Dr. Harrison advised them against doing anything. The danger of infection, he said, was quite small, because the shunt's southern tip had to be far above the abdominal cavity where they would be operating. The surgeons went along with his advice, but Dr. Atella was on the unit now, as she had been on the 9th diagnosing Jesse with an ileus and on the morning of the 10th writing in his chart that he looked good when he was merely drunk on Fentanyl. One of the nurses had made a comment to us about Atella's taking credit, today, for diagnosing what Carol the resident had suspected two days before, that Jesse was perforating. I didn't care for Dr. Atella, nor she for me. She was abrupt with the nurses and only somewhat less so with parents. Will got along with her best, getting her to talk about her husband's new Italian restaurant.

I had a fantasy.

I imagined Dr. Atella in New Haven, the owner of her own highly successful Italian restaurant where the waitresses throw your food at you. Given the prerequisite of superb cuisine and a world-class chef, this idiosyncrasy constitutes the main charm of the place and makes it an essential stop for out-of-towners. Rose, for that is Dr. Atella's name, is said to be the biggest contributor to the Mayor's campaign. You might think that would make her restaurant a drug-free zone, but she is known to go out alone at closing time and chase the crack dealers off her block. If you do not see yourself getting close to her, you do want to know her well enough that she will stop at your table to be introduced to your guests, or at least not snub you when you hail her from across the room. That the help do not love her might be inferred from their behavior with the patrons, but such a peccadillo is less jarring in a restaurant than on an ICU where more is at stake than the quality of the Lobster Fra Diavolo and Chianti.

Having read a perforation as a kink in his intestine, Dr. Atella was now taking an interest in Jesse's shunt. She came into the room. Jesse was barely awake or was shutting down to conserve energy. I mentioned that Dr. Harrison had discussed the shunt with the liver surgeons. Dr. Atella asked me what he had said. I replied, I think, with the timeworn rap about its tip being above the peritoneal cavity. She made a dismissive hand gesture.

That's not what I meant.

Why don't you talk to Dr. Harrison then?

It's eight o'clock on a Thursday night.

I don't care what time it is!

She walked out of the room. Gail and Rachel were standing next to Jesse. Eyes closed, he raised his eyebrows. I followed Dr. Atella to the nurse's station.

I can get his home phone. I'll call him myself!

I thought I remembered finding Dr. Harrison in the New Haven phone book, but I hoped Dr. Atella wouldn't call my bluff. If she did and I couldn't find his number, I could call his service at Yale-New Haven Hospital and make my request sound urgent enough for him to call me back, or to call Atella. But she looked down at the desk and said nothing. I walked away, fuming.

Dr. Wolters, the surgical resident from the night of the 9th, was on the unit. His manner was less brash now than two nights ago, in fact not brash at all. He seemed genuinely concerned about Jesse. Somehow, I knew he was aware of my run-in with Dr. Atella. Perhaps he'd been standing near the desk when I came out. I made a comment, inviting him to take my side. He shook his head sympathetically and said this was a difficult situation for everyone. I thought I might end up liking him yet.

A half-hour later Dr. Atella came back into Jesse's room, all smiles. She had called Dr. Harrison, she said, and what a nice and helpful man he was. He agreed with her that they should try to assess the condition of Jesse's shunt. I was not impressed. A neurosurgeon in New Haven gets a call from New York at eight o'clock on a Thursday night after his patient has had a liver transplant followed by surgery for an intestinal perforation. Of course he's going to go along with the attending physician's assessment, not risk making a long-distance mistake that could cost his patient his life and him a lawsuit. Dr. Atella said she would request a neurological consult.

Two hours later a blond-haired neurosurgical resident walked in. He did not introduce himself. The ICU resident and Angela, Jesse's nurse, were in the tiny room with him and us. We waited for him to start his examination. He turned to us.

Would you mind leaving the room? I don't want to have an audience.

We left like sheep, in single file. As we cleared the threshold Angela, Jesse's killer nurse, said to the neurological resident, You were rude to those people. That wasn't called for, the ICU resident snapped at her. I don't care, said Angela, he was rude. We stood in the hall outside, parents and stepparents, spouses and ex-spouses, knowing the camaraderie of a shared hatred.

The neurosurgeon came out a few minutes later and expounded on his thinking about whether to externalize the shunt, which apparently meant capping it off somewhere on Jesse's chest, or leave it alone. Whether he saw externalizing the shunt as a temporary or permanent option for closing off a possible source of infection, we didn't know. We listened politely as he answered our questions with information about hydrocephalus that Rachel and I could have recited in our sleep.

Will had a wild look in his eye. His fuse was shorter than mine but his wit usually kept him in check. The neurosurgeon talked about how the shunt was placed to drain into the abdominal cavity and how it was hard to tell whether it was working or not. Then, referring to its probable location far above its original dripping point, he said, And children grow.

There you go, said Will, straight-faced.

His timing was perfect, his tone and delivery matter-of-fact and friendly. It was a small victory on a dismal evening, but we were happy to take it.

The next day I told Dr. Meyer we didn't want this neurosurgeon to have anything to do with Jesse again. She said she would pass on our request. It was a hollow request in part, and I knew it. They might keep him away from Jesse, and from us, if it was a matter of a consult that could wait for someone else, but if he was on and push came to shove we weren't going to refuse to let him see Jesse. I passed him once or twice in the hall after this evening and often had the occasion to be around Dr. Atella. I kept my best face on for them both, for I had learned a key principle of life on an intensive care unit. Be nice to people on the way down. You may meet them again on the way down.

May 12th, evening. Dr. Dorand sat on the large square wooden table in the surgical waiting room. It went well, he said about Jesse's third operation. This was the re-exploration he had told us, two days earlier, that he'd want to do to clean out Jesse's abdominal cavity again and make sure there were no other perforations. We told him about the shunt wars. He shook his head and looked genuinely amazed.

I could have told them the shunt was not an issue because it's not in the peritoneal cavity. We saw that when we did the transplant.

We had a long discussion about communication. We told Dr. Dorand we wanted to be informed about everything that was going on with Jesse. He gave me his beeper number and said we could call him anytime we needed to.

Jesse was swelling up. There were no plans to take him off the ventilator because the swelling made it hard for him to breathe. We waited all day for the liver team, then missed them when we ran out for coffee. I tracked them down on the pediatric unit. Dr. Lanier, the chief of gastroenterology, introduced me to Dr. Swanson, the chief of liver transplantation.

He's the real boss.

Dr. Swanson was a stocky man of medium height. His fingers were thicker and fleshier than Dr. Dorand's, proof that a surgeon's hands need not look like a pianist's, if a pianist's need to. He was well regarded in his field, I knew. Months before I had talked to a high-ranking surgeon at Pittsburgh through a friend. He had good things to say about the transplant program here and about Dr.

Swanson.

We talked about Jesse. Dr. Lanier ran down a few items on Jesse's condition, then paused.

Jesse is as sick as you can get.

When I came back to the PICU I told Gail and Rachel I had seen the liver team, and not much more than that. I went into Room D. Jesse woke up. The knowledge that a thick piece of plastic was stuffed in his mouth, gagging him not breathing for him, came into his eyes. He fought against the tube and mouthed something to me. I leaned down to read his lips. He went under from the sedation.

Gail and I went down the street to The Three Gentlemen for dinner. She couldn't understand why I was so upset. Things were bad, she said, but no worse this evening than the last. I went down to the basement to a pay phone and called Dr. Gardner in New Haven. After fifteen minutes the waiter asked Gail if anything was wrong. I'm sorry for your troubles, he said when I came upstairs. It was the last time I held back anything about Jesse's condition from Gail.

Morning, May 14th. Jesse's ventilator tube and nasogastric tube, which went down to his stomach through his nose to draw out blood and acid, were gone. We thought this was a good sign until Rachel came in and said she'd run into Matt, the chief resident, at the grocery store. Matt told her that Jesse had pulled his tubes. He had missed a dose of sedatives during the night and woke up enough to start yanking.

Late morning he became agitated and tried to pull out his A-line, a thick needle straight into an artery in his neck. They restrained him with layers of gauze wound around his wrists and attached to the rails. We couldn't watch him every second and couldn't count on catching him even if we did, he was still that fast, that strong. They sedated him to keep him from moving around and using up precious energy and muscle mass, and also, I guessed, to keep him from seeing how deep a hole he was in. They considered using a paralytic drug, but said they would do that only if he was completely sedated so he wouldn't realize he couldn't move. But how could he move if he was completely sedated? In his dreams?

They took X-rays of his chest and abdomen every few hours. We had learned how to help. Somehow, he managed to work his way down the bed between X-rays, so we had to pull him back up into place to position the plates under him when the technician rolled in the machine for the next series. It was timing not strength the nurses taught us, a hand cupped against an underarm and a hand under the thigh, a steady thrust forward, not too fast not too slow, in sync with your partner.

His belly was pushing out. Third spacing had started. The fluid inside the blood vessels, the first space, leaked out to the area around the vessels, the second space, and from there to the third space, the lungs, abdomen, hands, and feet. With less fluid in the blood vessels, Dr. Meyer told us, blood moves too slowly to the kidneys. They started him on dopamine, a drug to help the blood flow to his kidneys and heart, and reintubated him, that is, put the breathing tube back in his throat, because the fluid in his chest was making him pull hard for a breath.

Inside Jesse's body a ferocious battle was taking place. His blood sent a distress signal from trunk to nethermost limb, calling back every ounce of inner strength he had stored up over the years. Rachel was stitching a pillow for him. I liked the symbolism and made Rachel-Penelope his mother stitching a pillow for Jesse-Odysseus rocking on the sea of himself, steering by the line of each stitch like a trail of lights on the water leading him home. She asked if I thought she should finish the pillow and give it to him.

No, keep going.

Carol the resident came in and looked at the blood in Jesse's ostomy bag.

What do you think it's from?

It could be low platelets. Or necrotic bowel.

Necrosis. Death of animal, plant, or tissue. Jesse's intestine is dying? A false alarm, I learned later in the day, and Carol didn't know I was alarmed.

His blood pressure went down. They doubled the dopamine. His right lung was filled with fluid that pressed on his heart. The surgical fellow came and put a chest tube into his left lung. The fluid rushed into the tube and down into a container on the floor. Dr. Atella took us into the conference room and put up the before and after X-rays on the fluorescent screen to show us how much better his lungs looked now. I was happy for Jesse. The oohs and ahhs were for Dr. Atella's benefit.

Later we saw Dr. Lanier on the unit.

Don't think Jesse's doing better because he's not intubated. This is not an upturn. His condition has worsened. This is the time when we want to see improvement. You don't want to stay on a plateau for too long.

This is a plateau?

Evening, we weighed him on the Tuna Scale, now part of the daily ritual of critical illness, to see how much fluid he'd put on.

But he had a stable night. The next morning his chest X-rays were good, and his liver tests. He was putting out urine. Dr. Lanier came by and talked with us.

Some things are going in the right direction. We'll wait and see.

That evening they decided to do a CAT scan to look for fluid on the brain. It took four of us to move Jesse and his bed out of the room. Jenny, his nurse, and I took the head. Will and Fashion Statement, the resident, took the foot. Fashion Statement was dark, gorgeous. In another lifetime she may have been Judith who used the beauty of her face and the music of her speech to slay Holofernes, but two and a half millennia sat stonily on her shoulders and sent tendrils to twine about her larynx, causing her to slouch a bit and reducing the lark-like timbre of her voice to that of a thin reed. The yellow scrub falling off her right shoulder was alluring, but not worthy of her past glory.

It was almost impossible for us to get the bed with its oxygen monitor, oxygen tank for the trip, and poles with meds hung at three of its four corners through the double set of doors for Room D, originally an isolation room for bone marrow transplant patients who wouldn't be going anywhere for a while. We couldn't angle the bed because it had to go straight from the inner doorway into a five-foot vestibule and through an outer doorway the same width as the first, thus going through two tight openings at the same time. Both openings were an inch or so smaller because of the doors, but the inner door swung a hundred eighty degrees to leave an opening the size of the doorframe. The outer door in its narrow vestibule swung only a hundred twenty degrees, so we lost half an inch there. Finally we jostled and squeezed the bed and pushed it and Jesse through the wide double doors to the unit, down the hallway, and to the elevators.

We worried about Jenny. She was an experienced nurse but older than her peers. By the end of her twelve-hour shifts with Jesse she was physically and mentally spent and could easily make a mistake on his medications. We would have to talk to Dr. Meyer about her.

The elevator started to close before we had the bed over the bump between hallway and elevator floors. Will hit the rubber edge of the left-hand door to send it back, only to have it return a moment later. We got the bed over the bump and in and pushed its head against the back wall, then realized that Jenny and Fashion Statement had forgotten to get in. The bed seemed to fill the elevator. Its right side was snug against one wall. There was a narrow alley, disappearing every few seconds when the doors sprang back, between its left side and the other wall by the control panel. Jenny, wide as an alley, struggled at the doors. Fashion Statement stood back, silent. We tried to help Jenny get in while not paying so much attention to her that the doors closed and took off with Jesse on his bed, alone and rudderless. Jenny hesitated at the gate. Will turned to her.

Get in!

She obeyed him immediately. He gave her a boost as she climbed up and over at the right side of the bed using the bars as hand and foot holds. I grabbed her arm to steady her and barely kept her from keeling left and falling on top of Jesse. We turned to Fashion Statement. Her face was impassive, as if carved in marble to commemorate her bloody victory over Holofernes. Suddenly, face still frozen, she jumped up, over, and down in one silky motion and pushed the button before either of us could lay a hand on her. The doors closed. We wondered if we should run downstairs and meet them in the basement. We guessed that after this dry run they'd be able to get Jesse and the bed off by themselves. If not, they would not both be able to get off without him. We waited. Jesse came back alive. The CAT scan showed no inter-cranial pressure.

Next morning, the 17th, Jesse was coming around. He's getting quite strong, Marion, the night nurse, said to us at the end of her shift. He pulled at his white gauze restraints. Leslie, the day nurse, was too gentle. She loosened the restraints. I tightened them after she left.

Strong or not, he was unconscious or semiconscious from drugs and ammonia in his body that rose as his new liver failed. The immunosuppressant drugs they gave to keep his body from rejecting his liver weakened his body's ability to fight sepsis. The antibiotics they gave to fight sepsis were bad for his liver and kidneys. Should they try to save his liver or go after the infection with all they had? His liver had to work a little or he'd die, but they had to treat the infection or he'd die.

He had stopped putting out urine. His kidney numbers went up. He burned up calories and fat without moving. His blood, full of acid, soured the drugs it carried and hurt his breathing. He needed albumin, a protein, to keep fluid in his blood vessels. His liver wasn't making it so they gave it intravenously, but his kidneys couldn't handle that. Because they weren't getting enough fluid. Because the fluid was leaking from his blood vessels.

Dr. Dorand and Dr. Lanier came by on rounds. Dr. Dorand said Jesse's kidney numbers were up and they'd decided to start him on dialysis.

How long will he need it?

Five days.

I thought he was joking, gently mocking my desire for certainty. Yet it seemed that Jesse had passed a certain checkpoint in critical illness. Now, all the machines he was connected to had become part of him and taking them away would be unnatural.

But his heart and lungs are good, said Dr. Dorand. Rejection and infection are still the issues. If we go back in, it will be to look for infection.

He went over to the nurse's station to check on lab tests. Dr. Lanier stayed with us. He seemed more optimistic today.

If the infection in Jesse's liver turns around, his liver might turn around. If his liver turns around, his kidneys will kick in. And magically, everything will change. The swelling will go down, the bleeding will stop, and he will wake up and get better.

He moved when we talked to him. We didn't know when to talk and when to be silent, when it helped him to hear our voices and when it upset him. The doctors told us he wouldn't remember any of this when he got better, that Versed, a drug that kept him calm, would also give him amnesia. I was skeptical. We all had too much to lose to want to know the truth on this point.

We played music for him on his tape recorder. Gail wanted something soothing. Rachel wanted to play his tapes, mostly alternative rock and not soothing. I stood in the middle, as always, and put on Van Morrison, *'Til We Get the Healing Done*, which became a kind of theme song, and more raunchy tunes, *Gloria* and *Good Morning Little Schoolgirl*. Rachel liked the tape and thought Jesse probably did, too. We knew he liked Seal, but I didn't want to play *A Prayer for the Dying*. Rachel thought it was fine, Jesse loved the song and it would call out to him.

That evening I stood by his bed and took his hand.

Picture yourself getting a little bit better each day, Jesse. See yourself sitting in a chair. Then see yourself taking a short walk down the hall, like you did after your colitis surgery. Then see yourself taking a longer walk each day. See yourself putting on your clothes and going down to the cafeteria. Like we did that day, remember? Then see yourself walking out of here.

He answered with hand squeezes and leg twitches.

The next day they went back in. Dr. Dorand talked to us in the surgical waiting room. He said the liver looked good.

Later, back on the PICU, Dr. Lanier made his rounds and talked to us in the hall outside Room D.

We're in uncharted territory with Jesse.

We were learning about Jesse's doctors and their specialties. The liver team was the surgeons, the gastroenterologists or GIs, a nurse, Cindy, who was also the clinical coordinator for the team, and a social worker. The team made late-afternoon rounds. The attending surgeon led the way with the attending GI at his side. A surgical fellow and a GI resident followed, with the coordinator behind and another resident or medical student bringing up the rear. The social worker with the team usually came on her own at odd times. The attending surgeon was in charge, then the attending GI. The GIs followed Jesse's medical condition and the surgeons followed what they had done surgically, studying his liver and blood and kidney numbers written in pencil on the large chart taped to his door. The GIs were medical doctors, as opposed to the surgeons, who were, What? I asked Gail.

Medical doctors practice medicine. They don't do surgery. Surgeons do surgery. They don't practice medicine.

OK, but what does practicing medicine mean?

Doing everything but surgery.

The impression, mostly unspoken, that I got from the medical doctors was that surgeons know how to cut and splice, take out old body parts and put in new ones. They are highly skilled technicians, magicians even, but they don't know how the body works when it's healthy and what disease is when health vanishes. And they don't know the person. Fine, I thought, but if you take that logic far enough, why not conclude that the old-time general practitioner who made home visits forty years ago was superior to them both?

And there was more, it seemed, again mostly unspoken, to this interdisciplinary catfight. The specialty you chose was not a matter of skill and interest alone but a reflection of who you were inside. Medical doctors treat the person and transplant surgeons trade in body parts, but it isn't the nature of the work that draws the GIs toward people and the surgeons away from them. No, the influence works the other way. The GIs are drawn to their discipline because they want to care for the whole person, while the surgeons are undersocialized individuals who lack the ability or inclination to deal with the person unless he's asleep on an aluminum table.

I didn't buy this analysis. For one thing, it let the surgeons off the hook. For another, it didn't fit with my experience. Jesse's first neurosurgeon, Dr. Lynd, was a compassionate individual, if reserved and a bit severe. Dr. Harrison, his second, was a pleasant fellow. He always asked, during grade school years at Worthington Hooker on Canner Street, if Jesse knew his red house a few doors away from the school. This was part of his examination, no doubt, to see whether Jesse understood his question, how observant he was, whether his speech was clear or slurred, and how his eyes tracked, but Dr. Harrison pulled it off with aplomb. Dr. Giselle, who performed Jesse's colitis surgery, was a gentleman from the old, fatherly school of medicine. If a sheen of ego overlay his manner to match his custom-made suits, it could have been far worse for someone whom colleagues and patients alike revered as the Zeus of gastrointestinal surgery. Dr. Dorand was a sensitive type, and sociable in his way. Dr. Rand, a surgical fellow, swung back and forth between the exception and the rule depending on whether he was with Dr. Dorand or Dr. Swanson, who was more distant, and uncomfortable with family members in meetings that did not conform to the hierarchical.

Which doesn't mean the GIs and surgeons didn't often perform true to theory. Dr. Lanier took time to talk with us. Dr. Dorand did as well, but you could see that Lanier felt a special burden of conveying Jesse's condition to us in lay terms. Dorand, by contrast, would sometimes stand at the foot of the bed and talk about Jesse as though he wasn't there. We had to motion him to the back wall when the talk got dicey.

The PICU doctors followed Jesse's condition from minute to minute, making decisions about intubating and extubating, feeding or stopping IV feeds, holding or giving blood products. Here on the PICU the surgeons were the final authority for surgical cases but had to share some power with the PICU docs. Here, too, the families had power, even if we were pushing the envelope, a double set of parents asking questions and making suggestions, and Jesse here longer than most patients, who usually go up to the floor or die within a few days. On the surgical intensive care unit, the SICU, off the high side of the pavilion, however, the surgeons ruled and visiting hours were strictly enforced.

Given the difference between the Sick-you and the Pick-you, it wasn't surprising that, except for Dr. Meyer whom they regarded as a true intensivist, the surgeons didn't think much of the PICU staff. We didn't share their view, but you could see why Dr. Meyer was the exception that proved their rule. She had the gift of simultaneously conveying a sense of high drama and of absolute calm. She came onto the unit one morning when a little girl from India was coding, that is, dropping like a stone toward death, blood pressure and breath gone for good in the absence of immediate medical intervention. I saw Dr. Meyer, far down the hall and apparently lost in thought, walking from the direction of the lab. She glanced up, shouted What?!, ran down the hall gathering information from the resident and nurse, and gave orders as she put her hands on the little girl, all in the space of seconds. They brought the little girl back. She died the next day, but Dr. Meyer, you felt, was always on the case for every patient on the unit. She listened to everyone, nurses and family members as much as residents, and made your observations her own, or let you think so. We wondered how she relaxed or made time for her husband and baby, but as long as she was here there was always something else that could be done and so, there was always hope for Jesse.

The GIs and PICU doctors had a certain bond. They spent time around each other and their patients and shared the knowledge that surgeons could cut but only medicine could make whole. The PICU residents made fun of the surgeons' preference for studying numbers on the liver chart over looking at the patient on the bed five feet away. The liver surgeons looked down on the GIs as well as the ICU docs and nurses, but from not so lofty a height, having to live with them. The GIs treated the surgeons, especially Dr. Swanson, the chief, and Dr. Dorand, the assistant chief and chief of pediatric transplantation, with deference. When Dr. Dorand came in with the team we watched the others shift as he shifted, turn as he turned, freeze like us at mock inattention when his tics got the better of him, and wait like us with baited breath for his assessment of the day. And both surgeons and GIs were part of the liver team, the group that handled the most difficult and complex of all organ transplants. Their arrival for rounds resembled, as Rachel put it, the arrival of a herd of bull elephants headed for town. You heard them coming, or heard wild reports of their approach, from this direction or that, trampling undergrowth and peasants alike as they came, and you felt the ground tremble beneath your feet long before you saw them.

What did Jesse, with his vast experience, make of this? He had always paid as little attention to doctors as possible except to be wary of all of them. But perhaps his understanding of medicine and surgery was just as acute as he needed it to be. This one cuts, that one doesn't, but that one can tell this one that he needs to.

The 19th. My boss was in the City on business. He came by and took me out for lunch. He was the new point person for behavioral health, meaning mental health and substance abuse treatment, for the Department of Psychiatry at the Yale School of

Medicine. A year and a half ago he had hired me to run a homeless outreach project for the community mental health center that the department runs. I had already talked to the clinical director of the outreach project. She had stood in for me for the presentation at the medical school and said it had gone well. My boss, too, thought it had gone well. We talked about his new duties for the Department of Psychiatry. He was meeting with some suits in the afternoon to try to sell the department's services and expertise. I felt as though I'd walked into a strange place and time that I knew quite well but only in the most superficial way. I talked about Jesse and his operations and the equipment he was connected to. My boss shook his head and said how tough it was to make it back when you're on life support.

Jesse's on life support? What's he talking about?

Jesse had been in the hospital only two weeks, but we'd grown close to Dr. Dorand. Perhaps we thought his vulnerability made him eligible to wield a knife on our son. And we could always count on him to give a positive spin on a blizzard of bad news. If Dr. Lanier was a poet with a metaphor for every visit and every change of condition, Dr. Dorand was a philosopher-scientist searching for clinical confirmation of his theory that the universe was weighted ever-so-slightly toward health over disease. Jesse's bilirubin was up, but all the blood products he was getting could cause that. If all his liver numbers that should be down were up, Dr. Dorand found a couple that were promising, if not exactly where they should be. I had persuaded myself that he liked Jesse and that his unending search for a crevice to hammer the next spike into was made up of more than fear of having Jesse's death logged against him. Or perhaps our affection for him came from his having taken the time to talk to Jesse before he was changed.

Three months earlier, Cindy had told me in hushed, almost religious tones, that Dr. Dorand wanted to meet Jesse when we brought him in for his last clinic visit before transplant. It was clear we should regard this as an honor. I tried to prep Jesse.

What questions would you like to ask Dr. Dorand, Jesse?

I don't know.

I ask a lot of questions. Maybe it keeps you from asking questions that you have. After all, it is your body.

Shrug, little smile.

I suggested that he ask how long he'd be in the hospital after his transplant. Also, how long he'd have to wait after the transplant before he could have an ileoanal pull through, where they would take his stoma, the round red bulb end of his small intestine that peeked out from the side of his belly, pull it down, and sew it to his rectal muscles so he could have near-normal bowel movements again.

Shrug, little smile.

We went in to the clinic. Jesse's name was called. Dr. Dorand sat behind a large mahogany desk in a tiny office. Jesse and I sat in chairs facing him, knees almost touching the desk. I asked my questions, then Jesse his, with some encouragement. About eighteen days, if there are no complications, said Dr. Dorand of Jesse's hospital stay after transplant. About six months, he said, of the time between transplant and pull through. His shoulder jerked occasionally as he talked and his pinky finger tipped forward and punctuated, by contrast, the subtly pictorial movements of his hands. I noted, pleased with Jesse's sense of etiquette, that he did not react visibly to Dr. Dorand's tics. It was odd, but we, his parents, never worried about Dorand's ability to perform the most delicate of surgeries, although Jesse may have. We joked about him in the hall outside Jesse's room, just as we joked about Dr. Swanson's too-tight scrubs or interpreted the faraway look in Dr. Boyd's eyes, but we assumed that Dr. Dorand's tics stopped when he worked. Jill, the evening nurse who knew everything about everyone here, confirmed this for us.

Jesse and I left the office. A few minutes later Dr. Dorand came out and met with all of us, Gail, Daniel, Cassandra, Rachel who had just made it in from work, Jesse and I, in a small waiting room. He turned to Jesse.

I have no problem going ahead with a transplant for you. You're young and you have your whole life ahead of you. Marriage, children, or whatever it is you want. And getting the pull through done, if you want that. I know I would.

He was reaching out to Jesse and Jesse was hard to reach. He just wanted to get this over with and forget about it.

But there is about a seven-percent chance that you won't make it.

I looked at Jesse. He showed no reaction.

Dr. Dorand stood with us now a few feet behind Jesse's bed, as we had taught him. He was ready to go and getting nervous, but Gail and I had taken positions on either side of him. Gail asked him what he thought about Jesse's condition. There was a long silence.

It worries me that he's not getting better. It's puzzling. There are no positive cultures. It could be a bacteria or virus we don't usually see. Or a toxic reaction to medications. Or his spleen. The clotting is bad. I don't think he's still infected but the damage is done. And the longer things stay neutral the more things can happen.

What about a second liver?

We're not there yet. We're thinking about it. I still think the liver can turn around.

There was another pause.

But it's possible he's not turning around because of the damaged liver. I'll talk with Dr. Swanson about it.

Sunday, May 21st. Rachel and I waited for rounds all Sunday afternoon. Gail and Will had gone home. It was a beautiful late-spring day in Central Park near the hospital, but the air itself was tainted in here. The silence made Jesse seem more ill and made hope seem a cruel thing to entertain. Dr. Swanson came by, just back from a liver conference in Chicago. We talked with him outside Jesse's room.

He can beat this. He's young and strong. That's the best thing he has going for him. If there comes a point when I think he can't make it, I'll tell you. My advice is, put down the notebooks. Take a walk in the park. Have hope. It will get communicated to him.

What about another transplant?

It's not indicated at this point.

It was a pep talk, and it came at the right time for us at the end of a long sorrowful weekend. We felt better and took his advice, in shifts.

Jesse's blood pressure went down during the night. His weight and abdominal girth were up. His stomach was tight as a drum. His intestine was still, no movement to show that his digestive system was working even a little bit. They stopped feeding him. The fluid in his abdomen pushed hard at the base of his lungs. His left chest tube, for he had two now, wasn't draining well. They put in two new IV lines, one in each arm. He was in DIC, disseminated intravascular coagulopathy, Dr. Meyer told us, where the body's fiber breaks down the body's clotting products. The cure for DIC is a blood transfusion, but blood transfusions can make the bleeding worse. He oozed and bled from surgical wounds and bruised without moving. The bag on his side filled up with blood. They put goggles on his eyes to protect them from a virus, cytomeglia, that he was at risk for now. Dr. Dorand and Dr. Lanier made rounds. Dr. Dorand started.

Jesse's condition has gotten worse. He probably won't last more than another day or two.

What will happen? I asked.

They won't be able to maintain his blood pressure, said Dr. Lanier.

Dr. Dorand gave me an embarrassed smile and shook my hand. They went on down the hall. Rachel was crying. I put my arm around her, unsure whether I should. We agreed that we should make phone calls, and split up. I was hungry. I went down to the cafeteria and got something to eat. Then I called Gail and went back upstairs. Jesse was bloated, bloated and gray to me in the dark. All the claptrap about saying It's all right to let go went through my mind, but I couldn't say goodbye to him out loud. Gail arrived. We sat in the NICU lounge and talked about the funeral. I wondered if Rachel and I would fight over it.

five

They are not my favorites, these superheroes he drew with their too-perfect bodies, and there were thousands of them, winnowed and tossed over the years, destroyed by water in the basement here one summer, lost in other ways, unaccountably, and those, only the ones he did on my watch. Rachel has her own, I'm sure, and her own treasures lost in a flood at her Milford home on the Long Island shore a few years ago. Perhaps I like them least because I see him at three years old in his Superman outfit with his fist in front of his face declaring that he knows everything in the world, will never forget, and won't tell anyone, when I knew he felt like no superhero inside. Please, I wanted to say, tell me one thing about Jesse and you can keep all the other secrets of the universe to yourself.

His dream of a perfect body may have begun as early as hydrocephalus, but I think of the first Star Wars movie, shown in what was then a novel phenomenon, the multiplex freestanding cinema, even if the gravity-defying feats of that movie were performed by spaceships, not their pilots. We walked past endless rows of cars and up the pale concrete steps to the cinema. It is the new church, I thought, devoid of history or dirt or communion, built to sunder people from place and prepare them to seek out the stars. Inside on the big screen, the perfect vehicle had been created to consecrate this new church, a revelation of jump cuts from one scene or corner of the universe to another, where each set was a vehicle for movement from here to there, a revelation of a world freed from the bonds of gravity and filled with conflict to compensate for its incurable homelessness, its only connection to place and history its implied yearning to be, for the new era it ushered in, a source of nostalgia, a long time ago in a galaxy far far away. Yet didn't we glide down those steps happy? Didn't we long to reach our own vehicle and strap ourselves in for takeoff? We, too, might push the right button and disappear into hyperspace, fast or was it faster than the speed of light?

This superhero hangs at waist level ten feet from where I stand by the open door to the new basement going down to Jesse's bedroom. The wall it hangs on is the other side of the passageway in his grandmother's apartment where he checked his hair. Its free-floating bottom is level with the kitchen floor. The stairwell ceiling, with no stairs running in the opposite direction to the second floor, is level with the kitchen ceiling, but the descending steps make the opening appear cavernous.

The drawing, a few strong pencil lines on a large sheet of paper, shows a densely muscled superhero touching down on a sidewalk, right leg first left leg trailing. His hair is crew cut. He wears a half-mask from hairline to nose. Five collar points flare out below his jaw to match his flared shoulder pads and flared boots and the lines of motion flaring out from the pavement on either side of him. His fists resemble small atomic explosions. His belt holds several small leather pouches with snaps, energy sources for various super powers or pillboxes for various diseases.

The stairs to the old basement, off the hallway that connects the kitchen and living room, are narrow, with a low ceiling to accommodate the stairs to the second floor of this 1940s Cape. The stairwell ceiling needs taping and spackling where crumbling plaster meets sheetrock halfway down. My study is to the right of the stairs. Gerrymandered scraps of kelly green rug cover the concrete floor and are the source, Gail claims, of an odd smell, like mold but not that of mold, which comes with autumn and at other times even with the dehumidifier chugging away by the door. The walls are tan faded from white. The fluorescent light box overhead needs framing or removal. The Formica-top metal desk from a United Illuminating tag sale holds a large monitor and keyboard connected to a computer that sits on a board game on the floor to protect it from minor flooding. To the right of the desk over the computer and its tangle of wires is a narrow table for the printer. Two metal file cabinets stand side by side to the left of the desk. A two-sided bookcase the former owner built to box in the water meter protrudes from the wall opposite the desk. Four bookcases painted green, brown, white, and blue stand at the perimeter of the room. Everything looks half-finished and is void of personality but for three of Jesse's drawings, a couple of Daniel's and Cassandra's, and a vividly colored Superman poster from the *Death of Superman* series on the walls. But this study is not without its utilitarian virtues. I felt no compunction about making five hundred-odd holes in its walls with pushpins through index cards corresponding to dates and events from my Jesse notebooks. That stage, as the grief dramatists call it, has been broken down, leaving a pockmarked image behind.

A stack of folders full of drawings sits on the blue bookcase. A set of outsize childhood drawings, which Gail discovered near the oil tank around the corner, sits on top of the metal file cabinets. I spread them out on the floor around me and turn the pages, stopping at a few.

Here are superheroes, Comet, whose muscular right arm ends in a huge fist, the arm and fist of power that appear over and over again in Jesse's drawings, the albino Whiteout with reptilian face missing both nose and mouth, and Nighthawk, thin for a superhero, who stands on a beach of black sand crumbled from the bank of shale behind it and looks out at the winedark sea.

And enemies. Behind Nighthawk, a batlike creature emerges from the shale, leaning at Nighthawk's angle. A mandala-shaped demon's flanged hood and horns make ten halo points around its head. Its ten sharp teeth bite dreams into nightmares. The Thangorian god, archenemy of George 10, stands naked in a raging fire. Twisted ram's horns grow from his head. His eyes, even in pencil, are bloodshot. Fangs curl from his mouth. His penis dangles in the fiery breeze.

Here, bands of superheroes, the earnest and the comic, travel together with carnival energy, an air of the grotesque. Streams of light freeze on hitting the air and hang from the eye sockets of one. A group of flying figures converges on a winged dragon, but optical illusion makes them explode outward from the dragon as the center and source of its power. A dwarf female, in a Maria Bonaparte decadent mask with wings that stretch up on either side of her red bouffant hair, shows legs that are shapely but too thick for her miniskirt. Next to her is a diminutive hero in diapers with long claws for hands, and next to him a robot that looks soft, vulnerable, with square ears and rectangular eyes. Hovering over them is a batlike creature with a face part man part horse and wings like an undiscovered continent ending in fists.

Here, superheroes rise up from a standstill as though flight is an act of will not aerodynamics, and gently touch down on the vertical like Christopher Reeve, more graceful than any helicopter. A Blakean would-be angel with rounded shoulders seen from above emerges from a deep pool. Another moves forward with breaststrokes that carry him across those same dark blue, those still quiet waters.

At times the fugitive nature of their calling suggests what Jesse was struggling with. The Manta, a lithe hero with batlike wings, flanged cape, and pointed ears, holds a hose that curves from behind his back. I am the vengeance that goes splishy splashy in the night, the caption above him reads. The Amazing Mr. Higgins, a bespectacled intellectual with tiny metal frame glasses, big head on small body, wide mouth full of teeth, lightning bolts that flash from the top of his head, and a look of perpetual surprise at what his mind has just unveiled to him, appears in the opening frame of a comic book episode working out an impossible mathematical equation. In the next panel he stands, a child, between his proud farmer parents Bob and Ellie. In the next he goes off to public school, then college, and completes both with high honors in six minutes. Everyone is happy for him, everyone, that is, except Lally Liver, an angry troll-like creature in the last panel, who is extremely jealous.

Here, a map of a province of Eggnog III shaped like a brain with an elongated cerebellum. In the center are two protruding kidney-shaped eye sockets, Murgot's Snot and Urinal Lake. To the right of Urinal Lake is a misplaced pituitary gland in a shaded area called Outland of Mindless Ones. At the rear center of the cerebrum is Highbrow City. Near the brain stem along a tributary of Chrpp Lake lies the town of Gall.

Here, a folder full of early handmade cards. Some, like this one for Gail, protest too much. Happy Mother's Day Gail, it says, and I love you Gail the mommy you are very beautiful. Inside are drawings of witches with balloons and a crafty-eyed character staring down the head witch. Next, a king and queen glare murderously at each other as though his or her ham acting has brought down the curtain on *Ubu Roi.* The king, a male version of the queen, has an even bigger nose than her. Mother and Father are written above their respective crowns.

On the outsize pages, mazes that crawl across the page sending out tentacles of confusion, insoluble puzzles, it seems, that may engulf the hero on his quest. Spaceships sprout space flowers that bloom and pull them up by their cones. Asteroids and stars and men who may be comets drift like snowflakes big as apples to the ground.

A folder filled with Jesse's writings, early poems and later short pieces, mostly comic. Here at the back of the folder, though, is his unfinished George 10 saga. The computer file date on the first and longest piece I found, the Catalogue, was April 27, 1995, the day of his last, cancelled appointment with Dr. Gardner.

George Ten aka George 10 aka G-10 aka Georges Georgino Nalphace Ten the Third Esquire is twenty-four years old in egg years and two hundred seventy-six years old in earth years. This makes 11.5 Eggnogian years for each earth year and puts Eggnog on a slow revolution around its sun. Eggnog, then, must be farther away from its sun than the earth is to ours. This means either that the Eggnogian sun is much hotter than ours or that Eggnogian bodies have tremendous thermal insulation for withstanding the cold. George, at six-foot-three, weighs 397 pounds. Taken with the portraits I have of George, which show him as solid, muscular, but by no means overweight, this indicates that Eggnogian gravity is denser than ours, that space engineering and flight are more difficult there than here, and that Eggnogian interplanetary travel is all the more noteworthy for the obstacles it has had to overcome.

George has green eyes, dirty blond hair, eggnog skin, and 20/20 vision. His race is Fugitive Duatian/Monolithian. His aliases include Lord Charles, G-Wiz, Mabel, the Q, and Dirty Blond Beard the Space Pirate. His marital, political, legal, and health statuses, his weapons, hobbies, special talents, bad habits, career trajectory, and superstitions are given, along with his Eggnogian social security and Thangorian prison camp ID numbers and his license numbers for space cruiser operation, wild animal keeping, swashbuckling, and marriage, expired because he is a widower. Among the schools he attended are the Cardanzian Police School, the Kedesian Monastery of Rjuill Mastery, Flydrge's School for the Assassin, MIG's School of Alien Electronics, and Egghead's School of Advanced Knowledge. His vehicles and weapons include his space hopper, Eggwhipper II, his bioelectrical left hand, six boxes of rubber nipples, and special extra-smoky Duatian cigars. Seafood, galactic grain, manna, potatoes, eggnog and eggnog-based products are the chief elements of his diet. His grandmother is none other than the illustrious and exotic Jasmine Sarafina Almeena Bambilliana Potyuch.

The Catalogue gives information on planetary position and star map coordinates, elementary planetary composition, and moons for Eggnog III. It gives life spans, ruling powers, major industries, imports and exports, races, population, and population density for same. The latter, 112,323,131 Eggnogians per square mile, may explain that civilization's obsession with space travel. The Catalogue also contains the first few pages of an English to Eggnogian dictionary.

A - Q
ABACK - OYZAW
ABACUS - CACLTIGNH
ABAFT - HIBEND
ABALONE - SHILLGEB
ABANDON - NEOVEEAL
ABASE - IEP
ABASH - WUNTHEDA

ABATE - MEDFOFTAPRE
ABATIS - KILBRANSE
ABATTOIR - CAPLETTEGRE
ABBACY - METOH
ABBE - GLASAGAN
ABBESS - DOBBAGE
ABBEY - TEAAREE
ABBOT - LERROPNDOS
ABBREVIATE - ZYAL
ABDICATE - GEFBLEK
ABDOMEN - HOTAX
ABDUCT - PAPNAOLD
ABEAM - HAJYHAJY
ABECEDARIAN - KOOKIER
ABED - ZZLEEBZZ
ABERRATION - DEREWI
ABET
ABEYANCE
ABHOR
ABIDE
ABILITY
ABJECT
ABJURE
ABLATE
ABLATION
ABLATIVE
ABLE
ABLOOM
ABLUTION
ABNEGATE
ABNORMAL
ABOARD

ABODE
ABOLISH
ABOMINABLE
ABORIGINAL

This is no mere transposition of letters. A is Q but there is no Q in the Eggnogian equivalent of Aback. There is no symmetry in number of letters between English and Eggnogian. The A and Q and Aback and Oyzaw pairs have one and five letters each, but symmetry ends with Abacus and Cacltignh, which have seven and nine letters, respectively. The continuation of untranslated English words from Abet to Aboriginal shows that Jesse didn't give the A to Aberration definitions merely as examples to lend verisimilitude to his alternate galaxy. True, he skipped over some English words such as Aardvark, Aardwolf, Aaronic, and Abaca, but these might have been missing from the pocket dictionary he had in his room. Finally, the abundance of words rarely used in spoken conversation proves he was not creating a lowly English-Eggnogian conversational dictionary for earthly travelers on some future intergalactic shuttle, but a bona fide, scholarly English-Eggnogian dictionary.

He protected one George 10 story with a password I had taught him how to create. Coming back to it just weeks before we went to the hospital, he couldn't remember his own code. We tried every combination we could think of, and I've had time to wish I'd done then what I did much later, take it to an expert and have it decoded. I came home with disc and password on a scrap of paper and stole down here breathless. I brought up the file list in the directory and clicked on the filename George10. The screen asked for a password. I typed in EGG3MRZBRZ, pleased to see my initials in the dead center of the code. The file came up. I sank in my chair. It appeared to be only the Catalogue under another name. But scrolling down on the screen I saw, in the middle of the document after Vespas, 11th planet from the Eggnogian sun, a new section labeled History.

The story begins with a recap of a civil war in the province of Duatia between those who favored cloning and those who were against it. The anti-gestaters, we are told, broke into the gestation chambers and found three gestation pods belonging to George 10 the Second. They destroyed one of the pods and damaged another. The damaged pod was repaired, leaving no visible signs of imperfection. Two weeks after the break-in two healthy Eggnogians, George 10 the Third and Charles Browning Miggilicutty, were born. The story does not tell us which infant suffered the invisible damage. We know from the Catalogue that George suffers from chronic tomatoed eggnog disease, but the same source tells us that t.e.d. is common to all Eggnogians. The stage set, the main part of what, as it turns out, is only a fragment of the History, begins.

George and Charles lived with their father on his asparagus farm in the province of Cud. One day an armada of strange ships descended into the atmosphere. George 10 the Second and his sons flew up in their sky-plowcycles to greet the visitors. They thought the ships were bringing the farming supplies they had ordered. But no, they were invading Thangorians, mortal enemies of all Eggnogians. A beam of light leapt from one of the ships and knocked George 10 the Third out cold. He woke up, shackled with his brother along with many other children in a prison that overlooked a huge arena. The brothers looked out from a tiny window in their prison cell and saw a group of prisoners, including their father, being herded into the arena. Suddenly a centaur emerged from a blazing portal at the other end of the arena. Alone among the prisoners, George Ten the Second mounted a valiant defense, but finally the centaur over-

powered him and clove his skull in twain, shouting out I AM MAELSTROM. George 10 the Third swore to avenge his father's death, but before he could begin to make his plans he and his brother were thrown into the arena with the other captured children to face an assortment of wild beasts collected from all over the universe. The brothers fought fiercely but Charles succumbed. Moments later a claw slashed George's chest and he went down in a field of red.

I walk back through his drawings in my mind. There are many of the bearded George Ten the Third but I don't recall seeing his father or brother or Maelstrom, although it's possible he drew them without naming them. The story moves on.

George woke up. His eyes were glued together from dried blood. He heard heavy objects like bodies being thrown onto wood like the bed of a cart and he heard a man named Jonah speaking to his companion.

Well, Ronanin, this is the last load. We must find a way to stop Maelstrom.

It is written in the stars, Ronanin replied, that one day a savior seeking revenge for some past wrong shall rise up to oppose the dread lord Maelstrom and his vicious armies of death and shall emerge the victor. But wait! This one yet lives.

Jonah and Ronanin lifted up George 10 and took him to a huge golden monastery. Upon his recovery George began his studies of the Great Rjuill under the Lord High Priest Ronanin's tutelage. One day after finishing his schoolwork George 10 went into town to check on a delayed supply shipment. He arrived to see mangled bodies lying everywhere. He raced back toward the monastery but tripped, fell, and blacked out.

This motif, having George black out whenever it's time to switch to another part of the story, could have used some work.

> *Back at the monastery an armada of Thangorian battle cruisers had opened fire on the priests, destroying their golden edifice and leaving the bodies of the monks and priests Swiss-cheesed beyond recognition. Only High Priest Ronanin survived. The Thangorian guards captured him and brought him to the Lord High Commander, who demanded the names and locations of those whom Ronanin and Jonah had taken from the arena. Ronanin stood in silence. The Lord High Commander ordered him to be taken away and tortured. But he had one more thing to say to his archenemy.*
>
> *Years ago we had one of our agents pose as an injured prisoner. When you saved him, Ronanin, he was really infiltrating your monastery, gaining your trust, and sending us the information that made possible this attack that was launched upon you today.*

We might expect Ronanin to doubt the Lord High Commander's word as a matter of principle, or at least to wonder how a spy could give the Thangorians precise information on the monastery's location but could not, over the course of some years, tell them who else had been taken alive from the arena. Perhaps suspicion is Ronanin's tragic flaw. In any case, he breaks free of his captors. As he teleports himself away he mutters, Beware George 10 for I shall be back and you shall pay! Here, the story switches back to George 10.

> *George 10 arrived to find the monastery in ruins. He began his mission to search throughout the planet for survivors. Finally he reached Highbrow, the legendary city of the ultra-intelligent*

and was taken to Egghead, the Highbrow chief. Egghead raised George as his own child and taught him the warrior's art. Years later George went out into the universe to seek adventure, always as a loner until the citizens of the planet Banana12 hired him to defend them against a band of fugitive Thangorians. The Thangorians surrounded him but were routed by a talking wolf, Aaarroooow, an experimental Thangorian lab dog who was exiled after a traitorous wolf unjustly accused him of cannibalism.

This meeting marks the beginning of the greatest superhero partnership in the history of the universe, if an idiosyncratic one, being a mixture of good deeds and shameless plundering. The story now skips over the next few years to a point when George 10's exploits have won him fame and fortune.

After becoming rich enough to buy a large ship and hire a crew, George 10 was shot down by bounty hunters trying to win a bounty that the ruling beings of the universe had placed on his head. But George and his crew escaped in their evacuation pod. Then a band of pig men on an uncharted planet hired them to kill a rogue dragon that lived in a cave outside of town.

The dragon, Shali-Dazire, saw them coming and toasted the three crewmembers with his fiery breath and was about to do the same to George and Aaarroooow when George noticed an amulet hanging from its neck. He smashed it with his sword. A million worlds, an angry scream of defeat rang out as the charm that held Shali-Dazire was broken! Shali-Dazire apologized for his behavior and vowed to follow George 10 for restoring him to the sanctity of his mind.

In the last incident this fragment recounts, George 10 lands his new ship near the arena where his father and brother were killed, and enters in disguise.

> *A scarred figure awaiting battle looked vaguely familiar to George. As the bell rang, a six-armed monster appeared from behind a portal at the other end of the arena and flung a battle-axe at the scar-faced warrior. The warrior dodged the weapon, jumped on the monster, and reduced it to a bloody pulp of matted fur. After the battle, George met the warrior, named Bane. The Bane told George that Maelstrom had won his freedom in battle and that he, the Bane, was the new arena champion, fighting for his own freedom. George offered to free the Bane in exchange for his help in destroying Maelstrom. The Bane was reluctant, but when he learned George's name and history, a smile came over his face. He agreed to George's terms. They escaped the arena and returned to George's ship to find that frog-like aliens had smashed it beyond repair. With a sinister smile the Bane announced that he knew a former prisoner, a space pirate, who could help them. The space pirate arrived with his crew. As George thanked them, a robed figure snuck aboard the new spaceship and hid in the shadows.*
>
> *Now I shall have my revenge, he whispered.*

The fragment ends here. The Bane, with his scarred but familiar face, must be George's twin brother Charles, and Ronanin must have convinced him that George sided with Maelstrom to kill both their father and him. But George, too, is blinded by his passions. He can't see, for example, that Maelstrom is merely a Thangorian pawn. Inserted here in the Catalogue, I think of this story as one of hundreds to be told. Perhaps Jesse would have reworked it, as he did with some of his best drawings, if he finally had been able to break his own code. Would he have delved deeper, extending the

Catalogue to include the arts and customs, the ethics and etiquette of Eggnog III? Would the Catalogue have recorded his growing isolation? Or would he have put it aside because he had found a way out of his own maze and come home after many adventures?

Here, his Odin dream. Rachel and I sat in our chairs at the foot of Jesse's hospital bed, in July I think. My ears burned with envy as Rachel told me the dream he had told her one weekend in Stamford two months before we brought him to New York.

My friend and I made a pact with Odin. My friend needed protection from a gang that wanted to kill him. He initiated the pact and Odin promised to protect him from the gang. But Odin broke the pact and the gang attacked my friend and he died in the hospital. I decided to seek revenge. I would find Odin and kick his butt. I asked around and heard about a cave that had just been unearthed that might lead me to him. I went into the cave and got lost in one of the thousand tunnels but finally I came out at a lake. Charon the boatman was there. I paid him to ferry me across to the Land of the Dead. When I got there I met Odin's son and befriended him. I talked about his father and how I'd heard a lot about him and wanted to meet him but I didn't reveal my true motive. He took me to one of the high goddesses who could help me find his father, but she knew I didn't belong in the Land of the Dead and she tried to poison me. I made an excuse and didn't eat. She gave me a horse and I rode off to meet the three sisters who were the three fates. They were behind my plan one hundred percent. They gave me a fresh horse and directions to Odin's castle. Finally I arrived at Valhalla, the place of the fallen warriors. My friend was there, but Odin was not the mighty warrior I expected. He was a weak old man. But I had to finish my quest so I challenged him to battle. He refused to fight so I taunted him to shame him in front of his warriors. He tried to ignore me but I kept it up. I called him a cowardly old man. Finally he agreed to do battle. I kicked his butt. Odin's clown who was a jokester told Fenrir the wolf that the chains that made him Odin's pet were imaginary. Fenrir the wolf broke his imaginary chains and killed Odin. My work was finished.

So much betrayal, in the George 10 story and even in his dream! By whom did Jesse feel betrayed? His old man? His doctors? His body? I don't feel betrayed by anyone, he would have said, it's just a story. He might have gone on to say that betrayal and revenge are staple themes of the myths and comic book legends whose wisdom he drank from, assuming he had talked in such terms. I like to think he learned his Norse mythology the same way I learned mine, later than he, finding Padraic Colum's great forgotten book *The Children of Odin* in the Naugatuck Public Library. Jesse must have known, from Colum or another source, that Odin was not only a selfish doddering old man who stole earth's bravest warriors to strengthen his own forces for the final conflict with the evil forces outside Asgard. Long before he was shriveled with age and fear, Odin sacrificed an eye at the well of wisdom to save humankind from the monster Surtur, who would destroy it with fire, and from Niflheim, the place of darkness and dread, which would gather it back into nothingness.

Jesse believed in sacrifice, too, up to a point. John, his therapist, gave me a story he wrote for him at John's request that he write something about himself.

Jesse was a young Norse Thunder god when he first realized that carrots were evil aliens planning to take over the world. The omnipotent entity of the Multiverse, the All, also saw this and since he did not want to directly interfere with human affairs he set this task upon Jesse. He gave him cosmic awareness and the indestructible anti-carrot bands. It was a long hard battle but after many years Jesse was able to change the evil carrots into harmless veggies. He gave back his bands and cosmic awareness to the All and then was able to lead a normal happy life free of all nuisances save one. People who would not accept him for who he was. The End.

He was willing, even eager, to give up his cosmic awareness for a normal life, but he refused to pay for normalcy with his inner sense of who-he-was. He understood that sacrifice may ennoble the world and diminish the sufferer, who has spent his moral and imaginative powers in the act of sacrifice. He saw Odin's shameful descent into a vain and doddering old man basking in the faked adulation of his warriors. He came in as the warrior that Odin once was and reproached the old man with the image of his former self. But without looking to sacrifice his body. He refused to accept the poisonous cup the goddess proffered, and friend or no friend to keep him company, nothing in the dream persuades me that, having kicked Odin's ass, he had any intention of sticking around in the Land of the Dead.

six

Notes to memory, memory to notes. A bit more memory required here, as I recall.

It was May 23rd and it was standing room only in Room D. We watched from the doorway, rapt with the drama of CVVHD, continuous vasovascular hemodialysis. CVVHD, slower and less intensive than standard dialysis, promised to be gentler on Jesse's body than the lumbering machine the nurse had been wheeling in for his daily two-hour sessions. It was less likely to cause a sudden plunge in his blood pressure but would still clear poisons and remove fluid, if more in the manner of bailing his leaky vessel with a thimble than a bucket. Dr. Broward, the nephrologist, pointed to a square box on a stand and lectured the nursing staff on its mysteries. Every few minutes he rushed out and through the double doors off the unit and then returned to take up his lecture again. If we let him past our watch one time, we blurted out questions for him the next.

Our anxiety grew as morning stretched into afternoon. The PICU nurses had to be taught this technique, since CVVHD didn't come with a dialysis nurse to hook it up to Jesse, sit in a chair and watch his blood pressure, and troubleshoot if the lines got air bubbles in them and the machine stalled. Also, there were delays in getting the correct gauge dialysis lines. There were technical problems with the machine itself. And most formidably, there was bureaucratic warfare. CVVHD had never been used on the PICU, only on the SICU where the surgeons held uncontested power. To entrust its operation to novices, we gathered, was seen by some, administrators or surgeons, or surgeons whispering to administrators, or other mysterious forces, as setting a dangerous precedent.

Is that so, Dr. Meyer seemed to say with the barest of smiles as she went back and forth between Jesse's room and the phone at the nurse's station. Dr. Broward's unflappable manner was reassuring as well. It suggested that he knew they would work this out and that Jesse was strong enough to wait. But would Dr. Broward move mountains to make sure CVVHD happened? Would he bring in another, more experienced nurse to run the machine if necessary? And how many tosses of the dice were going against Jesse while this battle over pissing rights raged on?

Dr. Broward stopped to talk to us on one of his many trips back into Room D.

CVVHD is a side issue. It's only a device to support Jesse. The liver team and ICU are dealing with the critical issues.

But support was no side issue now, it was of the essence, and I thought this diminutive, even-keeled man was too modest. Perhaps he knew the mantle of saviorhood we were measuring him for.

Gail has a different memory. In Dr. Broward's place she has a male nurse from the SICU training the PICU nurses. And this rings true. Why not get someone who actually runs the machine to teach others how to use it? Yes, Gail allowed when I prompted her, there was a problem with the SICU, but it was a union issue, who could operate what equipment, and this was the reason they balked at training the PICU staff. And the machine itself. I said it was air clots that stalled it once the PICU was cleared to use it. Gail said it was blood clots, which I thought only clogged the machine and slowed it down.

My notes don't settle the matter. From May 22nd, the day of Dr. Dorand's one-to-two-days-to-live speech, until June 8th, they are sketchy. In one place I'm missing divisions by day for three straight days. I reconstructed them by reference to phrases like During the night or by recognizing once-a-day activities repeated over the three-day stretch. I talked with Gail about this not long ago.

I wonder why my notes aren't as good during this time.

You wonder why? Look at what was happening! We were in shock.

Was it any worse than what happened before?

I don't know. Maybe we were in shock before and you were on automatic pilot. And then it wore off and... I don't know. We were just trying to hang on.

I pursued her, on the question of when we had to hold down Jesse's legs during dialysis and when we didn't, when he was more awake and the dialysis bothered him and when he was more sedated so that it didn't faze him. She wasn't sure about my causal links, though they made sense to her, but remembered that we didn't have to hold down Jesse's legs from the 22nd to the 8th. Her memories become my memories, mine hers. I see the SICU nurse teaching the PICU nurses and I'm convinced she's right, but I'm just as convinced that Dr. Broward was on and off the unit all day and played a key role in this drama, and now she remembers him too. Have we both supplied true details to repair our fractured memories, or are we telling each other stories?

And Jesse? For a day or two CVVHD and Dr. Broward, not he, were the center of attention in Room D, but only because Jesse had survived the night. There was little he could do now but not be extinguished. He lay heavy, unmoving on his bed, hidden inside himself in sleep and sedation. Each minute he survived he beat the odds, and the noisy activity around him gave us hope. If something was being done then something could be done. But each minute CVVHD was delayed pushed the odds back up against him.

By late afternoon Dr. Meyer had prevailed. Jesse would get his CVVHD. But the machine, like Jesse, was delicate, uncertain, and proved how much he was moving in his waterlogged inertness after all. They started it. He moved his legs. It stalled. They reset it, a process that involved a painstaking series of maneuvers to remove air, as I recall, or blood clots, as Gail recalls, from the dialysis line, with time lost clearing poisons from his body. The CVVHD solution had dextrose in it, bad for his glucose level. They brought in boxes of a special dialysate with no dextrose, but it had lactose and his liver couldn't metabolize that. It was back to the big machine. CVVHD was a two-day wonder.

The next day Daniel and Cassandra visited with their grandmothers. I sat with my mother in the NICU lounge and broke down trying to tell her there was still hope for Jesse. Hope was this, that we were two days out from the one-to-two-days-to-live speech and he was still breathing with the help of a respirator. And hope was this, that when Dr. Dorand come by on rounds the day after his speech, he said, I'm mildly surprised that he hasn't deteriorated today.

We had lunch in the hospital cafeteria. Gail and I were afraid to leave the grounds for as long as it would take to eat. We talked with the children about how sick Jesse was. We wandered under the mighty glass rafters of the pavilion and saw Dr. Dorand go up the winding stairs to the surgical waiting room. I bought Cassie a stuffed dog, then walked with them all to the parking garage and ran off when Rachel beeped me. I picture them flanking the car with jaws half-dropped, but I know they were not so placed and that each of them, even eight-year-old Cassandra, was too careful to reveal so much dismay.

The next day, the 25th I think, Gail was back. So soon? Maybe the day after. We went out for coffee at Rich's Deli down the street from the hospital and bumped into Dr. Kostos, the newest of the liver surgeons. He reminded me of another Greek, a psychiatrist I worked with at the mental health center in New Haven. He was dark like him, like him thick in build rather than heavy, powerful with three thousand years of seafaring in his blood and the memory of sea salt that had toughened his skin. Dr. Kostos stood close and engaged us as if much was at stake in any conversation, about where to have lunch or the fate of his patient. I guessed that his intensity was partly cultural and partly his desire to command respect, as though, newest of the full-fledged surgeons here, he feared he might not. I was prepared to kiss his feet if it would do any good. As with the others, I judged him not only by what I could gather of his technical skills but by whether he seemed to care for my son. If the surgeons saw Jesse as a person who had a life outside the hospital and off an aluminum table, I reasoned, it would give them that much more to salvage when they cut him open.

Dr. Kostos talked about the trouble they were having trying to diagnose his condition.

There's a question about whether there are other infections. The cultures could be misleading us. And there's a question about whether Jesse's liver can bounce back.

He referred to Jesse by name. Dr. Dorand, closer to Jesse than the others because he had seen him upright, often referred to him in the third person, and you could see why he needed some distance. He knew what might be passing out of the world through his hands, or hands under his direction.

If Jesse needs another liver he can get another liver. This may be the time, while he's stable, to think about it.

So this was stable, and they were thinking about another liver for Jesse. You had to talk to different doctors who could give you different information for different reasons. Some wanted to make their own alliances with patients and families. Some had a different view than their colleagues and could point, wittingly or unwittingly, to fault lines where the team could be played. Some just wanted to help or were glad to be asked because the questions didn't often come their way. You never knew whether any of this did any good, and the danger of being played and swayed yourself was always there, but we were swayed already by every comment and look and phrase of body language from doctor, nurse, and recreation therapist. Scheming at least lent the illusion we were doing something, and that kept our hopes alive so we could be good for Jesse. We lived in another world now, where every conversation could mean the difference between life and death, or where this seemed to be so, and so we played the percentages and people, even those we liked and trusted, for every possible advantage.

That afternoon Dr. Gardner, Jesse's GI, and Dr. Hall, his pediatrician, came in from New Haven to see him and meet his doctors. We talked with them outside Room D. Rachel, behind me to my right, commented on how surprised we had been that Jesse got a liver so soon after coming in. I took a straight jolt to the heart, turned, and made a face at her. Later, she told me she hadn't understood that they didn't know about the arrangement to admit him. The conversation went on from there, but we had missed a beat. Drs. Gardner and Hall waited to talk to the surgeons, who didn't show. They talked to Dr. Meyer for a long time, then each went in to Room D. Dr. Gardner looked at Jesse from head to toe. She closed her eyes and held the railing.

Oh Jesse.

When she came out she asked me to walk with her to the PICU lounge. She had brought Amy, her ten-year old daughter, with her to do some things in the City after coming here. Amy gave me a letter she had written. It mentioned a drawing that Jesse had sent to Dr. Gardner after her last baby was born. It said that the drawing sat on a bookshelf in their living room and that she and her mother hoped Jesse wouldn't die.

The 26th. Dr. Meyer had threaded and sewn heavy dialysis lines into each leg near Jesse's groin. He had a deep purple bruise on his right leg and his testicles were ballooning up like a wineskin with the red wine seeping through and staining the skin. Dr. Meyer removed the line in his right leg. She tried to reassure us.

It looks bad, but it doesn't hurt him and it won't cause any permanent damage. But it will take a long time for the swelling to go down.

Dr. Dorand and Dr. Boyd made rounds. They guessed that Jesse still had an infection. They would do a CAT scan to look for abscesses in his liver and spleen. If there were abscesses in his liver and they could get him stable, they would list him for a second liver.

That evening we stood in the hallway outside Room D with Dr. Boyd and speculated on what might have been missed, something underlying Jesse's liver disease that could help them figure out how to rescue him now. Dr. Boyd rocked back on his heels.

I never bought the diagnosis of primary sclerosing cholangitis as his major problem. There were too many uncharacteristic elements. The ascites in his belly before and after surgery was puzzling. His spleen was larger than his portal hypertension would make you think.

We talked about some other autoimmune process, where the body attacks itself, that might be at work. And could there be something that looks like sepsis but isn't? I had heard about liver lobe transplants, where an adult relative gives part of his liver to a young child. I knew the answer, but I had to ask Dr. Boyd anyway.

What about taking a lobe from my liver and giving it to Jesse?

Dr. Boyd tilted his head back a little farther than usual and rocked. His eyes widened slightly as he looked at me.

I think he's too big.

That night I lay on my bed in twilight sleep, halfway between waking and dreams. I saw Jesse. He lay on a hammock suspended between two trees in a flat open field before a red sky.

The 27th. Jesse slept, barely showing himself at times with a leg twitch or a hand squeeze. He was up to a hundred eighty pounds and was so bloated his stretch marks were purple. He came into the hospital at a hundred twenty-five pounds, some of that, fluid pushing out his belly. The doctors guessed he'd lost fifteen pounds of muscle and fat during the past three weeks, so his heart was pumping for an extra seventy pounds of fluid. They pumped him up with dopamine to tighten his blood vessels and keep his blood pressure from crashing through the floor. He was due for a CAT scan but they canceled it. It was too dangerous to move him. But he must be rolled back and forth and hoisted on the Tuna Scale every night!

The oxygen level in his blood was down and the acid level was up. Dr. Reuben, the ICU attending doctor for the weekend, explained that when blood becomes acidic, breathing gets harder and medications don't work as well. He talked about the possibility of doing a tracheotomy, where a hole is cut in the throat and the breathing tube blows oxygen directly into the windpipe. Jesse would be more comfortable with it, Dr. Reuben said, and there was a risk of damaging his larynx and vocal chords if they left the tube down his throat too long. Less than three weeks before, a lifetime ago, we'd been told that the breathing tube was uncomfortable for Jesse but wouldn't hurt him. I thought about his swollen testicles, a wonder of the world, that didn't hurt him and wouldn't cause any permanent damage, and realized that such reassuring statements assumed a temporary problem, even one that went on for weeks. The unspoken prayer which followed all of them was, As long as it doesn't go on too long.

Jesse is remarkably stable given his condition, Dr. Reuben said.

In plain English it was an absurd statement, but in ICU it was quite logical. Critically ill but stable. Can't be moved because his blood pressure might plummet but now, while he's stable, is the time to think about a transplant. Jesse was riding the hammock between gravity and flight and in this state, earthly logic was suspended. Were we crazy, too, that He's stable made sense to us?

Dr. Boyd came in, alone, on rounds. He conducted a neurological exam, leaning over Jesse, placing his mouth an inch from his ear, and shouting JUSTIN! JUSTIN! His son's name. My son passed with flying colors, not so much as wincing. It was a quintessential Jesse moment, even if he was out cold. At his best when fully conscious he would have done the same, stubbornly refusing to acknowledge the presence of some fool shouting the wrong name dead in his eardrum.

We helped the nurses turn him on his side and stuff blankets behind him, but he always managed to land on his back again and take up his heroic quest to raise his right leg, place his right foot flat on the bed in order to balance the leg like a suspension bridge, then crook his left leg and lift it over the right, resting the ankle above his right knee. This was his favorite reclining position at home, in bed drawing or sitting on the back deck. Buried in his underground command bunker he was trying to take this position now, but could only bend his left leg a few inches and do nothing with the right. His right leg was more swollen than the left, but I suspected that its dereliction was a critically ill version of the right-side weakness he'd had since hydrocephalus, showing up mostly in an off-kilter running style.

His bed had a standard-issue mattress with a green industrial-strength plastic cover and the usual push buttons for elevating and lowering the head and foot. We'd heard about beds that could be adjusted for the body's pressure points and even weigh the patient. You'd think a hospital that sponsored the most high-tech operations available to humankind would have state-of-the-art beds for its sickest patients, but we had seen more sophisticated equipment in modest general hospitals. And this only stood to reason. Those hospitals didn't perform organ transplants, didn't attract the most skilled doctors, and so had to compete with each other over creature comfort and hospitality. And we? While rumors flew between nurses, ICU docs, and us that the liver team was talking about a second liver for Jesse, we worked on getting him a new bed and a larger room so we could maneuver him in and out for CAT scans and surgeries and so he might know the small kindness of a bed that would help stay the onslaught of skin breakdown from lack of nutrition and bed sores from lying in bed too long. And this only stood to reason as well.

Rachel had worked in pharmaceutical sales and knew how to lobby doctors and medical systems. For two days she made Jesse's new bed her reason for living. She asked Dr. Reuben about it and he said he'd look into it, in a way that told us it was the last thing on his mind. We heard via the nurses that the nursing supervisor, Anna, whom we had first met during CVVHD, was not pleased with Rachel's efforts. We gathered that Anna had something to do with the process of approving the bed and was miffed over not getting first shot at slowing things down. Fashion Statement, Naomi, quietly gave her blessing to the endeavor and said she'd talk to Dr. Reuben. She must have, because the next thing we knew a dermatologist showed up to assess Jesse's need for the big-ticket item Rachel had picked out from a catalogue.

The bed arrived the next day and, as the sales rep demonstrated, it was a marvelous bed, an airbed with a pillowed mattress. At its foot was a control panel with a touch screen to adjust for pressure points on the head, shoulder, buttocks, calves, and feet, to make the mattress firm or soft, to raise or lower the entire bed or parts of it, to weigh Jesse, no more rolling him from side to side and hoisting him on a sling, and for collapsing the mattress like a popped balloon for a hard surface to work on if he coded. On this bed a young man might wink at crocodiles basking in the sun and float serenely downstream, not with the sloshing motion of a water bed but on a bed of air, never suspecting, for he dreams, that he has modern technology to thank for soothing his aching bones and setting his imagination free.

Rachel taught the nurses when they came in to gawk. The bed was beyond my hammer and screwdriver skills, and she had earned the right to demonstrate its mercies.

It was May 29th. Dr. Swanson, Chief of Liver Transplantation, glanced at us where we sat in the neonatal lounge and kept going. I jumped on the elevator and rode down to the basement with him. Dr. Swanson was unprepossessing in appearance, of average height and a bit overweight. The vanity one might expect to see in one of his status was evident only in the way his gray eyes held you for a moment with a certain detached intensity and then moved on, and also, after continued observation, in his subtle air of one who is accustomed to being observed and thus observes himself, as though walking toward a three-way department store mirror on rollers that recedes before him. I was trying to develop a relationship with Dr. Swanson. He wasn't the attending surgeon on Jesse's case but he could nix a liver for him. I was angry with him, too, for the pep talk he'd given Rachel and me twenty-four hours before Dr. Dorand's speech. My guess was that, just back from his liver conference in Chicago, he hadn't conferred with the team before talking to us.

Jesse's either fighting infection or coming down with something, he said.

The elevator took us from the sixth floor to the basement and its intersecting tunnels that passed by obscure departments with rooms, barely large enough for a patient on a stretcher, that housed the latest breakthroughs in diagnostic technology operated by lab technicians who knew arcane passages in and out of the maze or who, having stayed too late one night, had become persons without homes and now, never left. Today the accumulated inefficiency of the hospital's rambling growth over the years, which dictated his roundabout travel from the SICU to the liver clinic, had delivered to Dr. Swanson a serendipitous meeting with another petitioner passed from the village priest to the Monsignor to the Bishop to the Cardinal and finally come hat in hand, seasick from steerage across the Atlantic, to Rome and him carrying another moldy petition for mercy that even he lacked the power to grant.

Or the infection may be gone, but the damage is done and it just keeps him on the tailspin that it started.

Can an infection last this long?

Yes, it can.

We talked about Jesse's liver.

The problem with the liver is not rejection, because the liver hasn't responded to the anti-rejection drugs.

There was a circular logic here, it seemed to me. I'd heard it from Drs. Dorand and Lanier as well. It went something like this.

Transplanted livers always respond to antirejection drugs.

What's causing the liver to fail, then?

Infection.

But the tests don't show any infection in the body.

They must be missing it.

How so?

Because transplanted livers always respond to antirejection drugs.

Sometimes, sitting quietly here at the kitchen table and not trying, I see Jesse before he was changed, frozen in time but covered with the fleece of the living, and talk of rejection or infection is a distant chattering of magpies. Other times, when I sit here quietly in another way, without bitterness or illusion, and read these notes, I know that Dr. Swanson was right, that rejection or infection did matter. The doctors had to protect Jesse's liver with drugs that disengaged the body's defense system. If infection was present, though, they had to treat it as well or risk the Pyrrhic victory of watching his body fall apart around his brand-new liver. But treatments for infection and rejection hamstring each other, and thus the dilemma and the endless debates, which, we gathered, were moving toward resolution on the side of treating Jesse's infection. You might cheat a little bit on the antirejection drugs and not lose the liver, or they could think about another liver for Jesse if this one failed, but infection could take him quick as a shadow down the street.

We're dealing with infection and a marginal liver. Let's deal with the infection. We will continue to support him.

We got off the elevator and signaled to each other that the interview was over.

Sit tight, he said.

Jesse's temperature and heart rate fell and his blood pressure shot up, a sign of septic shock or increased pressure on the brain. The episode passed. Dr. Mellon, a GI we knew from the liver clinic but hadn't seen on the PICU until now, was here. She ordered a neurological consult.

It's fairly miraculous he's as stable as he is. Retransplant might become an issue over the next few days.

I asked her what she thought about getting Jesse started on physical therapy. He was semiconscious at best but they were moving him more now. I thought a little PT might slow the process of muscle atrophy even if he couldn't do the exercises himself. Neurologist on the way to determine whether a new disaster had happened, glucose jumping up and down and raising the question of whether diabetes would be the next ingredient in the stone soup his body had become, and Jesse taking thirty breaths a minute there was so much pressure on his lungs from fluid pushing up from his belly, Dr. Mellon was speechless for a moment at what must have looked like my terminal denial of his illness. But it was she who said he was stable!

Yes, maybe we should be thinking about that, she said.

The neurologist, with thick glasses and black thick-soled shoes, walked in carrying a black bag. An Indian resident, towering over her at five-foot ten, walked two steps behind her. He took a set of long metal pins from a leather case. They stuck Jesse on the soles of his feet, his ankles, and his elbows. The neurologist made little eye contact with us and had little to say. After years of poking and prodding she seemed to respond more naturally to neurological movements than to subtle points of social interaction. Her posture and manner were not unlike that of a meter maid on a city street. Each knows she can hardly be liked, for each has the unenviable task of inflicting pain, one on the owners of inanimate objects, the other to determine if the object of her pain is capable of feeling it. She noted Jesse's right-side weakness. We offered the information about his long-time weakness on that side. She did not seem impressed. She guessed there was increased brain stem pressure and wanted to do a CAT scan. She walked out. The resident was two steps behind her. We knew they'd be back.

I studied Jesse's liver numbers, rows of days that corresponded to columns of lab results on the liver chart on his door. I put pencil check marks next to the dates he'd had surgery. May 6th, transplant. May 10th, discovery and repair of intestinal perforation. May 12th, clean him out and check for holes. May 18th, more of the same.

Dr. Lanier came in and went over to Jesse without saying a word to us. He did a brief examination. Rounding the bed on his way out, he shook his head.

Jesse has an incredible will to live.

We followed him out. He turned to us.

Jesse is not giving up on himself, so we're not giving up on him. We need to rethink what we're doing.

Gail and I talked. We agreed that he couldn't go on like this, being maintained, neither alive nor dead. We looked through my notebooks for a missing link. Pneumonia, 1983. Calcifications in his spleen, 1987. Episodes of coughing, 1988 and 1989. Mildly enlarged spleen, 1991. Diagnosis of ulcerative colitis, 1991. High bone enzymes, 1992. Nothing that leapt out at us, nothing to go on except our suspicions about his ever-growing spleen.

I looked at my notes again. July 11, 1983. I remember the hot sun and the New Haven humidity. I sat by the open French doors in the living room of our second-floor apartment, the first one Gail and I had lived in together, brushing polyurethane on a pressed-wood bookcase we had bought for Jesse's room. The can of polyurethane was open. Jesse sat on the couch eight feet away. We talked. Suddenly he gasped for air and we were in the car on the way to our health clinic across town. He struggled for breath beside me. They rushed him into an examination room and gave him a shot of epinephrine. Within minutes he was running up and down the halls. Could the fumes have done something to his liver or spleen? If so, and we could find out what that was, would it make any difference now?

Or could there be a virus on the PICU? A few days before we had speculated that Naomi, back from a quick trip overseas with her fiancée, might have brought in an exotic disease that attacked only those with weakened immune systems. Then I thought of a bizarre, wondrous drawing of a body in uproar that Jesse had drawn the day before his colitis operation in 1993. Did it contain clues, the wisdom of his body talking through his art to anyone who would listen? Trying to visualize the drawing, I saw a hand reach down to pull Jesse from the same hammock he lay on in my twilight sleep vision of a few nights before. If we could just do something for him, something so simple, something that was staring us all in the face, something to take away all the heaviness...

I walked down the hall to the PICU lounge and called Dr. Gardner in New Haven. I told her I thought Jesse had done everything we could ask of him and now his doctors needed to do something for him other than just maintain him. There was a pause.

I think one of two things is happening. Either Jesse has an infection that antibiotics won't touch and a new liver won't help... And he's doing to die. Or the infection is gone and he needs a new liver. If they've gotten the infection under control... Then they should give him a new liver.

I asked her if she would talk to the liver team.

I could call Dr. Lanier. I don't know if it will do any good. He always says, Oh I'll call you, I'll call you, when I catch him on the phone, and he never does.

We agreed that she would try. On my way back to the unit I passed Dr. Meyer.

Could I talk to you for a minute?

Of course. What can I do for you?

I was wondering. If they think they've got the infection under control and Jesse's liver numbers are still bad, then it seems as though the only thing left for him is a new liver.

Yes, I think they're thinking along those lines.

May 30th. Jesse was stable enough to be taken down for a CAT scan of his head and abdomen. They blew it, scanning only his head. He came back to Room B, the one we'd been lobbying for. It was directly behind the nurse's station and much larger than Room D, with a wide door that left plenty of room to push his bed through. His chest and shoulders were stippled with tiny red freckles beneath the skin, a minihemorrhaging. His neck and face and shoulders puffed up before our eyes. This was subcutaneous emphysema, the nurse told us, where air gets in between skin and flesh. She didn't know what had caused it.

It looks bad, but it won't hurt him, and it should go down.

Now, years later, I see there is only one logical explanation. The resident who had bagged Jesse, forcing air into his lungs from a thick black rubber pump attached to an oxygen tank, a procedure they used each time he had to be disconnected from the ventilator for a trip off the unit, had done so too exuberantly. The leaky pump of his lungs made a carnival sideshow mask of his face and chest and shoulders. Jesse had drawn something like this, a boy or young man with a vertical brush of hair at the back of his head left standing and the rest raggedly mown down. The young man stands in water almost to his shoulders. I think of his face as bloated but it is not. Instead, his cheek muscles are tense with the effort of disgorging a fish shaped like an elongated tongue with a large oblong eye and the line of an almost-human mouth. The young man's eyes are closed as if to concentrate on spewing out the fish tail first. Blood drips from his mouth below his bared upper teeth. His nose is broad and flat and his skin, with a hint of shading, appears dark. The shape of his face and the round, muscular, but relaxed set of the shoulders on a strong neck give him the look of a South Seas fisherman's apprentice. But why would anyone try to swallow a fish whole? An initiation rite? Or could the fish be part of him?

The respirator's bubbling was a cascade, almost deafening at first, in this empty space, as if speaking out for Jesse against his new surroundings. Soon we would we get used to the noise and partly muffle it with cards and photos transferred to these walls from Room D. Jesse was christened in his new home with a shunt tap. A neurosurgical resident, not the blond resident we had met before, inserted a needle through his skull into the shunt to measure his intercranial pressure. The resident had a hard time getting the needle into the eighteen-year-old rock hard shunt. He did not ask us to leave, but we did. Jesse's intercranial pressure was higher than normal, the resident told us when he came out, but it was nothing to get alarmed about.

The next morning we left the transplant center and joined our high-rise mates, stockbrokers and lawyers, young men and women in earth tone and gray and blue suits, in the courtyard outside the building. We crossed Third Avenue with them, then parted ways as they cut across a middle school playground to a subway kiosk on our right and we continued up a residential street lined with brownstones to the broad avenue that led to the hospital. We passed The Three Gentlemen, a Greek restaurant where you could sit quietly and talk over dinner. Two blocks down on the same side of the street was Red Fish Blue Fish, a busier, hipper, more frenzied establishment that specialized, of course, in seafood. We crossed the street to Rich's Deli. Rich, a Middle Easterner, knew us well by now, what we took in our coffee, what time of day we got espresso instead, and what pastry was likely to catch our eye. At the corner of the street that marked the hospital's southern border was the oriental deli. We had eaten there several times until weariness over their smorgasbord and comments from the cognoscente, the nurses, led us to seek out other spots. Most times that meant the hospital cafeteria and back to Jesse's room, or a brief respite on the circular stone benches under the glass rafters of the pavilion. Or, for low-rent lunches and dinners, David's across the street from the oriental deli, with reasonable food that came quickly and, except at noon, without pressure to shovel and leave. The waitress, rail-thin and late fiftyish, had a chronic sniffling cold. The waiter cum maitre'd cum cashier was too relaxed to be David. He brought you a glass of red wine filled to the brim, his balance centered on his large equator, and smiled proudly, either because the glass of wine he brought you was more generous than any you'd get at Red Fish Blue Fish or because he could bring it to your table and set it down without spilling a drop, while you had to bend over and sip before picking it up.

Back on the other side of the street leading to the hospital's main eastern entrance, we walked past sidewalk vendors with their tables and stands filled with shirts, scarves, sunglasses, beepers, and fast food. We came to the doors that talk and shuffled through. Dr. Dorand, on his way out, we supposed, from all-night surgery, acknowledged us.

Do you have a minute? I asked. We stepped away from the lines moving in and out.

We were thinking. If it seems as though the infection is gone, and Jesse is stable but his liver numbers are still bad, then wouldn't he be a good candidate for a retransplant?

Dr. Dorand took a half step back and looked at me as though expecting to find dumb luck.

I don't know who you've been talking to, but we've talked about it and we're planning to relist Jesse.

That's great! How long do you think it will take to get him a new liver?

About one to two days. That's the usual wait now. He'll be number one in the state.

That morning, though, a blood test showed that Jesse's clotting time was down, still higher than it had ever been with his own liver but low enough to make us all wonder if this one, which we could hardly call his new liver anymore, battered and bruised as it was, might finally be kicking in. But it was only a blip. They drew more blood and his clotting time went back up. He needed a new liver.

That afternoon Dr. Crane, a surgical liver fellow, made rounds with Cindy. He looked at the liver numbers and at Jesse and gave us a brief assessment. We waited for him to repeat what Dr. Dorand had told us this morning.

Sit tight, he said.

For a moment I thought it was a tease to make the good news that much better. It would have been a bad joke, but we liked Dr. Crane and would have let it go. But nothing in his shifting readiness to leave or his puzzled reaction to our glances persuaded me he was joking.

We saw Dr. Dorand this morning, I said. He told us Jesse was going to be relisted today.

Dr. Crane stammered and excused himself. Five minutes later he was back.

Yes, it's official. Jesse will be relisted this evening.

The next day, June 1st, was a shock. Dr. Meyer and Dr. Lanier were off service, a new term for us. They were attending physicians, we learned, only on alternate months. It had never occurred to us that this could happen. A vacation perhaps, but to be gone for a month! It tore Jesse's ragged hammock a little more for his soggy weight to work at until he fell through. It meant more vigilance for us, more questions, and an even closer watch on every event that took place in Room B.

Dr. Mann, the new ICU attending physician, was a pulmonary specialist. His rounds were shorter than Dr. Meyer's and he did less teaching with the residents. He had less to say to us and was less disposed to answer our questions or ask us what moment-to-moment changes we observed in Jesse. The collective breath being held here, with precise instructions from Dr. Meyer on timing and depth of inspiration and slow, even expiration calculated to wake no evil, followed by another collective breath, and the comfort this illusion had cloaked us in, were gone, and now we were left to figure out how to breathe on our own again. Dr. Lanier's absence was less shocking because he had not been on the floor and because we knew his replacement, Dr. Mellon. Still, pessimistic as he was about his chances, he was a voice in Jesse's defense and he was gone.

The next day Dr. Crane came in to cut out dead tissue from Jesse's abdominal wound to eliminate a possible source of infection before retransplant. He would do it in the room rather than the OR but it was best, he said, that we leave. We were happy to do so. Fifteen minutes later he came out. The dead tissue went deeper than he thought. It would be safer to do the procedure in the OR.

The bed was soaked with fluid. Between the cutting in Room B and the OR, Jesse lost twenty pounds. He bled profusely during surgery and needed a complete transfusion. They found a perforation about to happen in a section of bowel they had sutured before. This time the problem was not a surgical accident but poor nutrition and overall illness. Jesse's liver looked bad, Dr. Boyd told us, but there were no signs of infection.

That evening I stood in the hall outside the double doors to the unit and added up the pluses and minuses of the day. Jesse had shed a lot of fluid. Good. They might have to replace the remaining dialysis line in his leg. Bad. Putting in another line would not be easy with his bleeding problems and Dr. Meyer was not here to do it. Bad. Other lines were being changed as his veins broke down. Also bad. They found a second perforation in the offing. Good that they found it, bad that it was there to be found. Would they change their minds about retransplant? Were other perforations waiting to happen? Tina, leaving the unit at the end of her shift, walked by, flirting with one of the male residents.

The fourth or fifth day of June, I think, and days beyond the one- to two-day wait Dr. Dorand had predicted. Livers are slow, he told us. We waited each night thinking this would be the night. One more day was time for Jesse to get stronger and one more day was time for him to have a downturn that would force Dr. Dorand to pull him off the list.

Don and Leslie had come in with their baby, Jessie, a few days before. Jessie was nine months old and had biliary atresia, an infant form of liver failure. Her only chance was a liver transplant but it was unlikely she'd get one. She was too sick and too few livers became available for babies. Leslie stayed at the transplant shelter. We were friendly with her. Don was a truck driver. He carried a beeper on the road and came here evenings or took time off from work. I wondered what would happen to them if their baby didn't make it.

Don joked with us about having the surgeons carve out a lobe of Jesse's new liver for her, but I knew he wasn't joking. That evening I called Gail, home with the children, at the pay phone across from the NICU lounge. I told her, incredulously, what he had said. When we finished I walked back down the hall toward the PICU. Don was sitting on a plastic chair in the hallway not far from the phone. He leaned forward, elbows on his knees, head in his hands.

The fifth of June. Jesse had lost thirty-five pounds from his peak weight. There were calculations and recalculations of fluids to give him as much nutrition and as little volume as possible. They couldn't keep up with his nutritional needs, they said, they were only trying to cut their losses. His pupils changed sizes, back and forth from left to right. His heart rate jumped around. He was restless, but it was good to see him moving. They wheeled in a machine to scan his kidneys. It showed no blood flow. Dr. Gregory, a nephrologist, said his kidneys were gone.

Drs. Crane and Mellon came by. They talked about the possibility of a double transplant, liver and kidney.

How much more dangerous would that be, doing both at the same time?

There's no significant difference, said Dr. Crane.

What about one of us donating a kidney?

Do you have the same blood type?

None of us was sure about his blood type.

It might be a good idea to check that out, he said.

We gave blood in the hospital. Only Rachel had Jesse's blood type, O-positive. She could give him a kidney and she was ready to go. We saw Dr. Gregory in the hall and asked him what he thought about doing a kidney transplant at the same time as the liver transplant.

A double transplant would not be feasible. A kidney transplant would be five years down the road. In the meantime there's dialysis.

Later, Dr. Dorand did rounds with the liver team. We asked him about the double transplant. He shook his head in disbelief.

A kidney transplant is way down on our list. And a double transplant would be very serious. That's something we're not even thinking about.

It was one thing he and Dr. Gregory agreed on, but Dr. Dorand insisted that Jesse's kidneys would bounce back with a good liver. Dr. Gregory, spotted down the hall, joined the team at Dr. Dorand's request and stuck to his guns. True, the portable renal scan was not as sophisticated as the larger stationary machine in the basement, but the pictures were conclusive. The kidneys were gone. Dr. Dorand turned to me after Dr. Gregory had left.

I'll be amazed if Jesse becomes a dialysis patient and needs a kidney transplant.

They'd had these fights before.

Days of waiting and watching Jesse ride the hammock.

June 8th. We got a call at 5:20 a.m. They might have a liver, coming from the same hospital in Dallas that was giving Mickey Mantle a liver transplant today. On the unit, Angela brought in the consent form for the surgery. Rachel and I did our usual polite dance around who would sign. I deferred to her. A few minutes later Gail made a comment to me about the consent form. Angela overheard it and told Rachel. Rachel came up to me as I was looking for some food we'd left in the patient refrigerator and told me what Angela had told her.

Do you mind my signing the consent form?

No, I lied.

We were doing well for divorced parents living together with their critically ill child on an ICU, but the cracks were beginning to show. I'd grown weary of Will's bluster. Gail and Rachel were polite, even friendly with each other, but the combination didn't work. Rachel and I had assumed our permanent seats, she at the side of Jesse's bed near the windows, I behind its foot at the back wall. She hogged the time with him, I thought, playing the mother role to the hilt. I was dumbstruck to hear my own bitter words, rehearsed in hundreds of imagined confrontations, come from her mouth much later, in July, that she felt Gail and I were belittling her role, pushing her to the sidelines. Now, in early June, the competition was only working up to that pitch, but no issue was more loaded for me than who got to sign the consent-to-treat form. Still, I wasn't looking for a fight with Rachel.

Jesse vomited in the morning. They stopped feeding him. We were afraid this might make them pass on the liver but they took him, unconscious, to the OR around 5 p.m., almost twelve hours after the call to the transplant shelter. We sat in the disheveled surgical waiting room with magazines and newspapers and leftover food piled up on every available flat surface. After a few hours I started cleaning up, tossing food and newspapers and making neat piles of the magazines. I drew the line at arranging them by title and issue. At 10 p.m. Dr. Dorand came in.

The transplant went well. There was a lot of bleeding in his gut. We'll try to cauterize the spots that are bleeding. If that doesn't work we'll open up his stomach and sew it. We'll know in two to three days whether this one will work.

He reached out his hands for Rachel and me. An hour or two later Dr. Mellon came in, smiling. She'd been called in from home but didn't seem to mind. Who cares about Mickey Mantle, she asked. The bleeding had stopped, but Jesse had varices, swollen blood vessels around his esophagus and stomach. They would have to watch them. If his chest tubes stopped draining they would take them out tomorrow. If things were going well they would take out his breathing tube.

Are you still thinking about a tracheotomy?

We won't do one as long as he doesn't need long-term respirator help.

What should we worry about? Other than everything?

We'll be watching for infection. The signs to watch for are elevated temperature, elevated enzymes, and oozing from the wound.

She stood up to go, and smiled, remembering something.

And there's blood flow to the kidneys. So there is hope for them.

We went back up to the NICU lounge and waited. They wheeled Jesse by. He looked so young, so peaceful, so innocent and helpless. He was a dark pumpkin color when they took him down. Even his palms were orange. His skin tone was almost normal now. They took him to his room and said they'd need a half-hour with him. Rachel wandered down early. When she came back she said she'd overheard one of the anesthesiologists say to the other, That's an awfully small hepatic artery.

Finally they let us come in. Jesse was swaddled in blankets under a heat lamp because his temperature was low. He was putting out urine. When I found a moment alone with him I leaned down close and whispered in his ear.

Jesse, you're getting better. We're so happy for you.

seven

Light, I need something light for what this lamp reveals, the door to his old bedroom across the hall from ours. A poor double entendre. Jesse would have made better use of it.

His sneakers, that will be light enough. Rachel bought him great clothes, but she must have left him to do her own shopping this time and paid for the sneakers in the box when she got back to the shoe store. I glanced at them when he came home with them still in the box. They were Nikes or a like expensive brand.

Nice sneakers, Jess.

Thanks.

Then we saw them on him.

What size are those, Jesse?

I don't know.

Did you try them on in the store?

Yes. They're fine.

We looked at them at the bottom of his seventeen-year-old five-foot-four skinny frame.

They look big, Gail said.

No, they fit me.

Take them off for a minute, will you, hon? I'm curious to see what size they are.

They were 13s. He took seven and a half. We joked with him so he wouldn't think we were blaming him or his mother.

They're fine.

They're five sizes too big, Jess.

I like them.

We like them too. They're cool sneakers. They're just way too big for you. We'll get you some others.

He'd worn them outside, so it was too late to take them back. We gave them to the guy down the street. He's six-foot six.

I sat on a white wicker couch with blue stuffed cushions across from an imitation white leather couch. Next to me, an unfinished bookcase filled with paperbacks, mostly offbeat contemporary fiction. Silk flowers in an earthen pot and a brass hat rack on either side of the front door. On the wall facing me, a silk rug with black and white squares bordered in black squares, a collector's item that Rachel bought for a song when we were first together. Through an archway, the kitchen with faded linoleum and chores that Jesse did or didn't do on the days he was here, alone after school or the two of them, evening and morning routines. A hand-carved cutting board darkened with grease hanging from a nail next to the narrow gas stove. A wicker basket with dried flowers on the table. Jesse's tiny bedroom off the kitchen with a new loft bed to free up floor space. Next to the archway on the living room side, an antique wooden type case mounted on the wall, with different-size bins for different-size type, filled with small lead and wood and ceramic figurines. Everything in here from good secondhand stores, poor man's furnishings but for the silk rug and clashing with just the slightest shift in balance, but here, a certain panache, a sense of story, or an invitation to imagine one.

Rachel and Jesse sat on the couch across from me. Jesse's dog, a mixed Terrier that appears in a few of his drawings, jumped up on their couch, then mine, to be petted. This was, I guess, late spring 1989. Jesse's split schedule had got old after Gail and I bought a house in Naugatuck the year before. Jesse took the school bus from Betsy Ross Arts Magnet School in New Haven on Thursdays and came back here. I picked him up after my work in New Haven running a social service agency for abandoned and neglected youth. We drove up Route 63 to Naugatuck for the evening and back down Friday morning to get him to school and me to work. He took the bus back here in the afternoon, I picked him up, and we drove back up Route 63 to Naugatuck for the better part of the weekend and back down to New Haven late Sunday morning. Jesse wasn't doing well in school and had few enough friends in this neighborhood. Maybe Naugatuck could be a new start for him. Even Rachel said it might be time for him to live with his father. She and I, and Gail and I, talked about the idea for months before asking Jesse. When we did he was noncommittal, as he had to be to honor his Hippocratic Oath to first do no harm to either of his parents.

Rachel and I went over the reasons once more from our couches, careful to assure him that this had to do with practical matters alone, not who he wanted to be with most and who was most desperate to have him. Everything was Yes he was ready and No he wasn't saying Yes because he thought he should. We agreed we'd make the switch over the summer before he would start eighth grade at Hillside Middle School in Naugatuck. We talked about his dog and cat and school to bridge to my exit. I walked out onto the narrow porch with the hanging spider plants. The door closed softly behind me.

Months later Daniel stood here in the hallway and blocked Jesse's path from his old bedroom to the living room. Jesse shoved him aside. I told him not to push Daniel, that he had to ask him to move.

I was trying to get to the living room. He wouldn't get out of my way.

Another time they were wrestling and hitting each other on the living room couch. Gail intervened.

I told you you can't hit Daniel. You're bigger than him.

Yes I can, he hit me.

No!

Yes!

No!

Yes!

I smile. To remember such things is to tell how garden-variety the problems were, how much my worries were bound up in what might happen next, not with the thing itself. I thought I could handle anything, even see Jesse miserable now if I knew he'd come through whole. But boys will be boys is a lie, too. There were fights between Gail and him, fights between Gail and me over him, Rachel always in the picture for Gail and me because Jesse was in the picture. I had three raps to choose from when his sullen resistance pushed Gail to the edge and I was calm enough to think. One. We're the adults. We have to do better than him. Two. We'd be dealing with this stuff with any teenager, especially with divorce and two homes. Three, jump off the cliff myself and hope she pulled me back. To hell with it! Let him live full-time with his mother! The whole thing is impossible! At best any of these raps bought time for hope to return. But when I saw and smelled his window frame stained black on the outside and realized he'd been pissing out his bedroom window, I was more afraid than angry that he would do something so bizarre, then lie about it under my bare-bulb interrogation until he confessed he couldn't wait to get into the bathroom.

Then why didn't you tell whoever was in there that you needed to go?

Ow no.

He didn't know, so we must fill in the blanks. He didn't ask because he couldn't, or didn't ask because he enjoyed the control his silence gave him, and enjoyed the control out of a sadistic withholding of his needs or because it was a place where he could take some control over his life, as John, his therapist, might say. Or he didn't ask because his confession was a lie, he was pissing on us by pissing on our house. Jesse and I had trained each other to circle around his rage like wolves around the last bloody scrap of meat. Love for spouse and family was hardly the issue then. The issue was not wanting to put any of us through another divorce, to have to choose between him and Gail, new home and family ten years in the making. Hoping to forestall such a choice I told her it would have to be Jesse, not because he deserved it but because he needed me more. The children would have her, and spend time with me. Or I think I told her so.

And then, when was it? After Jesse got sick? Or just before, late 1990 or early 1991, that things changed? Perhaps he sensed that he was in trouble, because in his tentative way he was reaching out. There was a softness in his demeanor, a yielding, a spontaneous hug. I wrote a poem for his fifteenth birthday around the image of a warrior dropping his weapons so I could embrace him. He was embarrassed, as I am, thinking of it now. It expressed a wish and was a plea for a moment that was passing as I wrote it, a door that had opened and was closing, an unexpected but possible blossoming if only fate did not control us, or because it did. I felt, at moments, that I was seeing the true Jesse, the one who wanted to love and be loved, as Gail said.

He withdrew behind his shadows again, at least with Gail and me. But things had changed for good between Daniel and him. Daniel told me the story a few weeks ago, about the time when they became friends. He was in Jesse's old room holding the door closed to keep Cassie out. He broke a piece off Jesse's bureau in the struggle.

Could it have been the desk, Dan? The desk was next to the door, remember?

Maybe. So I said, Jesse I broke your desk! He said, I know. I said, We're going to get in trouble. No we're not, he said. Yes we will. No we won't, he said, don't worry about it.

I remembered it now. The next day Gail and Daniel and I were in the kitchen.

Hey Gail, remember how angry I was the time that Jesse broke the leg on his desk?

No, she didn't remember that. A little air hissed out of me.

Well, it was Daniel who did it, and Jesse never told on him.

No no no I remember now! said Daniel. I ran to the door and hit the part of the wood on the top of the desk! That's what broke off!

Gail remembered that too. Daniel went on.

I said, Uh oh, Jesse, I broke your desk. He said, Who cares? I said, We're going to get in trouble. He said, No we won't, forget about it.

They laughed. The rest of the air hissed out of me. I settled in my chair and brooded over Jesse's lack of care for his belongings and all it implied to me then.

Gail was the first to recognize that something was wrong in the spring of 1991, that Jesse's many loose and foul-smelling bowel movements were more than the back end of candy and junk food from Marty's Corner. His bowel movements irritated me at first. They were part and parcel of the difficult child he was at that time. But I saw, when Gail pointed it out, that he was pale and had lost weight. She thought he might be anemic. Then one day she saw blood in the toilet bowl.

We went to our health plan in New Haven, an HMO, dirty word now, but they were good to Jesse. The place was in mourning, and so were we, for Dr. Warren, Chief of Pediatrics. His wry sense of humor had made for the right mix of distance and warmth for dealing with Jesse. The two of them played Othello before the era of the five-minute visit. He commented to us on the competitiveness Jesse hid so aggressively outside of Othello's borders. There were no games in the savage unforgiving psychic world that illness had opened the door on and pushed him through. Having learned what effort was required to have the courage to go on, he was afraid.

Dr. Warren recognized Jesse's great fear and great courage. Shortly after we moved to Naugatuck we had taken Daniel in for a routine visit with him, before we knew he'd been diagnosed with throat cancer. For once my medical instincts were better than Gail's. Didn't Dr. Warren look good, she asked, noting his lost paunch and lost beard. Younger, she thought. I didn't think he looked good, or any age in particular. His slightly pudgy softness was finely tuned to his gentleness. Now his face was off-kilter, drawn downward as though trying to make sense of the rest of him. His sudden thinness made him appear taller than he was. His white dress shirt hung straight down and showed all the emotions, anger at being draped over an impostor, grief that what gave it shape had abandoned it, and knowledge that the jig was up, which the rest of us did not want to face. An injustice had been done to Dr. Warren's body.

We went through most of the practice looking for a new pediatrician for Jesse before finding Dr. Hall, who knew more about intestinal disorders than the others in the department and was most like Dr. Warren in possessing a temperament that might outlast Jesse's silence. Dr. Hall sent Jesse for an upper and lower GI series in the summer and fall of 1991. Gail and I sat with him in his office as he explained that the tests pointed to inflammatory bowel disease. I'd never heard of it. He sent us to see Dr. Gardner, a gastroenterologist. I'd never heard of one. She performed a colonoscopy, pushing a lighted tube up Jesse's rectum into his colon. It confirmed that he had ulcerative colitis, an autoimmune disease that turns the body against itself and makes the colon fertile ground for angry red sores that bloom on its inner lining down into the rectum. Diarrhea and bloody stools, abdominal cramping and fever are its angry manifestations. It puts you at high risk for colon cancer, but it can weaken you enough to kill you quickly, without cancer. Medications can control it, steroids that give you a moon face, insomnia, and vivid frightening dreams. There's no cure that leaves the body intact, but take out the colon and you take colitis with it. I wondered whether moving to Naugatuck, away from his mother, his beloved dog and cat, attending a new school, and the household stress he helped to produce, had made him sick.

Dr. Hall called me at home. He would be available to Jesse and us for routine medical issues and would be in regular contact with Dr. Gardner, he said, but Jesse's care would shift mostly to her. I was annoyed. We had chosen him, not some myopic specialist, because of the supposed expertise he was now asking us to get from someone else. Much as I'd now read about ulcerative colitis, my mental armor shielded me from understanding the concern I heard in Dr. Hall's voice.

I didn't like her much at first, this Dr. Gardner, this Gastro Person, as Jesse called her. Seeing her on the street or in a restaurant, say Dr. Atella's, momentarily decoupled from the need to assert her authority or have the right answer, I might have taken her for an attorney with Wiggin & Dana, the top law firm in New Haven, assigned to the plum Yale-New Haven Hospital malpractice account and the clenched jaw that comes with it. She was tiny as Rachel, even thinner, attractive but stern. She walked into the cramped examination room and took in both of us, Jesse bland and silent on the examining table where the nurse had parked him to take his vitals, I with notebook and pen in my lap. She allowed a perfunctory smile but her manner was clipped and informational. I guessed that she was irritated with her new patient's silence and his father's legalistic note taking. I caught myself trying to please her, to give the cheap smiles and studied nonchalance with Jesse that might correct, through hints at his unstudied depths, her impression of him as a passive-aggressive teenager sure to join her short list of difficult patients. She was yet to be seduced by his vulnerability.

Tell me about your bowel movements, Jesse.

Shrug. Just have to go sometimes.

About how many times would you say each day?

Two or three times.

Jesse, it's more than that, I said.

Shrug.

I wondered how often we'd have to see her. The patient is a poor informant, she wrote in one of her early chart notes. True enough, I thought. Who has several caretakers in his life, the note went on. So what, I thought. Who brought him in and took down her every word like Boswell with Dr. Johnson?

No one could tell how badly Jesse felt except to say that he must. Dr. Gardner performed a digital exam on one of our early visits with her. There was blood on her gloved finger as soon as she stuck it into his rectum. She talked to me outside the examination room. We were starting to work together.

It's hard for me to believe that Jesse's not in more pain than he says he is.

We adopted the rule of thumb that if Jesse said something hurt, it really hurt. He itched. His liver functions were abnormal. He had loose explosive bowel movements on high doses of prednisone. Dr. Gardner was surprised.

Most new patients show dramatic improvement at first. And why is there itching now?

Was she missing something, she wondered out loud. She suspected sclerosing cholangitis, the narrowing of the biliary tree going into the liver, and sent him for a procedure to test for it. He had it, in an early stage. She worried about his enlarged spleen. There was no good explanation for it. She tested him for hepatitis. He didn't have it. She asked about travel to parts of the country with a high incidence of some disease or condition I've forgotten the name of. He had never been to those places. She asked if he had been given blood as a baby. No. She asked about fevers, itching, stools, appetite, physical activity, and respiratory problems. I told her about the polyurethane incident. Nothing was consequential.

He hated school, high school now, and wasn't doing well in it. How could he? He must have spent a good part of his time wondering whether he'd have to run to the bathroom. I got a call from work one day to come get him at the nurse's office with a change of clothes. We made an arrangement with his teachers that he could give a signal and leave class if he needed to go.

We found his friend Nicholas to be shifty and manipulative but decided, almost too late, to let it go. Nicholas found Jesse's talents and elusive rebellion fascinating and Jesse had the perfect audience in him. Nicholas taught Jesse another way to rebel, even if Jesse could no more copy his flamboyant style than he Jesse's silence, exile, and cunning. Perhaps it was Nicholas's influence that led Jesse to make a clay penis in art class and leave it for his female teacher to fire in the kiln.

Late 1992, early 1993. Jesse's right hip had given out on him in the fall. He had a soft spot in the ball joint. There was nothing to do about it but put him on crutches when it happened. His face ballooned out from prednisone, which wasn't as effective as it should be for stopping the frequent bowel movements and diarrhea. Other drugs didn't help much. He had acne. He was tired all the time. Who knew how much of this was colitis, how much insomnia from prednisone crawling inside his skin and the unrestful sleep it gave him with dreams of being shot into deep starless space? Down in his room to clean up the mess one day, I found medication on the floor and got frantic with him. Gail bought him a medication spacer, a good one with a carrying case, spaces for each day of the week, and moveable plastic dividers for morning, noon, and night doses. Jesse lost the moveable dividers and the medications got mixed together. We put in replacement dividers and those disappeared as well. At this distance I see that he did about as well as most do with medications they don't want to take, let alone pills that puff out an adolescent's face and feed acne and bad dreams. And the space between the pill dividers was too narrow, making the pills hard to get at. The whole kit was too small, elegant but too small.

Here on the kitchen table, a Jesse's Writings folder with another George 10 fragment, George 10 versus Ronanin, subtitled The First Battle. He had other battles planned, then, between pupil and mentor, now archenemies.

George 10 had just left the vast atmosphere of the planet Monolith when a dark robed figure appeared before him. The dark figure held out its hand and released a glowing ball which floated toward George 10 and then exploded into darkness. George heard the voice of Ronanin vowing revenge for the monastery and the death of his fellow monks. But George failed to see a Cyclonitron Magral net take form behind him and slip over him. He ripped at the net but it burned his right hand. He blacked out from the pain. The next thing he knew he woke up inside the arena. Again he saw Maelstrom rush out and strike down his father. Again he watched himself slay savage animals in a blind rage. Again he saw his brother disappear under a horde of wild beasts and himself fall in battle. Then he was left alone in the arena. Ronanin appeared at a distant corner.

Now is the time for your death, traitor! Ronanin shouted, and struck down George 10 with an intense energy blast. Before blacking out, George managed to reach inside his jacket and punch a button with his good left hand and teleport himself away to his space ship, Eggwhipper II.

A few weeks later George called council with Aaarroooow and Shali-Dazire. They agreed to return to the arena with George to settle the score. They stopped at the Highbrow Village of Eggora to pick up weapons and supplies. Egghead of the Highbrow was violently opposed to George's plan and used every trick in his book to keep him from going. Finally, seeing their determination, he agreed to help if George and his friends would have dinner with him and stay the night. He prepared a special dish, called Al-pi-mythnagor-smalthu, or I shall heal you and restore your health and strength if you get in a good night's rest. Egghead warned them that the food would make them sleepy. Within minutes they were snoring away in the Recognition Gel Chamber.

That night George 10 had a dream. The ghost of his father George 10 the Second appeared before him and whispered, Beware the betrayal of thy kin! Beware the betrayal of thy kin!

George 10 tried to speak to the ghost but could not. It was as if his mouth had been glued shut. He tried to move toward it but could not. It was as if his feet had been cemented to the floor. Then, suddenly as it had come, the ghost disappeared. George heard a loud noise, turned, and was struck down. As he fell to the ground he awoke from his dream.

I'm going to have to talk to Egghead, he said. He never told me that stuff I ate would have side effects like this.

George ate a quick breakfast with his companions and then boarded Eggwhipper II. Over the roar of the engines he screamed to Egghead on the ground.

Why didn't you tell us that food would give us weird dreams?!

Barely audible in the din, Egghead replied, It doesn't!

A great patient-physician exchange! The rest of the fragment tells that George 10 blew off Egghead's reply, thinking the Eggman must have misunderstood him. He and his crew landed near the arena and used the ship's cloaking device to disguise it as a sandbank. The fragment ends here.

It's sleep paralysis, prednisone inflamed, that Jesse describes, where the dreamer is unable to awake from his dream. Some who study it say you are not sleeping or dreaming at all, that your brain is awake but the rest of your body, which shuts down during sleep, has not received the message. All the signs of sleep paralysis are in the dream. The glowing ball floats toward George yet he is unable to duck it. A voice booms from out of sight. George, standing outside himself, sees himself do battle in the arena. He experiences a blackout or blackness or an abrupt change in scene, or wakes up from or goes into a dream, six times in the story fragment. He is enveloped by an outside force, the Cyclonitron Magral net, yet his loss of motor function is both willed and unwilled, an outside force invading the dream and an enemy within, for with no net around him later on in the story George tries to speak but cannot, tries to move but cannot.

Sleep paralysis started for me in late adolescence, a physical conviction of impending death through suffocation, with lungs, breath, and limbs paralyzed. It may be a rehearsal for death, so that death cannot be as fearful because the dreamer has played his part, and death its, many times before and with greater ferocity, one hopes, than on opening night to come. I wrote about it once, disguised in a Strindbergian dreamplay. A man is pinned to the floor of a polished wooden arena with invisible metal bands. From the four corners of the arena pins and needles roll themselves into steel cylinders, then back into pins and needles. Back and forth they change in rumbling, deafening tune with each other, rolling closer and closer to the center, then starting over again at the four corners of the arena. Have you seen the new torture, a voice crackles over ancient loudspeakers. It's all done by illusion. Nothing touches the victim. The victim screams but no sound comes from his throat. They carry him out, limp.

Could Jesse have read it? Much of his drawing paper was the blank side of my scrap paper. I usually checked it, but I might have forgotten that time or not thought much of it. If he saw it, then perhaps the play was not the thing. Could the Multiverse, the All, have planted my frozen dream in me so I would write this monologue that Jesse would read one day and begin his own rehearsal for death?

May 1993. It was strange to be out here in the sticks, twenty minutes from Yale-New Haven Hospital, for a bone marrow biopsy. I suppose this was one of a few satellite offices for Dr. Oran, and the first available appointment came up here, in Ansonia. Dr. Oran was kind and thorough in explaining the procedure to Jesse. He made only one mistake, but it was a big one. He told Jesse the procedure wouldn't hurt.

Jesse took off his pants, placed a paper apron over his legs, and sat at the edge of the examining table, as instructed. Dr. Oran came back in and had him lie on his left side with his legs curled up, then took a long thick needle and slowly pushed it through the skin to a vertebra in his lower back and through it into the marrow to extract a tiny sample of that life-giving substance. Jesse winced hard and let out a small groan. After it was over he got dressed, slowly.

It hurt. A lot.

Outside, we sat in the car in the parking lot behind the medical building. I looked at the white aluminum-sided three-story houses in front of us beyond the parking lot fence.

Dr. Oran was wrong to tell you it wouldn't hurt.

Shrug, a mournful nod.

Tell you what, we'll stop and get something to eat on the way back home. Whatever you want.

Little smile.

Where would you like to go?

I don't know. Anywhere is fine.

So he was going to leave it up to me. Probably Friendly's, I thought, balancing, always balancing money against the desire to let go, to do something full and unqualified for him. But he had a bad accident on the way home. I reassured him that it didn't bother me, that it wasn't his fault, all the flapdoodle one has to say and all of which is true, but none of which can cover the other's shame for having lost control at the place where privacy and dignity coexist. We got home. I put my jacket around him and shooed everyone away. We went downstairs to the washing machine. I found him some clean clothes.

Why does this day fill me with sorrow for what Jesse went

through when he went through so much, yet fill me with a sweet propinquity, too, that I was with him when I was with him for hundreds of procedures and office visits and blood draws? It was one of the most painful and least sedated of all procedures he had outside of the hospital. There is that. It did involve his spinal column, fearful enough for any parent but reminding me of the unruly watery cushions over his brain. Or was it because of his need and my desire to protect him, and maybe, this day, that I hit the right notes?

The biopsy yielded no advice on why Jesse's blood cells and platelets were down or what to do about his huge spleen, which can slow bone marrow growth and thus its production of blood cells and platelets. There was no evidence of tumors or lymphoma. It hadn't occurred to me that Dr. Gardner was looking for them. It had occurred to Gail, who didn't say anything to me until after the tests came back negative.

We drove in to New York and met Rachel for lunch, then walked to Dr. Giselle's private office in the East 70s. Thin women ages twenty to fifty walked past us wearing the same black dress. The thick squares of Coke bottle glass by Dr. Giselle's front door were circa 1950s. The reception area, sunk three steps below the front desk, was cozy, smaller than I expected. Posters of art exhibits long gone hung in their aluminum frames. The wicker furniture and outsize glossy magazines reminded me, uncomfortably, of an upscale hair salon.

It was June 1993. A month before, we had seen a surgeon, Dr. Morgan, at Yale-New Haven Hospital, where my health plan had a discount. Dr. Morgan explained the procedure in layman's language and with sensitivity for what Jesse was, a scared adolescent looking for a safehouse from his body. He would cut out Jesse's colon, then cut an incision in the side of his abdomen to create an opening, or ostomy, and then pull the end of his small intestine through the hole, exposing a rounded pinkish-red bulb that would deliver feces to a plastic bag with an adhesive flange stuck to the skin around the ostomy. If this were to be a total colectomy, Dr. Morgan would remove the sphincter muscle along with the colon and that would be that, Jesse would have a bag on his side for life. But we were talking about a subtotal colectomy here, where he would remove only the inner lining of the rectum and retain the sphincter muscle. This would set the stage for an ileoanal pull-through a few months later in which he would pull down Jesse's small intestine, close the ostomy, use the last foot and a half of intestine to create a pouch to store waste, and sew in the pouch just north of the anus. When successful, the patient has more frequent and, at best, toothpaste-consistency bowel movements, but does not have an ostomy bag. I asked him how many bowel movements Jesse could expect to have after his pull through.

Six to eight a day.

He sensed our collective wince.

I can't make what God made, you know.

I appreciated his humility as a man, but his statement did not inspire confidence in the surgeon. No one would come looking for such an operation if he could get by with what God had given him.

Dr. Gardner talked with Dr. Morgan afterwards. How many operations did he perform each year? Where did he train? How did his results compare with the rest of the field? She wasn't satisfied. She wanted someone who knocked off a couple of these before lunch. I don't care how much he's published, she said, I care about his technical skills. She talked to the top gastroenterologists at Yale, asked them for names, and made phone calls. She came up with a doctor in New York City who had pioneered the ileoanal pull-through operation, and talked the medical director of our health plan into paying for it.

Dr. Giselle, portly, in his mid-fifties, opened the door by the front desk. A nice touch, I thought. He could have had an aide usher us to the inner sanctum of office and examining room. His manner was courteous, gentle, and confident. I tried to decide whether his reddish blonde hair, a half-shade too youthful for him, was dyed to cover the gray or to go with a very expensive hairpiece. His office was unpretentious, a small surprise given his reputation and the part of town we were in. Photographs of his children were propped on the cherry wood breakfront behind us in front of cherry wood paneling. The desk was matching cherry. Dr. Giselle's was not the largest office in here. That was the first on the left as we walked down the hall and was reserved, I guessed, for the senior partner who came in these days only to visit off the front nine.

Jesse was polite but volunteered no information. Dr. Giselle saw, from his diffidence and our breaking in with answers to questions he did not answer quickly, that Jesse was not to receive too much information in one sitting. He took him into an examining room next door and came back alone a few minutes later.

You know Jesse will probably need a liver transplant some day. I assume Dr. Gardner has talked with you about this.

I shook my head yes, but I must have looked like a puppet on a string with head bobbing mechanically and a frozen half-grin on its face. Dr. Gardner had not talked with me about a liver transplant.

The spleen and the sclerosing cholangitis won't get better. My impulse is to remove the spleen when we do the pull-through.

Could we find some other word than impulse, I wondered.

Dr. Gardner shook her head when we talked about a liver transplant after the meeting with Dr. Giselle.

There is no reason for Jesse to have cirrhosis. The only evidence he shows of liver disease is a mild case of sclerosing cholangitis.

She wanted one more piece of information for Dr. Giselle before the surgery, though, an arteriogram at Yale to measure liver pressure and rule out cirrhosis.

Dr. Schiller came out after the procedure. He was in his thirties, tall, gangly, and made intermittent darting eye contact with Rachel and me. Rachel's take on him fit the profile of the brilliant youngster whose discomfort in social settings dovetails with parental expectations that propel him through pre-med, medical school, residency, and fellowship before he has time to recognize that the adolescence and young manhood he might not have negotiated well in the first place have been stolen from him. My interpretation, more cynical or more paranoid, was that his halting manner and sidelong eye contact, as if choosing words that fluttered past a few feet behind us, gave away his arrogance, if an arrogance in compensation for what Rachel had pegged as a phenomenal lack of social skills. I gave him this, he must be good at what he did or Dr. Gardner wouldn't have let him near Jesse. Dr. Schiller told us about the high portal vein pressures he had measured.

And what does that mean?

He looked at us quizzically, and took a beat to respond.

Cirrhosis.

We would have known it was lethal if we had heard only its name, the association with chaos of the body in its harsh alliteration, the sense that the tongue wants to hold back utterance but, once committed, spits fury like an avenging queen whose child has been sacrificed on the altar for the sake of a fair wind blowing Troy-ward.

What I knew about the liver was that the French had a reputation for ruining theirs with too much wine. I learned that it is a wondrous organ indeed, sitting inside its lower rib cage on the right side of the abdomen making chemicals from food, removing alcohol, drugs, and medications from the blood, making bile for digestion and proteins for clotting, keeping hormones in balance, storing iron and vitamins and minerals and sugar until the body is ready for them, even making blood before we are born. In cirrhosis the liver scars and tightens up. Primary sclerosing cholangitis, Jesse's problem, sometimes goes with it, choking off the bile's flow as the portal vein backs up trying to push blood into the hardening liver. The blood takes detours into veins and secondary vessels around the stomach and esophagus. These become engorged, or varicosed, and can pop into the bowels, bleeding suddenly and furiously. A statistical link exists, I learned, between ulcerative colitis and liver disease. The cause for this link is not known.

Soon Jesse would spike a fever and be admitted for a few days, delaying his surgery. Now, though, we sat with him. He seemed distant, depressed, withdrawn, from the sedation, no doubt, but I saw him bundling himself up against an ill winter. Rachel told him a little bit about the results without using the C-word.

Does this mean I won't be able to have the operation?

No, honey, it doesn't mean that.

First it was her turn, then it was mine to leave the room so he would not see us spilling tears over him. I went around the corner and sat in a plastic chair, then went into the bathroom facing me. When I came out a young woman brushed by me, disgusted. I looked back at her, surprised that she was so upset at having to wait, and saw the sign, WOMEN. I felt sorry for myself, of course, and wanted her to feel sorry for me, too. Still, a part of me marveled that one could cross the path of personal disaster and have no inkling of it, and that one's typifications, Men, all alike, probably sprinkled the edge of the bowl, could be altered not a jot nor a tittle in the face of it. An unreasonable expectation in a world of a thousand sensations a day and one I violate myself, now as then, Snooty bitch, pain for you would be running out of lip gloss.

Now they wanted to keep Jesse's spleen because it served as a backup for the liver, and now it was unlikely that Dr. Giselle could perform a one-stage, meaning one operation, ileoanal pull-through, a feat he had perfected. The high pressure in Jesse's portal vein, close to what they call a dirty area, rendered the final connections at the rectum a risky business, and the portal hypertension would not go down until the portal vein was pumping blood to a new, sleek, soft and supple liver fresh from someone else's misfortune. Dr. Gardner hoped that Jesse would get used to the bag and the ostomy and not want to go through another operation, but Jesse was not looking to get used to the bag or the ostomy. Unknown to him, I pray, I was struggling with my own distaste for his wearing a bag, my own wish that he be physically whole and have his first sexual encounter with all outward parts intact, no extras, at the moment of truth.

In late July, Dr. Gardner gave me a letter to hand deliver to Dr. Giselle. It was a psychological masterpiece in two pages. She reviewed Jesse's medical history in dry technical language. She gently reminded Dr. Giselle of the finding of cirrhosis and portal hypertension and the resulting complexity of Jesse's upcoming surgery. Slowly, ploddingly, she reviewed the current plan as if trying to reassure herself that she understood the ways of big-city surgeons. Dr. Giselle would do the one-stage pull-through if possible, she said, but he should be assured that she, and we, were behind his doing a lesser operation, the subtotal colectomy, if warranted, or, if necessary for Jesse's safety, a simple ileostomy, removing the rectal muscles and eliminating the pull-through option. She knew mistakes could be made, information forgotten, and egos get in the way. Sprinkled throughout the letter, under a tone of deep respect and a counterbalancing assertion of her own expertise, was the dual message, Don't be a cowboy and Don't let your surgical fellow take over the job. She had spent many hours seeking her wizard and selling him to my health plan. Now that she had him she was working against his technical brilliance and his quest to push the envelope of gastrointestinal surgery. She explained, warned, worried, and threatened, in the most polite way, that Jesse was no ordinary pull-through patient. Subtle as it was, she softened the message at the end, adopting the tone of a worried mother who was quite fond of Jesse and had instructed her answering service to reach her twenty-four hours a day so she could be reassured and could serve as a link between Dr. Giselle and us.

She instructed me to remind Dr. Giselle of these three options when I saw him before the operation. Joking, I confessed my absurd fantasy of reminding him that we wanted to keep Jesse's spleen.

No no no. Tell him. You should do that.

She taught me never to assume that the doctor knows or remembers or has things under control, especially when he is a hundred miles away from her. Be respectful, frame your reminder as a question if you can, but always make your point. I suspect she'd have gone about preparing for the handoff in a similar way for any of her patients, but she had grown to love Jesse, I believe, and this lent fire to her efforts. She was playing the percentages now. It might not make any difference, but the percentages were what she had to play with, and so she was playing them.

Early August 1993. We sat at the kitchen table by the glass doors having breakfast, Jesse, Daniel, and I. The next day we would take Jesse into New York for his colitis operation. He picked up a piece of typing paper and a pencil and appeared to be doodling. Ten minutes later he was finished.

The head of the creature he had drawn, or its topmost head, has the brutal blind curve of the shark, or is it Moby Dick? A beanie with a propeller is its cap. Its small eye has a slit pupil. Below this eye is another, much larger, that appears ready to pop out of its socket. The profile of a sharklike mouth full of teeth closed tight in a baleful grin butts up against this second eye. Below the shark-like mouth is what may be a moustache of a second, much larger mouth that opens wide showing human upper and lower teeth. Thick secretions drool from the back of that mouth where the uppers and lowers meet. A tiny man tries to escape from the thin darting tongue that grabs him by its sticky secretions. There is a small bonelike shape behind this mouth and, to its left, a flower. An inch below the flower are more secretions, fertilizer I suppose, drooling from the bottom of a faint elliptical flap or gill that borders the flower. An umbilical cord with notches that resembles stalactites originates beyond the left-hand side of the page and brings nourishment to the creature through a bonelike not-human ear next to the large eye.

One viewer said the figure was being propelled to the right-hand side of the paper toward, what, the birth canal? After years of studying it in its bluish-gray frame by our bedroom door, it occurred to me that it might be Jesse's version of the principle, Ontogeny recapitulates phylogeny, the fetus, as we saw it first in the *Life* magazine photographs, reproducing ascending levels of the animal kingdom, bird, fish, shark, elephant, struggling at the most basic level to become human.

Below the ear and the second eye, a perfectly drawn elephant tusk with darker lines and shading than the rest of the drawing curves down over the second mouth. Below the umbilical cord, a fish's tail grows out of the creature's right side. Just below the tail and partly obscuring it, a large human ear seen straight on faces the viewer. Next to the ear is a beak with eyes above breathing holes. Above that is a third eye with an indefinable shape or hieroglyphic inside. Next to this eye and below the second mouth's puckered lower lip, a hand waves at the viewer. Below the fish tail and almost joined to the ear, a man's face in profile with rounded nose, puckered lips, and lidless eyes anticipates the unknown with a look, not of horror but of disorientation that might show on a face landing upright just after beheading. Below the beaklike mouth in the center is a bow tie. Next to it at the creature's left side are flames or a pointed or a flaming ear. Just below the bow tie is a mouth with huge bad teeth. A foot sticks out over the lowers.

Jesse put down his pencil. Daniel, sitting next to him, stopped talking and studied the drawing.

What is it?

A self-portrait, he said.

They seem innocent now, too innocent, those times, and there was nothing innocent about them.

Giving Dr. Giselle my chair in the surgical waiting room, boxing him in between Rachel, Gail, my mother, and me.

We did the subtotal colectomy. It went well.

How about the portal hypertension?

The portal hypertension is bad. Al Swanson came by to take a look at his liver. It looked surprisingly good. We don't know what his underlying disease is.

Waiting to see Jesse in our yellow surgical gowns and blue slip-ons over our shoes outside the recovery room.

Our shock and fright at the little bulbs with plastic tubes stuck into his belly through tiny surgical incisions to drain the fluid that accumulated in his abdominal cavity.

The tube they threaded down his nose into his belly when he threw up his first solid foods on the pediatric unit. It was horrible to see the fear in his eyes that something had gone terribly wrong.

This is nothing, the attending pediatrician said. We do this all the time after surgery.

Jesse hated the tube. He picked at it. It gave him a sore throat and he refused to talk over it. He wrote us notes instead. Rachel and I traded nights on the pullout sofa next to his bed and the Ronald McDonald house thirty blocks south. Gail stayed home with Daniel and Cassandra, and visited. The nurses acted as though we were babying Jesse, which we were.

The recreation therapists who tried to coax him down the hall to the activity room for groups he would have none of, not to meet other kids, not to demonstrate his artistic talents, not to be cheered up, not to participate, not for any reason. He was sicker than those who used the groups as a springboard back to school and friends and not as sick as the socialized patients for whom hospital activities were second nature.

The unfunny volunteer clowns in their makeup and hobo outfits who came by every evening. Jesse closed his eyes, feigning sleep. We resented their cheery sense of entitlement to invade his privacy, resented having to validate them by faking amusement in his stead. The three of us did get a few laughs out of them, after they left.

Endless walks up and down the hall.

The ostomy nurse showing Jesse how to change his bag.

Late nights on my turn here, trips down to the basement vending machines by the escalator to drop quarters for bottled water and Fritos. I ate slowly, carefully on the couch so Jesse wouldn't hear me and feel deprived of the junk food he loved.

Doctors' contradictions. There is considerable liver damage, Dr. Lanier told us. Jesse might go another twenty years with his liver, Dr. Roche, another GI with the liver team, told us. We sorted through these statements, chewed them to mush, and spoon-fed them to Jesse with a little sugar.

Downstairs, going to the cafeteria near his discharge date. I shielded Jesse from being jostled in the lunch crowd, then walked with him under the mighty glass rafters of the pavilion, worried over him, and felt as close to him as he would let me be.

Coming home. His grandmother on the front lawn dancing with bells on, as promised, and a Welcome Home Jesse banner the neighbors had made strung across the front of the house. He barely acknowledged either. He was grieving for his lost colon, grieving over the bag on his side. Now he would need a liver transplant before he could have the ileoanal pull-through and rid himself of bag and bulb. He was quiet and stayed in his room. Still, he talked about how much better he felt. He shook his head in awe at what ulcerative colitis had done to him.

He developed an incisional hernia shortly after the operation. Luck of the draw, perhaps, but I had to wonder whether, after all of Dr. Gardner's scheming, Dr. Giselle had turned him over to his surgical fellow at the end. When the hernia popped out, Dr. Gardner instructed us, Jesse was to lie down with his legs up. If it went down, fine. If it did not go down within a few minutes he was to press on it gently with the flat of his hand. If that did not work but he was otherwise OK, we must watch it closely. If the hernia, which was a piece of his bowel, got stuck, choked between the tendons, or if it turned blue, or if he started vomiting, it would have to be repaired. If not, no one was anxious to take Jesse back into surgery now.

By late fall of 1993 he was still feeling better, but seemed less spontaneously sure of that now. And his liver was worsening. Dr. Gardner performed an endoscopy in December. It showed small varicosed veins, varices, around his stomach and esophagus. She started him on medication to lower his blood pressure and pulse. She took me into her office after one of our visits.

I think we should start working on arrangements for a transplant. Jesse doesn't need one now, but he needs time on the waiting list.

At first my health plan wouldn't pay for it, then later it would. In between, it appeared that Will's health insurance would pay. I made a list of every conceivable question his insurance company might ask to make sure we left them no wiggle room to deny Jesse. Rachel and I talked on the phone several times a week. I worried about the part in Will's plan that said they'd pay for a liver transplant for minor children who lived with the subscriber.

What about the primary home part? We'll have to fudge that.

Rachel didn't think the primary home part would come up at all or be a problem. I thought it could be a problem. She got exasperated with me.

But my health plan came through anyway. Dr. Gardner talked with Dr. Roche about the hospital's transplant program and came away reassured. They did a lot of them and had a good survival rate, eighty-five percent at six months after transplant, even better for children and young adults. About two-thirds of the surgeries went well, he said. A third had minor complications. That's a hundred percent, I thought. Was this one hundred percent of all those who survived or of all transplants performed, that is, did the minor complications include death or were the deaths another category, thus reducing the success rate? And when the surgery went well, did the patient continue to do well over time? If so, what did doing well mean? But I didn't ask these questions out loud at the time.

We started what turned out to be a year of tests and procedures to determine Jesse's eligibility for a transplant before they would place him on the waiting list. The liver surgeons debated whether to remove the shunt as a possible source of infection. Dr. Harrison, Jesse's neurosurgeon at Yale, was against it. The surgeons were reassured by his assessment. Jesse had an echocardiogram. His heart was fine. He was vaccinated against Hepatitis B. He had TB markers and thyroid function tests. He had a neurological exam. There was no hemorrhage, no stroke, and his ventricles were all right.

He had neuropsychiatric testing. The psychiatrist diagnosed him with Aspberger's Syndrome, a mild form of autism. Those who have it lack the full capacity to empathize with others and make few close friends. We were wasting our time with talk therapy, the psychiatrist said, wasting our time trying to coax better school performance out of him, regardless of his intelligence. His therapist disagreed. Jesse could empathize with others, John said, and Aspberger's was a trendy but vague diagnosis that covered too much territory. He called the psychiatrist.

You mean Jesse could never fall in love, he asked, never get married, never hold down a decent job?

That, apparently, was what she meant. She backed off a bit and suggested pervasive developmental disorder, a less disastrous diagnosis, but it was not clear to me whether she did so because John's insights about Jesse had persuaded her or because, knowing the diagnosis would do him no good if his therapist threw it out, she thought half a loaf better than none. If Jesse really had this syndrome it was torture for us to push him to do things he was incapable of doing. But the horizon she pointed out for him was so bleak! If she was off by so much as an inch and we followed her advice, we would be doing him a grave disservice.

Still, there was nothing to keep them from transplanting him. I gave the hospital a typed list with a dozen numbers on it, home, work, and beeper for me, Gail's work and beeper, Rachel's home, work, and beeper, Gail's mother's phone, Will's work, school, and the neighbors.

Fall into winter 1994. Jesse's gains from eliminating colitis were lost to cirrhosis. His hernia bothered him. He had an irregular pulse. He itched. He got short of breath and his energy was down. Rachel called one weekend. Jesse had a low-grade fever and was complaining of dizziness. He was having dizzy spells at school, he had told her, where he blacked out for a moment and then got an intense headache. There was no forewarning, no nausea, no hot sweats, no palpitations, and no chest pains, the list Dr. Gardner went down with me when I called her. Jesse's blood pressure medication might cause these symptoms, she said, but we had to keep his blood pressure low because of the varices.

Gail got a call from the school nurse one day. Jesse had a bad headache and an upset stomach. When she picked him up, his color was ashen. He slept for hours. The next day he felt hot but his temperature was low. He vomited in school suddenly and violently, then felt fine afterwards. It could be migraines, Dr. Gardner said.

Cindy, the benefits coordinator, told us to pack our bags, then told us to unpack them. The false alarm shook my confidence in the liver team. We wondered if we should consider listing him elsewhere. I talked to a big-name surgeon at Pittsburgh, who reassured me about the liver team but said we might want to think about waiting.

Jesse sounds like a low-risk patient to me. He might do well without a transplant for a few years.

He was failing most of his classes. We switched him to easier ones. I gave him rides to school, dropping him off by the tanning salon at the far end of Mountview Plaza. This saved time sitting in traffic on Rubber Avenue to get to the main entrance to the high school, and it was a short walk for him on a dirt path that led down to the football field, or so I thought until the other day on errands at the plaza with Daniel. We decided to walk Jesse's short cut. We parked and walked along the side of the tanning salon to get to the dirt path. It must have been slippery at times and muddy at others, like this day. We headed toward the school, the football field at our left and the National Guard buildings facing Rubber Avenue at our right. A hundred yards ahead, beyond the parking lot at the far end of the football field, we saw the front steps of the high school in profile and the wide concrete terrace connecting the main building and its two wings. It was a good quarter of a mile from the plaza and it felt like more with our braking descent on the path downhill and the soft earth with its knobby grass.

Dropping him off by the tanning salon, I would worry about the kid who threatened to beat him up. I told Rich Barone, the social worker, that a strategically placed blow to Jesse's record-size spleen could cause massive hemorrhaging and kill him. I wanted to scare Rich so he would scare the kid. Gail told Robert, Jesse's bigger and stronger friend down the street, who said not to worry about the kid. The kid stopped bothering him.

Jesse was reaching out again, just a little bit. Things were better between Gail and him. He and Daniel had become even closer after Nicholas moved south. And he and I had our moments. Driving home from the hospital, the two of us, after a visit to the liver clinic, he put in a Nirvana tape he'd copied off a CD. He was nervous that I'd disapprove of his music, and I was prepared to reward him with mild shock at Nirvana's raw anger and rebellion tempered with modest appreciation, that maybe there was something here, even if my adult ears couldn't hear it. But no such performance was necessary. Jesse had botched the taping job, his first attempt on Will's state-of-the-art equipment. We listened to a half-minute of a distant, muffled roar and broke out in laughter, big rear-back whinnies, a moment of sheer lunatic joy we hadn't shared in years.

I thought I was doing it right!

For Christmas he bought Rachel a bird feeder at a hardware store a mile from her home. He hid it in some bushes. Rachel saw him lugging it home close to the big day and got Will to pick him up. For me, lights for the back deck for stringing alongside his grandmother's apartment during the summer.

By January 1995 the fatigue was worse. Jesse had to drop more classes. Hydrocephalus had delayed him at the outset and now he might lose another year at school. In mid-February he came upstairs for a shower. He looked pale but said he felt all right. He started his shower and vomited suddenly. Drs. Gardner and Hall worried about his shunt, and sent him to Dr. Harrison. Dr. Harrison was not worried about the shunt. There were more vomiting episodes. The nurse from down the street, whose husband had inherited the size-13 sneakers, came by regularly to check Jesse's pulse and blood pressure. Daniel was depressed, afraid that Jesse was going to die.

We arranged to have him driven home in the school minibus. I look back and wonder how he walked home as long as he did, how Gail and I debated what to do about this as long as we did, and asked him what he thought about it as long as we did, when Jesse's default position was always to say, I'm fine, it's alright, or I don't know. But then, neither did we. We wanted him to do as much as he could for as long as he could, and we were nearing a marker point in his illness between a time when he could still walk home from school and a time when he could not. This marker point would be both true and false, coming, as it would, both too late and too soon, at a time when he no longer could make it all the way and a time when he could still make it part of the way.

Outside, to the left of the railing that marks the southern edge of the back deck, is a fenced enclosure housing the collapsed shell of a small above-ground pool and the hunched shapes, barely visible in the early dark, of ancient barbells that may have been fashioned from Civil War cannons, scraps of splintered wood from the frame, drawers, and legs of a much-loved wooden desk that molded by the oil tank for years after its four-by-six-foot oak top was lost or stolen in the move from New Haven, scraps of cheap Formica-top end tables gleefully smashed and tossed that contend with each other in their naked skeletal forms, and green plastic bags filled with the detritus of fifteen years of marriage and the crock pots that come with it, and with toys that mirror the stages of childhood and were shed like skin at the end of each stage, to be blown under the cracks in the basement doors, slink down to the lowest level of the house, and be saved for years in bins and shelves until the emotions that clung to them slunk away, too, and they disintegrated inside, leaving papery shells and a hazy film of basement light. Only the very I of their I of the children will weather this fading, an orange crate painted with the letters of the alphabet, a pair of shoes, and survive my recurring basement cleaning frenzies. One day we will be gone and, unless the children intervene, the next owners will toss even these to make room for their own shed skin. Rocko's Moving will haul away the pile in the enclosure when I finish working in the basement. Soon, maybe next weekend, most of Jesse's furniture will join it to make way for a family room.

I see myself standing here with him by the glass doors. He takes some color on his face from the early sunlight coming through them. This can't be, because the table was by the glass doors back then and wouldn't have left enough room for both of us to stand here. Still, I see us standing here or close by. It is May 5th. We are about to leave for the hospital. I act as though Jesse will be coming back, that is, I am too nonchalant by half. Yesterday I encouraged him to pick up in his room for his return. This was a transparent ploy. We both knew it, and knew it together. He didn't smirk when I said it and he didn't pick up in his room. This morning, there's nothing left to be said. We stand on holy ground now, and we don’t want to disturb the spirits in here.

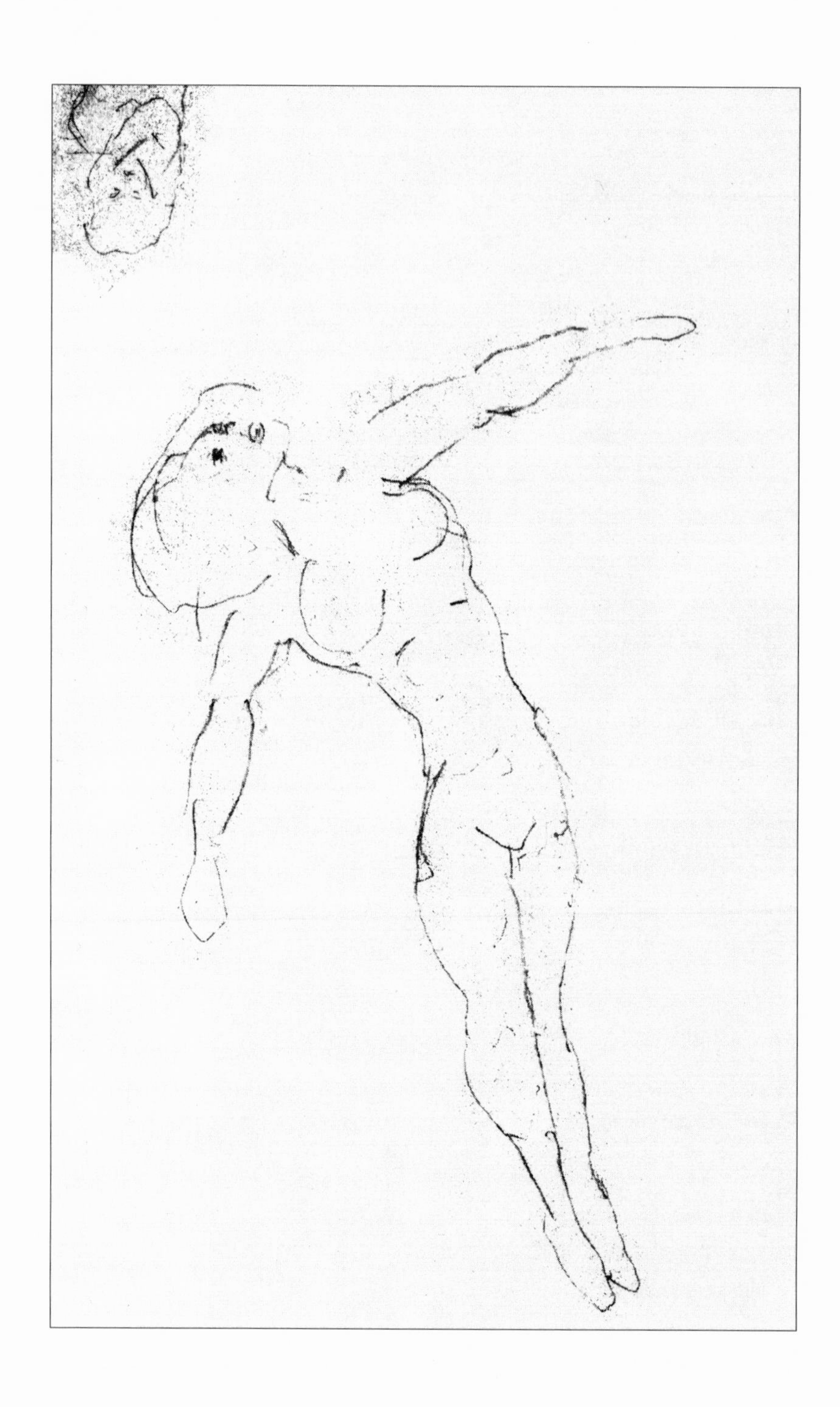

eight

Back to work. When my work is done, will Jesse be gone? And I? I have doled out my time and sympathies for family, work, and friends by the compass of Jesse and these notes for the past three and a half years. When they are no longer my compass, will I be better for having steered by them or, not so much worse, but nothing at all?

Late on June 9th. Terri told us, proud that she was the first to see him awake after his second transplant, that Jesse had opened his eyes and smiled at her.

We stood with Dr. Dorand behind the technician who worked the sonogram, gently moving the transducer around the area of Jesse's new liver. The liver looked good, but he had trouble seeing the blood flow through the hepatic artery. Dr. Dorand was satisfied, though. Rachel told him about hearing the anesthesiologist say, That's an awfully small hepatic artery, after the surgery.

The hepatic artery is small, but OK, he said.

Jesse had tremors in his left foot. Tia, the resident, thought they might be from liver function returning and, my notes say, his metabolism being metabolized. OK, Mike! We'd heard that flapping movements were associated with liver failure. The neurologist came by to check on Jesse. She smiled an ugly smile and shook her head at our liver failure worries.

No. The problem is that he needs to learn how to move again.

During the next two days Jesse looked around and nodded yes and no to questions. He had physical therapy. They gave him a Texas catheter, a condom with a small hose attached to a bag hung at the side of his bed, to replace the Foley catheter that had been stuck inside his penis for weeks. Dr. Gregory was surprised he was putting out any urine.

I still think the kidneys are permanently damaged, but I could be wrong.

And there was talk of extubating him, taking the breathing tube out of his mouth and freeing him from the respirator. Still, we wondered why his clotting time wasn't coming down faster, and we waited for that spontaneous alignment of what you see and what you feel in your gut that tells you things are good.

A second sonogram to look at the hepatic artery. The technician was able to locate the artery but couldn't see any blood flow through it.

The 12th. Dr. Dorand thought Jesse looked well, but he wasn't anxious, like Dr. Mann and the ICU staff, to take him off the respirator.

He needs to be stronger. I'd like to see him completely awake and aware.

He looked at Rachel and me, a signal that he was about to deliver an exit line.

You're here all the time. You have to be his advocates.

Then he went out to the nurse's station and pitched a tightly controlled fit with the nurses and residents about not taking Jesse off the respirator too soon. But how best to be Jesse's advocates, we wondered? Even Dr. Gardner, long distance, told me she thought he needed a trial off the respirator.

The next day Dr. Mellon looked less cheery than usual.

I'd like to see him doing a little better at this point. His clotting time is of some concern to us. It makes me wonder how his liver is doing.

Dr. Dorand came by later and said Jesse was making good progress. We asked him about the hepatic artery and what the questions that were coming up about it meant for Jesse and his new liver. He explained that the hepatic artery is one of two sources of blood and oxygen to the liver. The portal vein is the larger of the two. The hepatic artery mainly supplies the bile ducts in the liver. Because it's smaller, it can get clogged. You can live with a clogged hepatic artery for years, he said, but eventually the liver would have to be changed.

1:40 p.m., June 13th. EXTUBATED! There must have been a dozen people in Room B, Dr. Mann, the nurses, residents who'd moved on to their next rotation but heard the news, and us. Congratulations to Jesse all around.

But that night Jesse pulled hard for air. They intubated him on the day shift. Dr. Dorand, on rounds, was diplomatic.

It's good to see that he can breathe on his own. That his lungs work. That there's no swelling and that he's responsive.

Another sonogram was done. They couldn't see the hepatic artery.

The neurologist came in and had Jesse open and close his eyes and raise his right hand.

He's doing well.

Eyes open. Awake all day. Doing physical therapy. Awake and looking around. I read these notes and wonder why memory doesn't show me Awake and Aware and Looking around and Doing physical therapy. Is it the notes themselves, mostly clear during this stretch but a little flat, a poor prod for memory? Or is it Jesse's flatness, awake and then fading from the Fentanyl, which had kept him under for weeks and that still coursed through his blood while they tried to wean him off it? Or is it that I know what Awake and Aware are because we have July, when Jesse opened all his doors and invited us in?

I was about to go home for the first time since May 5th, to spend a day with the kids. Gail would stay at the hospital. Rachel assured me she could handle things here and said this was a chance for Gail and I to have some time together as well. I understood her plea to be left alone with Jesse and be away from us, to take a breath without the air of politeness, wheezing like a ventilator, that pervaded our days here. There was no sham in it. We were drawing on whatever reserves of goodwill we had for each other, on a dollop of social propriety, and on the love we all had for Jesse to be decent with each other so we could be good for Jesse. But Gail had to be here, if I wasn't. It wasn't about handling the doctors or watching out for Jesse. Rachel could do that as well as Gail or I. Competition to be a good parent in the doctors' and nurses' eyes was part of it, at least for me. But it was more than that. Bad luck, which I'd not given a thought in years because there was no bad luck, there were only circumstances and actors and actions and external forces that impinged on those actors and circumstances and actions to give us the illusion of luck of any kind, bad luck hovered around Room B and demanded our presence. Jesse's luck had not been good, but take us out of the mix here, one pair of our eyes to witness if nothing else, and the delicate balance we had helped to create might topple Jesse from his hammock.

Leaning down to say goodbye, I discovered that his left front tooth was cracked and half-crossed over the right from biting down on his breathing tube. Christ! They can't even save his two front teeth?! Cindy told me the dental team would fix it before he left, at no charge. Thanks, Cin! So what else could she have said? There was nothing else. She said what she had to say with the best of intentions, if awkwardly, and it was her job to say it. Sometimes the right thing is no longer an option.

I went home. The children tripped over each other's sentences as I walked in the back door. We went to an indoor playground in New Haven and crawled around in the tunnels and slid down the slides. It felt good to move my body in such absurd childish ways and to play Whack-a-Mole, banging the plastic heads of the green moles with a rubber mallet as they popped up out of one of their twenty holes in rapid succession, and to feel the thrill of victory as the prize tickets spurted out of their slot five at a time at the end of another successful mole whacking.

Gail took notes and called me with report that evening. Jesse had developed a bright red inflammation in his elbows and knees and a rash on his arms and legs, as though his body was a dark room making images on his skin of the illness it was manufacturing inside. The infectious disease team said it could be an autoimmune reaction, or an onset of arthritis from his medications, or serum sickness. Rheumatology said his joints were swollen, not inflamed, that there was no arthritis, and that the redness in his legs from the knees down was not a rash but a medication reaction. When the swelling in his left knee went down, his left elbow blew up. He was itchy and had a fever on and off and diarrhea. Yet he was alert, Gail told me. When he heard new voices he woke up.

I must have stayed the night and come back the next day to watch Jesse's mysterious rash come and go. And it must have been the next morning, June 18th, my notes aren't clear, that Gail and I were at the transplant center stretching our bones waiting for coffee. The phone rang. I picked up the receiver.

This is the PICU. Is Leslie in?

I called Leslie to the phone. She listened for a moment and ran out the door. Baby Jessie died that afternoon. Her bed was in an open area across from the nurses' station. The nurses pulled the curtains around it. One by one all the women, mothers and nurses, disappeared behind the curtains and emerged. That afternoon Jessie's father, Don, knocked over a newspaper stand on the street near the talking doors and was being cuffed when Leslie intervened and explained to the cops. Jesse was awake all day, looking around.

Dr. Boyd made rounds in the evening. We commented on Jesse's prothrombin, his PT, or clotting time, which was up a bit. Dr. Boyd looked at the numbers on the liver chart taped to the door, then over at Jesse, and then at us.

He's making slow progress. I have no explanation for his PT.

The ear, nose, and throat specialist came in and scheduled a tracheotomy for the following week. He said Jesse would need it for at least a couple of weeks.

Tina looked worried. She talked to us at the end of the room away from Jesse's bed.

Something started happening yesterday. The way he looks, his blood pressure.

Dr. Mellon thought so too. Jesse seemed depressed when he reacted at all. He had nothing to mouth to us. His legs were bright red.

Dr. Dorand made rounds late in the afternoon. He walked over to Jesse's bed and looked at him for a moment, then stood with us outside Room B.

He's getting farther away from danger with each uneventful day.

These are uneventful days?

I take as much comfort from his white blood cells and platelets creeping up as I worry about his PT and bile creeping up.

That night we helped Jill place and replace cool washcloths on his arms and legs and, as always, retreated to the NICU lounge, in shifts, draping sheets over our bodies to keep out the light and to scare off security guards who sometimes cracked down on those who were not NICU parents. The NICU lounge was enclosed by an elbow-high wood frame at either end and it felt enclosed, too, with its dark, soft, not-quite-clean blue couches and chairs and its dark blue rug and dim lighting only fifteen feet from the bank of elevators facing it. It was our refuge. The PICU lounge was too bright with its fluorescent lights on and too dark with them off, too sterile with its linoleum floor and plastic-covered easy chairs, and too depressing with its construction paper tree on the wall ripe with construction paper fruit filled with hopeful messages the mothers had written to their sick children. It was the NICU where we met people and had important conversations. Here in late May I had told my mother the dismal good news that Jesse still had a fighting chance. Here we napped or slept many nights, one or two or three or even all four of us when we couldn't risk going back to the transplant shelter. During the early days there was a sanctification to Jesse's suffering, or so I tried to ennoble a surgical accident in a world shrunk to the size of the hospital. It made a shroud around us to keep out intruding thoughts, our own or others', and intruding people, not part of the outer circle of sorrow for which we were the inner circle and Jesse its irreducible center. During those days his situation and ours were one. Later, the outside world and the simple fact that he lay in bed while we went out for coffee forced the revelation that our lives would go on even if his did not. Here, though, going into sleep or doze mode, we could follow him on his quest again, seeking beneath thought the wisdom of his body in our bodies, the secret that would lift him from his hammock. The NICU was nothing more than a place to crash, but in our sleep-deprived encephalic state it became a place for explorations beneath the surface of things to bring Jesse back.

When I see the pale Blakean goddess I found on his closet shelf floating across the page in light but bold pencil strokes with her half-finished arms and her crown of hair that must be blonde or Blakean white, I think of the NICU lounge, of its graces and its illusions. At the top right-hand corner of the page a little girl, the daughter, I have always assumed, of this floating goddess, dreams of meeting her mother again after a long separation, a meeting that will be sweeter for the separation. But where first glance at the drawing has the mother finding her daughter after a clean sweep of the cosmos, second glance has her looking beyond, as if she does not see the child or, worse, is not searching for her at all but shuddering at her own grace in flight. And the child, whose smile turns the corners of her mouth and shows, at first glance, that dreams and waking stand in such perfect harmony with her that she need not open her eyes to know her mother is near, at second glance is hedging her bets, steeling herself for the gravest disappointment of all, that mother is not coming back for her. Yet she will survive, resourceful daughter, the sly smile that crosses her face as her arm crosses her breast, distorting her body, proves this. A voice, hers, speaks to her.

That is not mother. See, her arms are not all born. Her hands don't have hands to hold you with.

She holds back hope in order to live and to keep pretenders at bay, and waits for her true mother.

And then it was the 20th of June and Jesse seemed better, though the redness and rash were still there and the specialists still had no answers. He put his right leg up and his left leg over it for the first time. He used an alphabet card. Tina and I tried to guess what he was spelling with his shaky hand.

B-A-L-N.

Blanket? You want a blanket, Jesse?

He nodded, and smiled at me. I got it right. Then he squeezed a rubber ball we'd bought from a drugstore down the street. Then blood gurgled from his stoma into his bag. They gave him blood and fresh frozen plasma and stopped feeding him. He was frightened.

In the afternoon they drew his blood pressure for his clotting time. It came back at nineteen seconds, close to twice normal. Dr. Mellon shook her head.

That can't be right.

They redrew his blood. It came back at eighteen seconds and now we knew something had gone seriously wrong.

Dr. Dorand made rounds with Dr. Mellon. They would take a sample of intestinal fluid, he said, and test it for infection, the most likely cause of the moderate fever Jesse had been running for the past few days. He was upbeat, though.

I don't see him as sliding downhill. I want to see him get more nutrition. He needs to get stronger.

The next morning Jesse's sheets were soaked with

bilirubin-tinged fluid from his surgical wound. The nurse weighed the soaked sheets and pads, then weighed the same number of clean sheets and pads, subtracted the second from the first, and estimated that he'd lost three liters worth of fluid in a few minutes. They took him to the operating room.

Gail saw Dr. Kostos come off the elevator to the surgical waiting room. He ushered us into a private room without speaking. We wondered if Jesse was still alive. We sat down with him, and waited. He told us that Jesse had perforated again, at a suture point from one of his six previous surgeries over the past six weeks.

I feel so bad for him. I don't know why it happened. Maybe it was just bad luck... His liver looks better than the last one, but it's swollen... We didn't look at the hepatic artery, but it's probably open... The tracheotomy was done.

There was this, then, that Jesse's mouth was free at last of the hard plastic tube he'd been gnashing his teeth on.

Time for a break. A walk, down the street half a block to the little plaza at Chestnut and Quinn.

Sunday night and the parking lot is deserted. Adrian's closed at noon and Marty's a couple of hours ago. The street is deserted, too, the quiet of Sunday evenings before summer and long days draw us outside. The center section of this little plaza that divides Quinn Street in half at Chestnut was built at the end of World War II around the same time as the Capes on Quinn and North Hoadley from Chestnut to Field. Before that, fields and apple orchards the men who play cribbage in Marty's are old enough to remember.

The plaza is a brick building a hundred thirty feet long and thirty-five feet deep. The north and south sections flanking Adrian's and Marty's were built in the 1960s. Marty's has been here since the late-1940s and Adrian's since the mid-1970s, but Adrian replaced another grocery store that had been here for years. Quinn

Street Pizza at the north end, a hole-in-the-wall takeout place with one table, is not going to make it. The kid who runs it isn't ready for his own business and regular hours. It was a yarn and accessories store when Jesse frequented Marty's Corner. Diana's Kut-n-Kurl is next to Quinn Street Plaza, then Community Liquor. The addition at the southern end set back from the rest of the plaza housed a sports equipment store next to Marty's that moved to Cheshire not long ago, and still houses Leo's Barber Shop, a sleepy establishment that operates only on natural light.

Adrian's Market is open every day. Adrian works the deli at the back and cuts meat and talks to the customers. A red ICE sign with blue borders and white caps of ice on each letter, cigarette posters of varying antiquity, and signs advertising childcare are taped to the plate glass windows. Next to Adrian's is Marty's Corner Patent Medicines, by the ancient peeling metal sign above the front door awning. The oddly spaced holes pocking the sign, like the open ends of Mason jars, must be sockets for light bulbs long since discontinued. A white square cross in the center symbolizes the availability, at one time, of the miracles of modern pharmacology. Inside to the left by street light and a radiationlike glow from the ice cream freezer at the far end of the store, is a long counter with cash register and lottery machine at the street end, red leatherette stools for the cribbage players and coffee drinkers along its length, and a Slush Puppies machine at its far end. On the wall opposite the counter are a rack of comic books and wrestling magazines, shelves of candy and gum, and an accordion-door telephone booth with a seat. The floors are hardwood. Looking in, I recall giving Jesse money to play the video games they had in what is now a storage room behind the ice cream freezer.

Fran, whose daughter owns the place, minds the store. He remembers Jesse looking at the comic books more than buying candy or playing video games.

Nice quiet kid.

He pointed out the front window from behind the cash register.

One time I saw a kid picking on him outside. I ran out there and told him to leave him alone. The kid said, Well, you know, he said this and that to me in school today. I said, I doubt it. Get moving, and don't pull your shit around here.

I thanked him, which felt odd with Jesse not here to benefit from the memory of Fran's protection. It sounds cozy, all of it, but what's distinctive about the plaza is not its quaintness or age but its entrenchment in the everyday and its refusal to take credit for anchoring the parcel bounded by Park, North Hoadley, Millville, and Field.

Down Quinn Street from Chestnut and turning up the driveway to the back deck, a scant breeze moves the bags filled with wrecked things behind the latticework fence under the floodlight, and I am thinking of Jesse's teachers. For three years I saw little of them. A call from Jen DaSilva, his tutor. A trip to the high school to pick up his honorary high school diploma from his guidance counselor, Chris Brinkman. The dedication of the arts display case we paid for. One of his teachers came up to me after the ceremony and said, I loved Jesse, and then disappeared before I could place her or her name. Calling Chris and Jen and telling them I wanted to meet with them, and Rich, and others, together or one on one, to talk about Jesse, but never getting around to it until a month ago and then, phone calls and phone tag and making appointments and I saw them all in the course of two weeks.

I sat with Chris Brinkman in his office. He hesitated, and why should he not, talking about the dead to a father who had waited too long to collect memories?

Jesse knew what was going on around him. Who the good and

bad teachers were. Socially, he knew what was going on.

Really? I never thought of Jesse as knowing what was going on around him socially.

He did though, in his own way. He'd make his point known with a couple of words. About his schedule, who he liked and didn't like, with one or two words. I talked with Jeff Byrne last year after you called.

Yes, I got sidetracked. I meant to get together with you before now.

He had Jesse for psychology. He said Jesse was quiet, but whenever he called on him he'd have something profound to say.

In psychology?

You should talk to him.

I wondered if my reaction showed in my eyes.

People didn't forget him. When students leave, they usually do.

I thought of a reason his teachers might remember him now, but I wanted to savor the moment.

He had a major toughness. He was a solid, tough individual.

A solid individual? Tough, yes, But solid?

He had to be solid to get through what he was dealing with.

Yes.

There was a little alcove outside Rich Barone's office. Jesse would wait in there. Once I passed by and I couldn't see anyone, but I felt a presence. I came back and looked between the two file cabinets. Jesse was scrunched up on a chair with his feet up. He smiled at me.

Rich Barone has a similar memory. I met him at one of the middle schools, one of several he has responsibility for, like a traveling preacher, along with the high school. We sat in a small square room with concrete walls painted yellow and a round Formica-top table with low plastic chairs too small to park adult butts on. I thought Rich would have the most to say of anyone, but he seemed tongue-tied at first. I felt as though I should be comforting him.

Jesse would let me know when he needed to talk. He would just appear. He'd be around the corner in the little alcove outside my office with a smirk on his face. I'd say, Hi Jesse, why don't you come on in? And he'd walk in. He wasn't looking for advice but for comfort. He expressed his needs in his presence, in being here.

He hesitated. It was a leading question and came too soon, but I asked anyway.

Did you see any changes in Jesse toward the end?

I think he was partly aware of the severity of his problems before anyone else and partly denied it. I saw more passive resistance, more bitterness. I rarely saw anger, but it was always down there. I think his bag was an embarrassment to him. Toward the end he wouldn't go to the bathroom at school. You could smell it. Jesse, I'd say, why don't you change your bag? He'd shrug.

Because of the incident with the bathroom stall, I wondered? For a long time I'd wanted to ask Rich about my idea that it was really an accident and that Jesse couldn't admit it or couldn't explain himself to us in a way that we would understand, but I'd always held back. Rich had been good to Jesse. So what if he misread him this one time? I put it out as an interpretation we had both made, that Jesse smeared the feces deliberately, but said that I'd asked myself at times whether it could have been an accident that just compounded itself. I described how that might have happened. Rich seemed to search his memory for the incident, and then to recall it.

Yes, I can see that. That may very well be what happened.

I was astonished that I'd carried this against him for so long, and it was over for him. It was not how he remembered Jesse.

I missed him for a long time, he said.

I told Chris a story that John had told me. He and Jesse would have a difficult session, with Jesse pushing John away just when he thought Jesse was going to open up. At the end John would feel frustrated, defeated. He said that as Jesse and I walked down the hall past his office, Jesse would give a couple raps on his outer door, and he was always glad to hear it.

It was as if Jesse was saying to me, It's OK, I'm still here, you're doing all right.

The story wasn't all that similar to the one about Jesse waiting in the alcove outside Rich's office, but I was caught up in the effervescence of memory. And so was Chris. He leaned forward and pointed, at me and my notebook.

Another thing that struck me. No one ever picked on Jesse. And students get picked on for the slightest reason. He was protected here. There was a silent understanding.

This wasn't literally true. I could count a few times when fellow students picked on him, but only on one hand. The spirit of what Chris said was true. You would expect a kid like Jesse to get hassled more than he did. I volunteered another story, about a time when Jesse and I were going through the checkout line at Stop & Shop and the bagger, who looked as though he could be the captain of the football team, said hello to him. Jesse barely glanced back. On the way out I told him he should say hello to people when they said hello to him. I did, Jesse said.

Yes, that's Jesse, said Chris.

I told the same story to Rich Barone as we sat in our student chairs at the middle school, with the same punch line, Jesse saying, I did.

And he did! And the guy knew it! said Rich.

He agreed with Chris that Jesse wasn't singled out at school.

Whereas someone more out there, someone like Nicholas, he

was ridiculed.

Gary Oettinger, Jesse's social worker for eighth grade at Hillside School, saw it differently. We sat in a counseling room on the second floor, starting from the basement, of the only building in the world, according to Naugatuck lore, with three first-floor entrances. The school, designed by Stanford White, is built next to a road that curves uphill around it.

I can see him as clearly as I see you sitting there. That's where he sat. I can see him just like I see you, I can remember his voice, but I can't remember the words.

I told him about Chris and Rich's theory that something in Jesse brought out a protectiveness in others, even in hardened adolescents.

I'm not sure that's what it was. When you can't get a rise out of someone, there's no fun in picking on him. It's not worth the risk. You don't know what he might say. Those who are a little different, who don't buy their clothes at the Gap, their gait is off, they're socially out of it, or the joke is over and they keep laughing, those guys take a beating. Those who are a lot different, like Jesse, there's awe, fear, respect.

I told John what Gary had said. He was skeptical. No, there was something that made people want to protect Jesse, he said. He hadn't yet figured out what it was. He was working on it.

Chris has a way of looking off when it's time to sum up the main points.

Who went through what he went through? What kind of man would this have made him?

I told him I hadn't known how to talk to Jesse about death, before we went in to the hospital and after, when he couldn't talk and was in such desperate straits. Chris shook his head.

I was in Vietnam. I saw everything. Some of the guys didn't handle it well, but I think it helped me. I'm not afraid of death. It's a gift, but it comes with a heavy price tag. Jesse could have taught you about illness and death.

Did you notice anything different in him toward the end? The last year? Before he went into the hospital?

I detected a sadness in him. He seemed calmer. Maybe he knew something you and I didn't know.

I've always wondered.

He began to isolate himself during the last six or seven months. Days Richard wasn't here, he'd be down by his door. And he knew Richard's schedule.

I didn't remember Jeff Byrne, the psychology teacher. I might have met him once at an open house. I came at the appointed time and we took seats in the student desk-chairs in his classroom. He looked at me quizzically, as though he wasn't sure who I was or why I was here. I reminded him.

It's been a long time. I don't have the greatest memory. I only had Jesse for half a year, the fall and winter of 1994, 1995, I think. When kids leave, I forget about them after a while.

He told me a story about four kids who flocked around him during senior year and of seeing one of the girls a couple years later in a restaurant and not remembering her name. He sensed my unspoken rejoinder that he remembered Jesse because he had died.

I've had other students die and I forget them too. So why do I remember him? I remember where he sat.

In the back of the class.

No, over there. Third seat, last row. He had his own look. His dress, his carriage. I remember black jeans.

He looked at my black jeans.

I wonder where he got that? I remember silver. A silver shirt? Silver and black?

He gave a quizzical look, which seemed to be his look, but at the moment it asked me to reflect back to him my memory of the silver and black shirt and my recognition that he had hit on something with this notion that Jesse had his own look. For a moment I wondered if the student he had talked about with Chris was someone else and whether he realized this as we sat in his class, saw that I did too, and, like me, was about to conclude that our job now was to find a way to end this blind date. Jesse did have black shirts, though, one with a science fiction theme and at least one with a white, if not a silver, design. I gave back a quizzical look, not of recognition but of jogged memory that said, Yes, Jesse had his own style and Yes, silver and black did ring a bell. It was enough to reassure Jeff that he was on the right track, even if we'd best not walk along it. And still I wondered if it was Jesse he remembered.

Did Jesse draw in your class?

Yes, but he heard what I was talking about. I'd call on him and his answer would show, He gets this.

Maybe, but I use this dodge myself when memory fails. Acknowledge the question, half-answer it, and change the subject to discourage further inquiry. I risked another leading question, quoting Chris Brinkman on Jeff's putative observation about Jesse's profundity. He gave that look again as if to say he, too, wondered if he had the right guy.

His thinking was more mature than others. He gave that off. His air, his answers. He had deeper perceptions.

You are trying to please me.

I wondered who he hung out with. What would become of him? I don't say I knew him well.

It sounds as though you made a good connection with him.

He shrugged.

I think you can make a connection without being close. I try to see if there's something unspoken.

I asked Chris and Rich and Jesse's high school principal who it might have been that had approached me after the dedication of the arts display case.

She's about five-four, dark hair, medium build, attractive, maybe mid-thirties. I think she might have taught Jesse English. Or maybe history.

Chris asked around for me. One lead after another came to nothing. When he finally suggested Ann Merola, now a vice principal, and I made the appointment with her, I still didn't know if it was she I'd been looking for until I walked into her office across the hall from Chris's. I had waited too long to talk to her and she grasped for specific memories, but like the others she remembered where Jesse sat, first row, fourth seat back in her class.

We connected around humor. He had a higher-level sense of humor than the others.

He got her jokes.

He would draw pictures on quizzes that told a story sequentially from the first page to the last.

No doubt, I thought, he was inspired by the old children's books we came across at his great grandmother's, where you riffle the pages to see a moving picture at the top right-hand corner.

He was quiet unless he was harassing me. I'd walk around the class while they were reading. He would have a science fiction book behind his schoolbook. I think he wanted me to see it, to get a laugh.

I laughed, that she had pegged him, and to encourage her to go on.

He was protective of himself. There was one time. We were standing by the window. He had his foot up on the radiator. He said his Mom was getting remarried and he talked about what he was wearing for the wedding. The next week I asked him how it went. He shrugged and said, Pretty good.

It was Mrs. Merola, another mystery solved from school papers I found in Jesse's room, with whom he had the ongoing feud about who was the real and who the fake Master of the Universe.

I drove the block over to Jen DaSilva's house, it was that cold. I had missed her a couple of times the year before and she had left a message I didn't get. By the time we finally set up this meeting I feared she would ask why I was still dealing with Jesse and I'd have to banish her to outer darkness. We sat in the living room and started with little things, how she worked at the public library downtown with the suspended kids and liked it but that it might be ending.

I tutored Jesse during study halls. He would draw action figures, demons, and caricatures, or talk about drawing or science fiction books. Anything but schoolwork. I'd say, Jesse, you're going to get me fired. He'd go on drawing his figures. Then he'd bring in words that I knew couldn't exist. Now, how would you use this word in a sentence, he'd say. I had no idea. Then he'd write his own sentence on the blackboard and show me the word in the dictionary. Or he'd make a cryptic comment on a subject and explain himself with drawings, weird figures on paper or intersecting lines that he drew on the blackboard. Now you study it, he'd say. You see what I mean? I never saw what he meant, but that was part of the game. Then he'd pull things out of that book bag of his. It must have weighed thirty pounds. He'd take out some book or drawing. Look at this! I'd say, Jesse, you're going to get me in trouble. No, this is important, he'd say. Look!

We'd work a little, then we'd talk or he'd draw. One time I put my foot down. This is absolutely it, Jesse. No more excuses, no more drawing. You have to work. He argued with me, but finally he gave in and actually did some work. I praised him up and down. See? You can do it, and you didn't do a single drawing! Two days later I found one of his monsters on a scrap of paper in my class book. He had dated it so I'd know he'd got me again.

We laugh. I tell her I know it meant a lot for Jesse to be able to spend time with someone who accepted him.

He created his mind. It was his playground.

Gary Oettinger had echoed this idea when we talked about Jesse's gift for verbal water torture.

It was his hobby. He would toy with me. I knew I couldn't beat him at it. If I saw one of his drawings and said it looked good, he'd say, What are you talking about? It stinks. If I said, You look good Jesse, he'd say, I feel terrible. It was mental sparring for him. I could look out the window and comment on how bright the sun was and he'd smirk. He always knew when you were trying to get him to talk about himself.

Listening to Gary, I realized there was nothing of what I had worried about most, no picture of an antisocial adult in the making. There was Jesse warding off intimacy to get me off his back or to parry with his teachers, and there was Jesse bobbing and weaving to avoid being interpreted and known, but sparring or serious, the repartee was a thing in itself. He wasn't setting up the authority figure for later gain or trying to reach a goal other than the immediate one of escape and, maybe, a small victory over his inquisitor. A wave of shame came over me as I thought of my imitation of him on the tape I'd made with Daniel and my unspoken charge that he'd been playing with Daniel's feelings. Even if it happened at times, how could I have forgotten the many times, on the tapes that Daniel played for me, where it had not? Where was the nastiness I imputed to him? There was boredom here and there, the older brother not caught up in the younger brother's magic. There was Jesse taking my part and Daniel his a decade later, coming up with solutions for the hero's dilemmas that his little brother shot down one after the other in order to maintain the conflict and thus prolong the telling. I remembered driving to New Haven with a couple of those tapes and turning up the volume on my poor-quality tape deck to catch their voices. The background fuzz from the tape was the sound of roaring engines fueling tales of artificial bosses, thousands of them, who worked for the real boss, an Artificial Boss himself but with capital letters. Here Jesse could relax, even poke fun at his own mythologizing.

D: Let's build a space ship.
J: OK, you build the thermonuclear reactor.
D: OK... What will you do?
J: I'll make the cheese sandwiches.

Political debates could be held over whether China was pronounced China or Shina. Phones could explode and fire drills could interrupt the action when imagination failed. Teenage ducks could commit drive-by paintings that transformed all the houses on the block from their normative polka dot to scandalous blue. Cars could swim, Martians might pass unknown amongst us but that they mistook toast for lemonade and lemonade for toast, and hospitals could be turnips as in, I'm sorry, sir, but since your infection hasn't responded to antibiotics we're going to have to admit you to the turnip.

Jen tutored him with other, tougher kids, as well as one on one.

He was a thinker, they liked action. He would listen to them brag about their exploits. They were all lies, but his eyes would get big.

Then he would draw and they would watch him. They were fascinated.

We talked about how Jesse shut away his illness from himself and yet had insight about his situation.

He was a little boy in a lot of ways, but an adult too, beyond his years.

Gary had talked about this, how any kid who got through a serious illness became different, wiser, because he was forced to.

I had a bad heart as a kid. I couldn't walk when I got out of bed. They put in a pig valve when I was about five. Up until then I didn't know what it was to have energy. When the good times come, you take them.

I mentioned to Gary about learning that only 385 people in New England were listed for liver transplants in 1995, and how I'd calculated from this fact just how bad Jesse's luck had to be, an adolescent among an older crowd waiting for a call.

But what are the odds that you and I exist? That your parents got together? That the sperm that got to the egg got there to make you? There's a better chance to have problems than to have been born. At least you're in the game.

We talked about dying young. Gary had a theory.

Everybody lives a lifetime because you only remember so much at any one time. By the time you're five years old you probably remember as much as you do when you're forty. The rest you forget. Jesse's lifetime wasn't shorter than ours.

On anyone else this would have looked New Age optimistic, but on Gary it looked good. As a child, he lay himself down to sleep between Lady Luck and Mister Death. I figured he'd earned his ray of sunshine.

Jen and I talked more about Jesse's illness.

I would never have known he was sick. He hid that away. He only let you see so much. I don't know if I ever got to know him.

The men I'd talked to said things like this as well, but with a wistfulness that was lacking in Jen, who seemed to have nothing to get off her chest. Still, we talked past nightfall. I talked about how hard it was to know what to say to Jesse about the possibility of his death, both before transplant, when he avoided the subject of his medical condition, and after, when he had a breathing tube stuck down his throat. Jen held up her hand, palm out, to stop me.

No. With all due respect, I think he had to work through this in his own way. If you had talked about it you might have made it more difficult for him.

Did you see any changes in him toward the end?

He was quieter, not as spontaneous. Still quick-witted. There were times when he was tired. He didn't want to leave. I would let him draw, or just rest. You know, everybody says these things will work out. I remember talking with Rich about home tutoring. We'll visit him, we said to each other. Things were going well, we heard, then suddenly there were problems. I thought the liver didn't take.

I told her a little of the story.

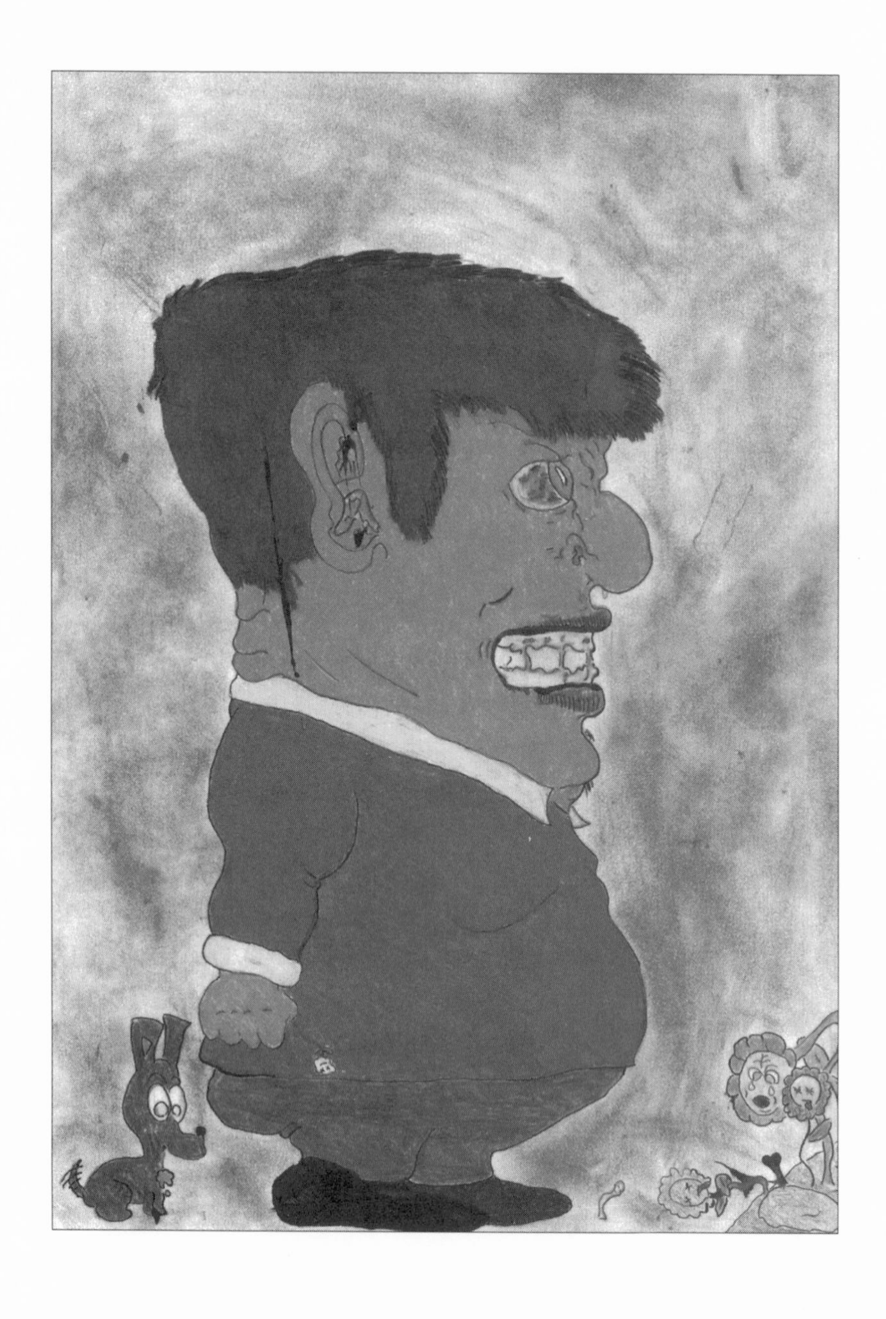

nine

Two stones, his headstone at the Carrington Cemetery off Route 63 going to New Haven and this one, just a good-size rock, in the back yard. JESSE is too faint to see in what little light seeps back here from the floodlight and drains from a pale bloodless moon, etched too shallow from Gail's hammer and screwdriver chipping to trace with a finger, unlike his name cut deep into buttery bluestone at the cemetery. And two trees, the sugar maple my mother and sister planted for him in Canada and this, a flowering cherry, next to the stone. Why not one of each? The enthusiasm of newborn grief? That, and a clever ruse to disguise mortality, like my dream of doctors, nurses, aides, and janitors tripping over each other around Jesse's bed, in the hallway outside his room, and at the nurse's station. They could not all be trying to save him and thus nothing so dramatic as death could be happening here. That this frantic dream activity mirrored what took place around him at life's end is proof only that the mind at rest retains a keen sense of irony.

Dreams every night at first, with their different themes. The theme of the mind holding on to old habits and not yet ready for a new one, which the dull call denial. In one, Jesse was dead but had come home with us to rest up for his next operation in New York. In another, his condition was hopeless, as confirmed by a ring of head-shaking doctors around his bed. They took him off the respirator and he did fine without it, yet this, Dr. Lanier told us, was not a sign of progress.

The theme of my growing doubts about his medical care, which my dreams turned into jokes against his doctors. We took Jesse to Stop & Shop for a procedure related to his ileostomy and he immediately felt better. Gail and I, in our surgical masks, stood next to him in the cereal aisle and conferred about having the other, more complicated procedures he needed done here as well.

And the theme of regret for what I had focused on and what I had missed. My favorite took place at Dr. Gardner's office. The nurse came out and announced that, since we had failed to hear his name being called a few minutes before, Dr. Gardner might not be able to see Jesse. I knew this was my signal to beg, which I did, and for the nurse to give in, which she did. Jesse, on the floor leaning over something, paid no attention to us. I told him to hurry up, annoyed that he didn't appreciate my negotiating skills.

I just have to do one more thing.

The usual passive-aggressive routine, I said to myself. Then he got up to go in. I looked down at a series of beautiful colored drawings done with great attention to detail.

And long episodic-symbolic dreams that lasted all night only to disappear down their holes in the morning as I reached out to grab them with too few hands. I managed to capture parts of one by forcing myself out of bed to the kitchen and my notebook. Jesse was in another room. We had decided to donate his organs. The man who was to receive them sat on a couch between his doctors, who were also Jesse's doctors. I looked at the potion, in a sake glass of course, that the man would drink before the operation, a concoction of purple and deep red flowers in water created by desert monks. The doctors sat blank-eyed, immersed in the Zenlike concentration required for transplant surgery, whose difficulty stems not from the technical aspects of the operation but from the problem, akin to that of the alchemist, of taking a living part from the hopeless and putting it into the hopeful with good effect. I was expected to wish the recipient well or say something meaningful and then be congratulated for the gift of life I was giving by proxy. I left the room without a word and went out to the lounge to have a good cry, but even my tears wouldn't run away to save themselves.

Then I walked through the chambers of a house of learning with books on shelves up to the ceilings and the smell of old wood. As I passed from the study into the living room I saw a door to my left. A voice assured me that I need not fear going through this door. I would see wondrous things, yet no harm would come to me. I dared myself to do it, then stepped boldly through the archway from the living room back into the study. It was the same room I had just left but I saw it differently now, vivid with color and promise and knowledge. I oohed and ahhed to express my appreciation for this vision and to take my attention, and that of the reassuring voice, off the fact that I had not walked through the door off the living room.

Then I was walking on a dirt road that led to a harbor. I saw Jesse with a girl who told him stories about himself as he drew her story. The first mate of his ship pointed me along an Oz-like brick path that led to the house of the girl's parents. Yes, they remembered Jesse fondly, they told me. How secretive he was, to have a girlfriend that I didn't know about! Then I saw him again, talking with a group of people about himself and his clothes, to their great interest. His hair was darker and he looked a little older.

Jesse couldn't have worn that outfit! He died before they were wearing those things.

I did not deliver the coup de grace of noting that Jesse would never have talked about himself or his clothes. I went home to write a letter to this pretender asking for a meeting, secretly hoping that he really was Jesse and that I would have the small disappointment of learning I didn't like him quite as much, older and on his own, as I did when he was in my care, rather than prove to my satisfaction that he was an impostor and that the first Jesse, the one I saw with the girl, was an illusion.

Then nothing at all for a season, and then one that made it through the cobwebs. I found out that Jesse was not dead, but had been living at his mother's. I was ashamed of myself for not knowing this and not having invited him over before now. I went up to him.

You look good!

He looked at me, face inflamed and rounded from prednisone.

I look good?!

I acknowledged the face problem. He told me he wanted to find an apartment and finish high school.

Fine!

I was excited, thinking about how I could help him do this, but I started crying. Gail told me not to, one because it would upset Jesse, two because he was here so there was no reason to cry. Using mental telepathy I told her I was right to cry, one because Jesse wasn't really here, two because I wanted to see if he would come over and comfort me, thus proving that he was here and proving to the psychiatrist at the hospital that he could show compassion toward others.

Gail's mother had a dream. Jesse lay on a mesh-covered lounge chair near a tree. A second tree stood at a distance.

The chair she described was not so different from the hammock I had seen him in. He looked bloated and very ill. Two figures dressed in white appeared. They helped him up from the hammock and walked away with him, each holding a hand. He looked back over his shoulder and she saw that he was the old Jesse. A beautiful dream, not less so for being an Italian Catholic grandmother's dream, but the interesting thing is that she didn't know about my hammock vision or the tree in Canada at the time she had it.

My mother and sister had a tree planted in Canada for Jesse in the fall of 1995. We went to see it in August of 1996, part of a visit to my mother's house in Rochester. The four of us took our car, my mother and sister took another. Crossing the border north of Buffalo you see the difference immediately. The trees, the landscape, the houses and lawns are picturesque, and that is the word, more ordered, flatter, English than here. Rain was predicted, but there was none. We drove to Niagara-on-the-Lake and Queen's Royal Park. Daniel and I lagged behind the others walking up the hill from the parking lot. He showed me his dinosaur chart with eons, eras, periods, and epochs and quizzed me on which was which. The tree overlooks the confluence of Lake Ontario and the Niagara River downstream from the Falls. A straight line where they meet, aqua on the Niagara River side closest to us and blue on the Lake Ontario side, stretches half a mile from a small peninsula housing Fort Niagara. Cassie and I sat on a break wall and watched the sailboats.

The four of us were in a foul mood. I felt badly for my mother, who found the park and picked the exact spot at the crest of a hill leading up from the street and down to the water with an unobstructed view of this congress of river and great lake vast as an ocean. The tree was taller than it was full and looked vulnerable, in the cracked sandy soil around it, to a high wind coming off the water. We thought it should have been planted deeper, right up to its knobby graft, and talked to the workers who were planting trees nearby. They said they would take care of it. A stone with Jesse's name on it that my mother had left at the base the day they planted it almost a year before was gone. She had brought a shellacked wooden JESSE to replace it. I tied it with rawhide straps to the main trunk high as my arms could reach and warned her that it, too, would probably vanish. I struggled to appreciate the weight of grief you try to hang somewhere but have no tools for the job. My sister took charge, spreading out blankets and commenting on the sandwiches, grapes, and drinks to buy time before the children begged us to leave. We walked into town and through a lush park with flower-lined paths. The sun was merely annoying.

My mother and sister drove back to Rochester. We stopped at Niagara Falls. The Falls are a shadow of what they were before being harnessed to produce electricity and slow the erosion that has moved them several miles upstream over the past few thousand years. Still, they drop upwards of a million gallons of water a second onto the rocks below. The park on the American side was colorful and fragrant but oddly sterile in the surrounding carnival atmosphere. No one wanted to take the ferry and get sprayed in a yellow raincoat at the bottom of the falls. I made a half-hearted effort to persuade them, not because I wanted to make the trip myself but because it's what you do when you come here. The tourists were pot-bellied Americans with campers and two children or foreigners, many of them, yes, Japanese families traveling together, the men standing side by side snapping photographs. We stopped for ice cream at a mobile stand after buying a dream catcher for Cassie, stupid gringos, from the Native Americans. I tried to figure out how many people we were, four or five, how many cones we needed, and if one of us didn't want one was that five minus one or four minus how many should we get? By way of this arithmetic lies madness. Licking around the edges of the cone in a race against the heat, I realized how miserable we were, ugly Americans whose children, walking from the U.S. to the Canadian side, stared dumbly at the customs official when she asked, Are these your parents?

Ripley's Believe it or Not, the Mecca of commercial freakdom that surrounds the Falls, was the high point of the trip. We snatched brochures and bought a program on the way out to remember See Lin Chung who had two pupils in each eye, Three-Ball Charlie who could put three balls in his mouth and whistle at the same time, Charles Somebody the tallest man in the world, and the two-headed cow. We shared with Ripley's the secret, omitted from the program, of the combination mirror and one-way glass where, on the one-way glass side in an adjoining room, you saw people, on the mirror side, watching themselves scratch their asses at the exact spot where you watched yourself pick your nose. Hearts pounding, we learned that if we knew of an unbelievable fact or item, we could submit it to the museum manager and become part of the legend of Robert Ripley's Believe it or Not.

I swam with Cassie in the plankton-breeding indoor pool of a not-too-clean Holiday Inn on the American side. Morning, waking up on the other side of twilight sleep, the ease of walking across the border played on me, how easy it would be to cross over and not come back. If Jesse's tree was in Canada then he was in Canada. We left in late morning and drove back to Rochester. Driving away from the soggy K-Mart universe that surrounds it, the myth of the Falls reasserts itself in some deep pool of the mind. The river that feeds the Falls, more strait than river it is so short, becomes the mighty Niagara again rushing to its repeated doom, certain of its part in a drama that is always about to happen, discovering and forgetting again and again that its glory is in its approach and the rushing anticipation of its plunge.

Walking in through the glass doors to the kitchen, our rose and green and cream wallpaper shows me a few images, the ram leaning down at the water's edge, a hint of rose garden and barbed wire, that fade back into the pattern when I take my seat.

Saturday night, June 24th, Edward, Jesse's night nurse, walked with us under the mighty glass rafters of the pavilion on the high western side. Back on the unit, Jesse was asleep. We had got a few hand squeezes and some eye contact out of him today. His clotting time was way up and his legs were red and swollen. The day before, Dr. Kostos had taken him back into surgery for a cleanup and re-exploration. He found cloudy fluid in Jesse's abdomen and a swollen liver.

Earlier this evening Dr. Kostos had made rounds. Jesse's liver was in severe rejection, he told us. He wanted to transfer him to the surgical intensive care unit to give continuous dialysis, CVVHD, which might clear out his cytotoxins, tiny particles whose existence, others told us, is largely conjectural. We pointed out to him that Jesse'd had CVVHD on the PICU and they stopped it because his lactate level went too high. He made a disparaging remark about the PICU staff, leaning close to me with expensive hospital breath. He was not pleased with our resistance. It had occurred to us that the weekend would pass quickly and with it, Dr. Kostos's role as attending surgeon. He wanted to give Jesse the best chance he could get, he said. Anything that might help, even give him a one- or two-percent better chance, was worth trying. But letting him come here would mean letting go of him a little bit more. The PICU was home. The nurses and Dr. Meyer, who was on this weekend, were here.

Edward pointed up to the mighty glass rafters of the pavilion.

This is the showcase area of the hospital. Where they put all the money. Have you seen it before?

We took the elevator past the stop for the surgical waiting room and up to the surgical intensive care unit, the SICU. Edward showed us its cubbyhole rooms with curtains for doors arranged around the island of the nurse's station. Nothing we heard or saw suggested to us that the SICU could do more for Jesse than was already being done on the PICU. We did learn, without a word from the SICU staff on duty tonight, that they would abide by none of our territoriality or our demonstrated disregard, on the PICU, for the limits set by visiting hours.

Sunday morning. Jesse was more sedated now than he had been a week ago. Dr. Meyer told us this was probably due to his liver not clearing his medications as well as it had before. She had heard about Dr. Kostos and the SICU, but said there would probably be no CVVHD or SICU, in a way that told us, It will happen over my dead body. But Dr. Kostos was on again that evening muscling us with cytotoxins. I told him we wanted to think about it for one more night. He looked at me with complete understanding and walked out of Room B.

Then Monday came and the SICU threat evaporated. Dr. Dorand seemed surprised it had been brought up at all. Jesse's legs looked a little less swollen. He tried to scratch his right leg with his left foot. We smeared A&D ointment on his itchy legs.

The next day he was restrained. He had pulled out his nasogastric tube during the night. Standing next to him and loosening the restraints to free his arms for a bit, he pointed to his head and mouthed, Headache. His heart rate dropped down, then went back up. Dr. Mellon thought this was probably a complication of sepsis, but wanted the neurologist to look at him. The neurologist didn't think there was any brain swelling. If there had been, his heart rate would have stayed down, not dropped down and then come back up. More likely, she said, there was something with the heart itself.

The cardiologist came. He said that Jesse's erratic heart rate was probably related to his kidneys, his general illness, and possibly a medication interaction, but his heart was fine.

Dr. Dorand made rounds. He was concerned about calories and nutrition.

His wound is not healing as quickly as it should because of lack of nutrition and his body being sick. I've thought about going back in to see what's happening, but I haven't seen any reason to.

This meant, we knew, that he would soon see a reason to go back in.

June 28th. Jesse had a restless night and slept most of the day. Dr. Boyd made rounds in the afternoon.

He's still fighting. He should get better soon.

We didn't know whether Should meant that Dr. Boyd thought Jesse would get better soon or that he'd better get better soon if he was to have any chance at all. We didn't want to ask for clarification on this point.

I called down to Room B from the open double doors to tell Ellie that Jesse's blood had arrived through the tube from the blood bank, and I thought of the early days standing in the hall outside Room D conferring with doctors and conspiring with each other. Now, doe-eyed sympathy and frightened looks, hushed steps past the door to Room B where the marked family kept watch over the marked patient.

The 30th. Jesse was a little more alert. He had some physical therapy, moving his arms and legs, slowly, with the physical therapist's help, and wincing. They did a sonogram. It showed blood flow in the hepatic artery but not inside the liver. Dr. Dorand was willing to take it.

If there's blood flow outside, I assume it's inside and that there is no bile duct blockage.

He talked about infection and rejection again, how the first liver was lost to rejection and how the problem with the second was infection. Still, this one was not going in the right direction, he said. We asked about a third liver. He said they would consider it if infection, not rejection, was the main issue, as he suspected. Notwithstanding this assessment, we asked him about an idea Dr. Mellon had been floating, of treating Jesse with an antirejection drug called OKT3. I had the impression she hoped it would work as something akin to the paddles that give an electrical jolt to the heart, to shock his liver awake and remind it of its many duties.

It's too powerful. He's not strong enough, and I don't think he needs it. In a thousand liver transplants here we've never lost a liver to rejection.

Except the first one you gave Jesse, I thought, according to your and Dr. Swanson's statements. But maybe that one didn't count, since they had let it go on purpose in order to deal with the infection that had invaded Jesse's body.

Usually it's not a matter of the liver not getting better, it's a matter of the patient not getting better.

It's a good thing I love you, I thought.

That evening James the medical student poked his head in.

We'll hope the next week is better than this one has been for Jesse.

Has this been a bad week for Jesse?

We turned the corner into July. Jesse was losing hair from the back of his head. The resident said it was from lying on his back, lack of protein, and prolonged sedation. I wondered if he'd grown used to being on a respirator and lying in bed and how much he remembered of his life before he was changed. He was awake and tried to speak, but only barked over his trach.

Dr. Dorand made rounds. He looked at the liver chart on the door and then at Jesse. He came back to the chart and pointed out two liver enzymes going the right way from a long row of numbers going wrong.

These are the first to come down with rejection treatment. Others should follow.

He wanted to get Jesse fed and get his intestine in shape, he said, and surgery would slow that down, but he needed answers about the condition of Jesse's liver and bile ducts and hepatic artery, and whether infection was still present in his body.

The next day, his clotting time came back at more than three times normal. He bled from his stoma and got blood to replace what he lost. He was shivering. They put him under heat lamps and blankets. He tried to say something but didn't have the energy to mouth the words. He was so skinny now. Dr. Lanier thought there was still infection they hadn't found.

In the meantime, I'm pushing the nutrition. That's one thing we can do for him. With a lack of nutrition the intestine gets paper thin and perforations occur. The first perforation was related to adhesions. We missed it because he looked so good. The second was due to his poor condition.

He pointed at Jesse.

The jaundice looks bad but the facial thinness is worse. That's one of the last areas of the body to go. He has a concentration-camp look.

After he left I asked Dr. Meyer if Jesse was at the point of irreversible weight loss.

No. People can live for months on the nutrition Jesse is getting and in the condition Jesse is in.

I didn't ask if people could survive this survival. His life was in little gestures now. Maria the day nurse stuffing pillows under his left shoulder to ease the swelling on the left side of his face, Jesse trying to wiggle away from the pillows and turn off his right side on to his left. Maria putting her face close to his and lip reading, I want to go home. Jesse signaling for us to put blankets on him. The light in his eyes when Tina walked into the room. Ellie, who told him he would go back and back and back, now calling him Jesse baby and getting a crooked smile from him. Marion coming in at night. Jesse, it's Marion, hmm? Jesse sucking on foam mouth cleaners, licking them like a baby he was so thirsty.

But only a little, OK Jesse, because they make gunk collect at the back of your throat.

On July 3rd they did another sonogram and couldn't see the hepatic artery. They took Jesse down. Dr. Dorand sat with us at the western end of the surgical waiting room by the high side of the glass rafters. The other side hadn't brought much luck, and another family had our spot tonight anyway. Dr. Dorand leaned forward, hunched and looking smaller with elbows resting above his knees and hands clasped. He told us the hepatic artery was blocked and that they had found another perforation about to happen at the spot where they had sewn the bile duct to the intestine.

He's not going home with this liver. He probably won't live for more than another day or two.

Fourth of July, a Tuesday that felt like a weekend with many of the regulars, both doctors and nurses, off. The PICU was quiet. Jesse was bleeding and didn't want to be touched. Dr. Lanier made rounds. Like a few other times when things looked dismal, I sensed that it was physically painful for him to be with us now.

We don't want to give you false hope.

I left unspoken the smart-assed reply that hope, by definition, is neither true nor false, but I was surprised that Dr. Lanier could be so out of touch with the reality of life on an ICU, where the next That's not bad, about a blood level coming back less awful than you expected, gives hope, and where even despair is part of hope's rhythm.

Jesse's face was an Edward Munch painting, dark green, wasted. They took many chest X-rays to gauge the fluid pushing up from his stomach into his lungs. The attendant wheeled in the machine. We told Jesse, almost whispering it shamed us so to say it, that it was time for another X-ray. We moved him as gently as possible, arms under his upper back and under the tender skin behind his knees to shift him up or down on the bed and lift him a few inches to place the metal plate under his back. He grimaced, then looked into the camera lens directly over his head and frightened himself. The X-ray technician who looked like Quasimodo was on, so it was understood that one or two of us would stay in the room to keep Jesse steady to make sure they wouldn't have to come back and take the pictures again. Other technicians would balk over this procedural violation. Rachel wanted to stay with Jesse this time. Which annoyed me. He might need one of her kidneys someday, and exposing herself to X-rays she didn't have to be exposed to was not a good thing.

Jesse oozed and bled from surgical wounds and into his ostomy bag and bruised without moving. Dr. Swanson sent back word to the ICU resident that there was no surgical solution to the bleeding. Over dinner at Red Fish Blue Fish, Gail and I talked about whether we should donate his organs. Could any of them be used? Later, Dr. Swanson came by the unit.

I said I'd tell you when there was no hope and we've reached that point. He's had enough and I think you've had enough.

Presumptuous of him to say so, we thought.

Later in the evening I called the liver surgeon from Pittsburgh at home. He had buttressed my faith in the liver team last year after the false alarm about getting Jesse ready to come in for his transplant. He had also made me uneasy when he told me we might want to wait, that Jesse sounded like a good bet to live for years without a transplant. Tonight he said age was in Jesse's favor, but that seemed to be all. I told him we'd been thinking about a third liver for him.

The odds of survival go down with each transplant. What does Jesse want?

I don't recall my reply, but I do recall that the question left me unsettled. Should we ask Jesse what he wanted when the alternative to a third transplant was so stark?

The next morning Ellie and Rachel confronted Dr. Dorand about the bleeding as he tried to walk into Room B. Jesse was oozing from his wound, he said, not bleeding. Ellie turned on her heels and got the chart. She opened it to the nurse's flow sheets and held it under his nose to show him that Jesse'd had more than sixty units of blood and blood products in the past day. He stared at it.

I didn't realize he was bleeding that much.

He ordered Jesse back into surgery, with a surgical fellow we hadn't met. We sat in the waiting room but for the first time, no one came to talk to us and observe the waiting room ritual that the surgeons here seemed to respect as much as we had come to rely on it. The fellow called the unit later and said she didn't know we'd been waiting there. Rachel, who took the call, didn't believe her. The right lobe of Jesse's liver was bleeding, the fellow told her, but there was no one major source of bleeding. Jill, the night nurse, said she didn't believe there hadn't been a big bleeder.

The next morning his eyes were open. He blinked for yes and nodded for no. He was stable, considering. They had stopped feeding him through his nasogastric tube because of the surgery, but hoped to start again, slowly. The only satisfying moment of the day came from watching Dr. Dorand's discomfort when we told him his fellow hadn't showed up in the surgical waiting room the night before.

Then it was the 7th and Dr. Swanson was outside Room B. Gail stood facing him a few feet away. Five-foot Rachel stuck her nose under his chin. The ICU staff stood bunched around Dr. Meyer at the nurse's station. I stood behind Rachel.

Jesse is not going to make it. A better day here or there doesn't matter when you're that far out there. It's like climbing a sand dune. You climb a few feet and you slide down to the bottom again.

Gail shot back a question as if to scatter the image before it took hold of us.

How long can Jesse's liver hold out?

Longer than it should.

Rachel interjected staccato questions at Dr. Swanson's windpipe. What about no surgical solution and then back in surgery? What about the different stories we keep hearing? What about this? What about that? A few feet away, Dr. Meyer mouthed a silent Yes! Gail kept up her end.

If Jesse stabilizes and gets stronger, will you give him another liver?

Probably not.

Well then that's it, isn't it?

Dr. Swanson flinched, barely but perceptibly, and corrected himself.

He would have to be extubated. Sitting up. Eating. Putting on weight. Talking. It would have to be a dramatic recovery.

Dr. Swanson looked down the hall as if his help might come from there. I shook his hand. He walked off the unit. It was

Mother's day on the ICU.

Later, we talked with Dr. Meyer.

It's in our court now. We don't need him. It's our job to get Jesse to the point where he can relist him.

We heard muttered comments about Dr. Swanson's performance, and encouraged them. In fairness, though, he must have thought we hadn't got the message the first time. We learned that Dr. Lanier, who wasn't aware of Swanson's No hope speech two days before, had insisted that he come up and talk to us. Still, we thought he had been ready to let Jesse bleed himself dry on the 4th, when Dr. Dorand took him back into surgery on the 5th. In any case, Dr. Swanson was our scapegoat now. If he served to focus everyone's attention and help Jesse a little bit more, then smack him on the rear end and send him off into the wilderness to slide up and down his own sand dune.

Gail took me aside.

If they're not going to transplant Jesse then let's take him to Yale where he can be closer to home. If he gets strong enough we can have him transplanted somewhere else.

I felt such despair that even Gail, more optimistic than Dr. Dorand, had lost hope for Jesse's chances here. I could see him being loaded into an ambulance and driven through Central Park to the Henry Hudson Parkway. He wouldn't make it past the river. I had always thought this was harder on Gail than on me, going back and forth between Naugatuck and New York, the children and Jesse, the constant pull and guilt no matter where she was, while I could feel guilty about the kids in fifteen-minute phone calls a day and then be sucked back into the whirlpool. And I had the nurses' and doctors' unspoken admiration, a father being here for his son.

I started to worry about my health insurance as the bill approached what I guessed to be a million dollars. I didn't know then that my health insurance company had negotiated what they called a global contract, so much for the first transplant and everything associated with it, so much for a second if Jesse needed it, and, I guess, anything that came after. That Jesse's suffering was a privilege of sorts, and our being here to watch his suffering a privilege too, was not lost on me. I had been feeling a subtle pressure, mostly self-inflicted, to get back to work as I saw my leave days drop past the halfway point of what I'd saved up. I still had enough to take me into August, counting the odd quarter hours I put in at the hospital, having documents mailed to me at the transplant shelter, marking them up, and sending them back to the clinical director of the outreach project. I thought about the parents who couldn't do what I was doing, and thought more about the patients who had no family to care for them, or those, like fifteen-year-old Matt across the hall waiting for a heart he didn't want, whose mother did not come often and, when she did, seemed distracted, sitting in a rocking chair before him in vague disapproval and not staying long. Matt refused to eat, except occasionally the junk food that parents and nurses brought him. We gasped in awe and salivated over the chocolate cake he made with the activity therapist, hoping he'd eat some with us. The nurses stand *in loco parentis* for such unfortunates so they won't be forgotten or deemed less worthy because they have no one to prove they are loved outside of an intensive care unit. It's not that the doctors would make such a conscious judgment, but that advocacy on an ICU is a hedged bet against a fog of weariness or hopelessness that might set in and lead to a wrong diagnosis when the odds are stacked against you from the outset or you wouldn't be here.

I close the notebook and close my eyes. I see myself massaging Gail's back in the dark, three years ago. I don't know why my back is so sore, she said. Rubbing her back, I remembered how I had rubbed Jesse's back after his first transplant. Rubbing Jesse's back, I had thought of rubbing my father's back when cancer was looking for nerve endings to draw pain from at life's end. But this is different, I thought. Jesse's sore back comes with liver transplants. It's an unpleasant side effect of death averted. Then Jesse's soreness turned to agony and I kept rubbing his back as his life drained out through a hole in his intestine. Rubbing Gail's warm back in the dark before making love, I thought I could feel Jesse's back again, heating up at the first pitch of fever that would burn his body to ash like his grandfather's before him.

August 1995. It was over and we were back home in a world we had been part of but that seemed foreign now. It amazed me that neighbors and strangers could walk down the street, go into Adrian's to buy a gallon of milk and go on their way, oblivious to the fact that the world had changed utterly. Jesse's absence from this house seemed unreal, and the world seemed brutal and corrupt for failing to acknowledge his absence. Some people were kind. Few knew what to say or do and few could help but be infected with the idea of closure. People gave us grief manuals, which all got it exactly wrong from the start. They focused on the griever not the one grieved over, as though the latter had never existed, or didn't matter anymore. They didn't understand that you have to keep the wound open, to maintain alertness for the moment of the moment when loss is a hot knife to the heart that brings us together again.

We were a ghost family and solitary ghosts, more of a family than ever for sharing this insubstantiality yet playing at being a family as we played at being ourselves. Cassie fussed over her babies and took them with her everywhere she went. She couldn't talk about Jesse. Daniel was the keeper of the scrapbook and writer of Jesse moments. At the cemetery that first winter he carried icicles he had pulled from the bushes and dropped them onto the crusted snow.

The father. Chink! The son! Chink! And the holy ghost! Chink!

When the unimaginable happens it can happen again. We couldn't protect Jesse and we can't protect them.

Gail, more sociable than I am and more needed by others, wore her wound openly and was hurt more for it, easy target for the rarely spoken but often implied question, Are you still going through that, a question more biting for the sense she got, even from friends, that as Jesse's stepmother she had no right to grieve over him as Rachel or I did, that she should support me in my grief and take care of children and household, and that enough was enough. She plunged into a deep depression, spiced by the trauma of flashbacks to Jesse in the hospital and a stepmother's special guilt over what she might have said or done or understood.

Anger was my shield. Suggest, by tone or wrinkled brow, that I was becoming obsessed about whether serious mistakes had been made with Jesse's medical care, and you made my shit list. Ask the dreaded, How are you doingGood question, with no pause between doing and Good, and you made my shit list. Squirm a quarter inch in your chair when I mentioned Jesse, and you made my shit list. Through it all I smiled like a villain and no one knew that he, like everyone else, was on my shit list. I laughed when Gail pointed out to me that the comically angry man we found in Jesse's room was an outrageous caricature of Will. Jesse had drawn it, I guessed, when he was seventeen and Rachel and Will became engaged. No doubt he was wondering what his place would be in this new family, yet the drawing suited my inner man now better than it had ever suited Will then. The man in the drawing has reddish brown hair, green eyeballs about to drip green fluid, huge head sans neck, wiener nose, blue shirt on dumpling body, green pants and brown shoes against an aqua background. To the right is a flower garden with wilted flowers. One flower is dead and lies on the ground. Two others weep over it, giving the garden the look of a newly dug grave. A worm sticks its head out next to the flower, too innocent to be Blake's invisible worm. Behind the angry figure a little brown dog with ears sticking up and big surprised eyes wags its tail hopefully. The dog is the most obvious culprit for the dead flower, but the theme is adult anger, a colossal force that sends its rays into innocent forms of life and destroys them, flowers first, and then, who knows?

Anger shielded me from my own ghostliness. The I of now was not the I of then. No gradual progression of blurred events sustained the illusion of continuity for me. There was my double agent who acted out roles he remembered well, who walked to the store like neighbors and strangers and, like them, bought milk at Adrian's, who observed those actions from afar yet experienced an approximation of whatever satisfaction, enjoyment, pain, the situation seemed to call for, and who did things, detached, that I had once thought were fueled by an inner self. How solid an illusion this concept had been for me!

Strange half-in half-out state, going into Jesse's room and thinking of some parental instruction I would give him while looking in his closet to see how much room there was for other clothes, not his. Gail wondering what was wrong when she picked up the telephone and it wasn't sticky from whatever candy he had on his hands. Jesse with us yet not with us everywhere we went. Driving north on Route 63 past Litchfield near the Massachusetts border with the leaves changing colors that first fall, I had a fantasy of living in a house in the country with fields and fences and woods and thought, what a mental break it is to take a drive away from home, Away from him, I thought, before I could catch myself.

Or sunset after rain in New Hampshire, two summers later. We crossed the highway strip from our hotel room and went down stairs built into the seawall just as the moon loosened its grip. Huge rocks buried beneath the ocean were beached. The sand exhaled steam and made a cloud that hung two feet off the ground. We walked toward rocks where people were gathering stones. Rocks and people would have been background filler for us in daylight but now they were marvelous, what happens when the nimbus of every live thing is tricked into showing itself. Walking back with Daniel, Gail and Cassandra's legs fled in front of us like a silent movie for having only shadows to carry. The sensation of being lost, as in floating on a pool with eyes closed and being deliciously wrong over and over again, gave way to a moment's panic, that we would not find the stairs but would wander the beach until the tide came in and the moon pulled us out. Later, the girls said we looked like us yet not us. They had wondered if they should come back for us.

Or fall, last year. Daniel and I went out to dinner. He was fourteen now and big as Jesse ever got. We talked about Jesse, as we always did when we went out to dinner. Daniel looked uncomfortable. I waited.

I realized that underneath all the joking he was really this unhappy kid.

Uh-huh.

Because of all the things that were happening to him.

Yes.

We talked about the hospital and what he and Cassie had done at home while we were in New York and the grandmothers and my sister were taking care of them.

I played with my friends. I hadn't spent any time with them in two years.

That's right.

Because I wanted to spend all my time with Jesse.

I talked with him about taking Jesse's hand in the hospital, and how much that meant to him, and to me. He shrugged.

I felt the pressure to do it. Like it was expected of me. Because

I was older than Cassie.

Was it hard for you?

No, it wasn't any big deal. Any brother would do it.

I don't know about that.

Well, I was the older one. Cassie couldn't do it.

No. She was too young.

I talked about the little regrets. He hesitated.

I thought you and Mom gave him a hard time.

About what kinds of things?

His room, things like that. Like, give the kid a break.

It hurt, but I admired him for his honesty and he drew Jesse from his shadows for me.

The world lapped at the sandcastle of our otherness. What had been alien, walking into a video store, say, too impure a few weeks before to ever happen again, became commonplace. In the early days of his death the loss of him was filled with revelations that would be obvious to anyone who wasn't consumed with warding them off. Driving to Cheshire to pick apples, the thought, We can't help Jesse now. Absurd, and one of many such jolts for those whose minds cannot take in catastrophe all at once but only in little draughts, like Mithridates, until loss is no longer a dark horse on the horizon but the little dog that lies at your feet.

His molecules have slipped away from his clothes, his bed, his desk, his drawings, and his pencils. There is less of him in every place I look.

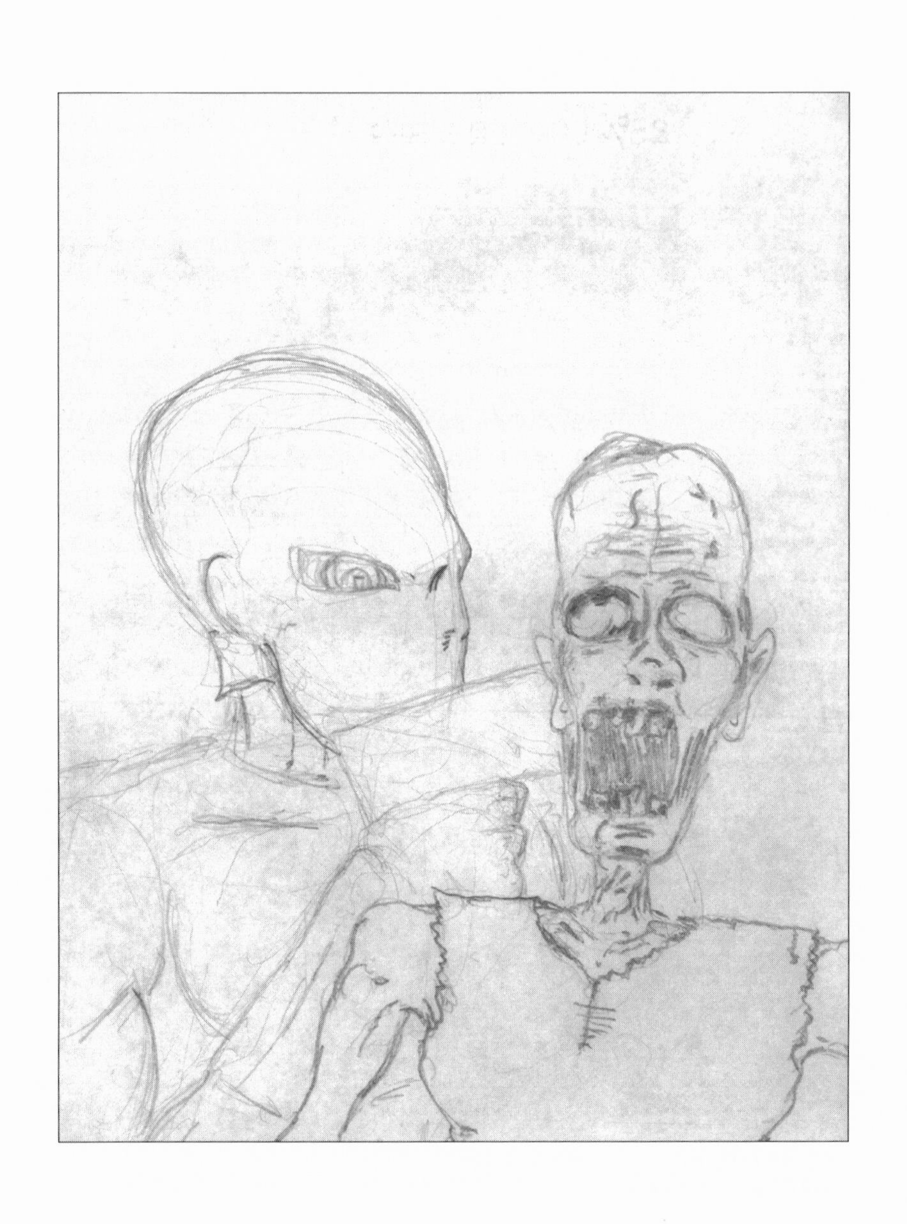

ten

Jesse journal number five. Now, no need for notes to memory, memory to notes, the notes mostly good here. I had finally learned that I didn't have to record every event and every medical detail, and had figured out how to catch moments in the midst of things or scribble notes I could draw on later in a quiet moment. How many times through for me now, this ritual of witnessing the best of times and the worst of times, the time of trouble and the time we were most alive?

July 8

Jesse woke up! He was trying to talk this morning, mouthing and signaling to Gail.

I want the sheet off.

OK hon.

She pulled it off him. He rolled onto his right elbow and started to get out of bed. She held him back.

No Jesse, you can't get out of bed right now.

Want to.

I know, hon. But not right now.

Why not?

You need to get a little stronger. Then you can get out of bed. OK?

OK.

She got him settled. We put the rail up. He seemed confused about where he was, but knew he was in the wrong place.

I want to go home.

Yes, we'll take you home as soon as you're better.

He nodded, but I think he wants to get out of bed, better or not.

Afternoon notes. Dr. Meyer made rounds. She was amazed at how awake and alert he is.

Hello Jesse.

Waved.

How do you feel?

Nodded, pretty well.

It's good to see you awake.

Yes.

You look much better.

Yes.

Over by the door she told us, There must be some liver function for him to be so alert.

Daniel and Cassandra came. Daniel walked over to Jesse. His face lit up and he waved with his right hand high in the air, IVs dangling, then held out his hand. Daniel didn't miss a beat, stepped forward and took his hand. Jesse, big crooked smile. Cassie stood at the doorway, then went outside, crying.

Outside Room B Daniel said, He looks like the same old Jesse. Then, moments later, His hands looked like clay. And they do. Even the palms are dark, the smooth earthy consistency of clay.

Then, Jesse looked like a puppet. Why a puppet? The thinness, angularity of his arms and elbows. His long thin fingers. Herky-Jerky movements from lack of practice and loss of strength. Then, a few minutes later, Daniel talked about blood smelling like metal.

Dr. Rand, the surgical fellow, came in and examined Jesse. On his way out he looked me hard in the eye.

If Jesse bleeds badly again, we will stop the bleeding.

He spoke with an emphasis I took to be a reference to Dr. Swanson saying there was no surgical solution to the bleeding a few days ago when Jesse was breaking the blood bank.

The excitement here is electric but held back, not to wake the demons. Jesse's beaten the odds again. But his gut is still sick.

Evening note. Angela, Jesse's killer nurse whom he accused of giving him extra lines right after his first transplant, is moving to Florida. Tina's leaving soon to work with pediatric cancer patients at Sloan-Kettering.

July 9

Jesse confused again this morning, about where he is, objects in the room. Rip Van Winkle waking up after 2 transplants among 10 operations. He motions for the shades to be pulled down. To keep unseen presences from observing him in this condition or to avoid looking them in the eye? He looks at his right leg, still more swollen than the left. He moves his arm, fearful, maybe, of his own emaciated appendages. With his free hand he points at the red light clipped to the oxygen monitor. He knows we'll have to put it back on if he pulls it off.

I can't stand it, he mouths.

We try to take his mind off it with the latest batch of cards and letters that have come in.

I wonder if home means health to him now or just getting away from this place. This is the flip side of Jesse awake and aware. He's able to appreciate what's happened to him and suffer awake what was done to him mostly asleep or half-awake before. Suction his trach. Clean the white sticky secretions bubbling out from his trach onto the tender skin of his throat. Give IVs for blood and antibiotics and nutrition and needle sticks for blood draws. Pull and turn him for X-rays, for changing sheets wet from wounds oozing through their bandages. Put pillows behind his back to keep the skin from breaking down. How exposed he must feel, he the most private of persons.

He's changed his mind about Brooklyn Ellie, who said he'd go back and back and back to the OR, weeks ago, a lifetime ago. He opens his eyes when she looks away and closes them when she looks back. She can have her way with him. He doesn't want the rest of us to touch him except for lube jobs, rubbing ointment into the dry skin on his legs and feet.

Afternoon. Rachel told me a dream she had a few months ago. My father and she were at my childhood home. My father was in his car. She went to open the door for him to get out. He looked at her, face filled with sorrow, and she woke up, afraid for Jesse.

Late afternoon. Jesse looks sad, discouraged. We talk to him, encourage him, tell him how well he's doing. He grits his teeth. Dr. Meyer came in a few minutes ago. He always listens to her. I wonder if she reminds him of Dr. Gardner. Both are motherly with him and both take charge.

How is your stomach now Jesse?

Nodded.

Is it OK?

Shrugged. OK, not great.

Do you feel like you might have to vomit?

Shook his head no.

Walking home to the transplant shelter, late. Puppet. Daniel said Jesse looked like a puppet. Dummy! The IV lines coming out of his hand. The impression that an invisible puppeteer was playing him.

July 10

Morning. Jesse mouthed to Gail.

My chest hurts. My back hurts. My stomach hurts. I want to get out of here.

He points people to their seats when he gets tired of their ministrations. But he's doing his own physical therapy, moving his arms and legs and raising his eyebrows. He waves to visitors, makes good eye contact as they say in the mental health coalmines, and seems quite aware of others and his surroundings. Brushes his teeth with a foam stick. Scratches himself. Folds his hands under the tubes on his chest. Raises his right arm and rests it over his head on the pillow. He likes to put it there and probably forgets that Liu the nurse told him not to do it because it makes his blood pressure reading go haywire on the monitor.

Why do I keep telling you to put your arm down, Jesse?

He shrugs, waits a few minutes, and does it again.

Afternoon. Dr. Lanier came in and gave Jesse a quick belly exam. He walked out of the room past us, shaking his head.

Jesse defines the word fight. He doesn't know what it means to give up.

We followed him out. He told us they've been thinking of cutting back on Jesse's meds, that it might help him overall.

So what do you think? About how he's doing?

I don't want to mislead you. Jesse is very ill. I see a little crack of light that I didn't see a few days ago. But that's all, just a little crack of light.

Late evening. Gail went home for a few days. Rachel and I waited for the liver team, late afternoon into the evening. The PICU resident called several times for med orders. Finally they gave them over the phone and we decided we could leave. We told Jesse we'd see him in the morning, first thing in the morning, whispering, not to wake him. Walking back to the transplant shelter, we talked about how proud we are of him.

For all his passivity, he must have developed an inner strength during all these years, and he's showing it now.

She's right, but proud or not, this is business, and the show he's putting on for his doctors is very good business. We're in the middle of a campaign for a third liver. It's his only chance to get out of here alive.

July 11

A quiet moment before the onslaught of the day. The initial euphoria is over. The X-rays torture him now precisely because he's awake to feel what the preparation for them does to his body. Another death sentence has expired but no one laughs. Jesse is blown toward and away from us with each wheeze and suck, wheeze and suck of his respirator, which the technician checks and adjusts, snaking out the tube and examining the droplets of condensation inside like a Greek priest examining a bird's liver. All that he needs now stands out in bas-relief against this shadow wellness. What he needs most is to get fed and not have any more perforations. The rest is maintenance, figuring out how much IV nutrition to give versus keeping down fluids that slip out through capillaries and move up into his lungs, causing pleural effusion, a phrase that might be beautiful, like the name of an exotic flower, in a language you didn't understand. Figuring out whether to cut back on the antibiotics, gambling the infection is gone, in order to help his digestion, which the antibiotics hurt. Figuring out how much Hyperale to give, superhero IV food so rich in nutrition it can build muscle mass but carries its own Kryptonite, glucose that can lead to diabetes because they can't stop giving Jesse this sweet poison that sustains him. Delicate balances, imposed from the outside, for a body that has lost its internal balance. A chest tube is the next level of external intervention, but brings with it a risk of bleeding. The blood bank is there for the bleeding, but IV blood increases bloating because, because, because his body is sick. And how long can his doctors keep the faith? The liver team never made rounds last night.

Dr. Stacey the liver fellow came in. A full-size Canadian flag that Rachel got for Jesse was taped up on the back wall over the window shade between Rooms B and A. Why Canadian? No one knows why Jesse loves Canada, he just does. He says he wants to live there someday. He pointed at the flag and mouthed words. His face twisted up in fear. Damn! But Stacey was impressed at his alertness and activity. We'll take it from her, and we took down the flag for Jesse.

Early evening. Dr. Dorand made rounds alone, late afternoon. We wanted him to see Jesse awake to feel the same shock and amazement we felt two days ago, as though he was something rare, an endangered species, and for that must have a third transplant. And lucid, not just awake, not wondering whether his hands and feet belonged to him or someone else. Bad timing, though. Jesse was sleepy and didn't look as good as yesterday. I was standing at the door, Rachel at the foot of the bed. Dr. D walked by me, looked at the liver chart on the door, and started to go in. Rachel, mischief in her eyes, waved him over. He hesitated.

Come on over.

What's she up to? Dr. D came over. Rachel stepped back, smiled, and motioned him through the narrow passageway between bed and outside wall. Dr. D, tentative, walked over to Jesse.

It's Dr. Dorand, Jesse. He's come to see you.

Jesse opened his eyes. He looked up and slowly stretched out his right arm. Dr. D looked at his hand for a moment, then took it.

Hello Jesse.

Jesse gave a faint smile and nodded as if to say, You did well, then rested his arm on the bed. He's become a different person. He's teaching us what he's learned.

Outside, Dr. D and I talked. I said it was hard for us to know what to think, with Dr. Swanson saying Jesse'd had enough one day and Jesse waking up and looking good the next. And what would we do if we agreed that Jesse's had enough? I asked. Dr. D shrugged.

We don't do that with pediatric patients. We don't take kids off the respirator. There's nothing different that we'd do from what we're doing now. You'd have to take us to court.

I talked about our fears that Jesse had been written off for a third transplant. It was only partly true that we felt this, but I wanted to keep Dr. D on track. He shook his head no.

Dr. Swanson and I decide who gets transplanted. Dr. Swanson is in charge of adults. With children, I decide… and Dr. Swanson agrees.

I talked about our last encounter with Dr. Swanson. I could see from his studied blankness that he'd heard about it. Tactfully as I could, I said Dr. Swanson seemed to be setting the bar at a height that Jesse would just fail to reach even in a best-case scenario. Dr. D shook his head no.

I don't think Dr. Swanson's standards are too high. He wants to see Jesse breathing on his own. Sitting up. Retransplant would not be a good idea for him now. He wouldn't survive it. He's probably a couple of weeks away from relisting, but maybe less. I still think it's a long shot, but we'll take a long shot.

I thought of the Fourth of July weekend and the dozens of units of blood Jesse got. Of the fellow not coming to see us in the surgical waiting room. Of something more subtle in phrases, tones, or slight distancings you couldn't call anyone on, and a retreat into specialization.

You know, I've been wondering. With all the perforations Jesse's had, it would be easy to see this as his fault. I mean, something about him, you know, that he just can't make it.

Dr. D was shaking his head after Perforation, so I knew I'd hit a nerve.

No. If it hadn't been for a surgical accident… he looked at me… I don't say mistake… during his first transplant… he looked through the window behind the nurse's station at Jesse on his bed… Jesse wouldn't be where he is right now.

He was about to leave, by the tilt of his head toward his chest and his shoulder jerking. I turned another ten degrees toward him as though he was merely shifting his weight. Time for truth telling, and the moment might not come again. I said I understood what he was saying about this not being Jesse's fault, but when you keep trying and nothing seems to work, it takes its toll on you. I pointed out Dr. Swanson saying there was no surgical solution to the bleeding the day before Dr. D took him back into surgery. I trotted out the surgical fellow stiffing us in the surgical waiting room the night of the 5th. That was wearing thin, but I'd only used it once on Dr. D.

It's true. In a depressing situation sometimes people back away. Out of sight, out of mind. Now we have to go back again and try harder.

He leaned forward to depart. Did he really think he could make his escape off a cheap Avis tag line? I leaned too. I wanted to make sure he knew how much we looked to him, more than the others, even more than Dr. Meyer. She could keep Jesse alive, but only he could get him out of here.

I understand that Dr. Swanson and everyone else thinks Jesse is going to die.

Dr. D shook his head.

No, because Dr. Swanson didn't think he would survive this week.

And neither did you, I thought.

And he was wrong. But that was last week. This is a new week… Dr. Swanson is a very smart man. He's more famous than I am. Sometimes I think he's smarter than I am. Sometimes I think…

He smiled. A good line to end on, but I couldn't let him go yet.

We're going to be here fighting, with Jesse and for him. Are you still the surgeon on Jesse's case?

He smiled again.

Yes.

And left. I overplayed the moral high ground, but what of it? Politeness and diplomacy have got us what?

Jesse alert and itchy after chest and lung x-rays. We were just getting him comfortable when the technician came back for the abdomen. He'd missed it on the order. I wanted to say No, you had your chance five minutes ago, don't drag your sorry ass and your

1950s machine in here now. But you can't do that, you can't take the chance that something like, um, a perforation, gets missed.

Talk of having Jesse sit in a chair and spend time off the respirator!

July 12

Jesse had a good night until 6 a.m., when Eden, pulling her first shift with him, woke him up to wash him. He got angry and started to bleed from his trach. She sedated him with Fentanyl. Now, he's sleeping.

Dr. Meyer tells us they're dropping Jesse's IV feeds down from 70 to 40 ccs per hour because of pleural effusion.

We don't want to put in a chest tube. We will if we have to.

We're happy she's back. There's never a shake of the head from her. Bad as things get, she's always got an idea and it never feels as though she's grasping at straws, even if she is. Moving around is important, she says. Oh good, then we can move him around, that's something we can do for him. Good bowel sounds, she says. We may increase his feeds later. Oh good, bowel sounds means feedings, and feedings means he gets stronger. That, cigars all around, and dancing girls for the surgeons gets us a third transplant.

Dialysis is a breeze now. Other times he's become agitated and had to be sedated, or we've had to spell each other pushing his right leg down with two arms and then leaning over him, chest and one arm on his right leg and the other arm on his left.

Gail's back. We are closer now than we've been in years.

A quiet half hour in the NICU lounge on a quiet day, Jesse mostly sleeping after duking it out with Eden last night. Lupe, the day nurse, is asking parents to write letters to the hospital administrators about why the nurses should keep their three straight twelve-hour shifts with four days off instead of going back to five eight-hour shifts. The law of supply and demand has shifted back toward management, which has corrected the nursing shortage with enticements like three straight twelve-hour shifts with four days off. Five eight-hour shifts, at forty hours a week, will buy four more hours per week per full-time nurse and save money on part-time nurses and per diems. The nurses say this won't work on the PICU, where twelve-hour shifts give more continuity for the critically ill patients who need it most. I can buy this up to a point. It's good to see only two nurses a day, and the idea that nurses here have to dive in and immerse themselves in order to be effective makes intuitive sense, but you could make a good argument for seeing your primary nurse five days straight with only two days off rather than three on and four off. A better argument might be that the nurses need this kind of schedule to cut down on burnout. But many of them are working second jobs, and letters warning about burnout aren't going to carry weight with hospital administrators anyway. Not that we're going to argue with the nurses. We'll write them a letter for limousine service to and from work if they ask us for it. It feels odd to me, talking to the nurses as employees, not as extended family members. It annoys me that the switch is so difficult for me to make, as though I've built an infernal cocoon around Jesse and the hospital. Even the world surrounding this cocoon is about him. Family, friends, all are measured by the quality of their attention to his ordeal. A job is about earning enough money to be here or having the leeway to disappear from it for a while. Seeing nurses as employees trying to make a living, bumping into them on the street off shift, is unsettling for me, as if someone is tampering with the delicate spin of the cocoon. But I can adjust to having my fantasies exploded. What I can't adjust to is the idea that overworked nurses are more likely to make mistakes. We all make them every day, but here the margin for error is almost nonexistent. Marion has had a second patient her last two nights with Jesse, and he counts as three or four by himself.

A little while ago, the vicious cycle of suctioning to bring up blood clots that, once loosened, cause more bleeding. The new blood must be suctioned up while new blood clots are forming. Standing next to Jesse, he looked at me and croaked over his trach.

Help me, help me.

I will Jesse. We're going to help you.

A few minutes later he was asleep and dialysis started. I walked back to the high-rise to do my wash. When I got back, dialysis was almost over. They'd pulled off six pounds in two and a half hours with ultrafiltration, the slow, gentle form of dialysis and the closest thing to CVVHD we can get. How frail he looked! How thin! Three mothers, Rachel, Gail, and Tina, were fussing over him, dabbing at the secretions around his trach in the tender hollow of his throat, suctioning his mouth, moving his arms and legs, straightening his wrist and laying it on his beanbag dog. Did he have enough pillows? Did he want them fluffed? Were his lips dry? Did he want some Vaseline on them? Pucker your lips Jesse. There you go.

At the transplant shelter, before lights out. Gail back home again after another whirlwind visit. Evening, walking to the transplant shelter under the glare of lights on the broad street that leads down to Second Avenue, Rachel said, It used to be horrible to watch him fight the suctioning. It's almost as horrible now to watch him lie there passively when they do it. And I, a few weeks earlier, walking with her along the wide bright-lit street, wondered if Jesse would swing on his hammock until he no longer knew any other way to be, and whether we would stop taping photographs on the walls to keep his image before his doctors and, instead, have to slap each other awake to remember him before he was changed. Tonight, Uncanada came to me, after that northern border country that Jesse has never seen but knows was meant for him. Uncanada, the crack in the door between life and death that medical technology for the unfortunate has opened a little bit wider. An air of fraud, of the arbitrary, hangs over Uncanada. Bits and shreds of what we supposed ourselves to be wander here where even God is a stranger to himself.

July 13

Jesse's mouth is full of yellowish-green secretions. He fights against giving them up to the suction tube the nurse waves before his mouth. He lies there impassive, eyes open but not looking at us, mouth shut tight. It's infantile and annoying. We lean down next to him with bad hospital breath and explain that secretions can give him an upset stomach, can make him vomit, can slow down his feeds, as if he doesn't know all this. They can also cause pneumonia, but we don't say that. He's probably thinking, Don't you people get it? If this is my life I'd rather be dead. Here in this one place, the privacy of his own mouth, he has the power to keep us and his doctors at bay. When he's had enough of the game or feels he's proved his point, he opens up and lets us suction him. We tell him how good that is.

Late afternoon. Matt across the hall went down for his heart transplant today. He's about five four, maybe ninety pounds. Our fattening-up campaign has had limited success, obviously. I hope his new heart gives him reason to want to sustain the rest of himself.

Corey in Room C is four and has been on the unit waiting for a heart transplant for months. They need the right size for him but not many come along for four-year olds. His mother and aunt walk him around every other day with his oxygen tank. They live here now. Each night one sleeps next to Corey in his room and one sleeps in the PICU lounge on the sofa couches you can't keep sheets on they are so slippery. The mother, Dorinda, is in and out of an abusive relationship. The father visits occasionally and seems pleasant and solicitous, but we've heard too much not to dislike him. The women are very poor but full of faith. They pray with us for Corey and Jesse and Matt. We stand in a circle, the mother, aunt, Gail, also full of faith, and me, here for communion's sake. If there's a God who intervenes in our personal troubles he's taking a bye on this one, or trying to make some other point

A new liver patient was brought in today. She's a little younger than Jesse. We thought she'd had a transplant and were jealous of the attention she was getting. Turns out she hasn't been transplanted but is here for a problem with her failing liver. Still, all the activity from the liver team made me fear Jesse would become an old story, like Kafka's Gregor Samsa, loved and worried over at first like Samsa transformed from person into insect, and then, failing to return to what he was, become more and more troublesome to all and finally be swept out, a weightless shell, along with the detritus of furious activity, the bandages, tape, gauze pads, and their paper wrappers that have landed on the floor around what used to be a human being.

Another liver patient, a little girl from India, went into cardiac arrest and was brought back. Dr. Meyer was just coming onto the unit when it happened. It was horrible to watch, but we're thankful she was on the job.

Rachel told me Jesse's dream about his friend getting killed. He had it a few months ago. Odin had promised he'd protect the friend, but didn't. Jesse vowed revenge. A trip in a boat across the River Styx to find Odin and kick his ass. I thought of Nicholas. Must ask Jesse about it when he's well.

July 14

A restless night. Jesse's belly is tense, distended. He's complaining of stomach pains. They stopped his feeds. He's still holding on to bilious secretions in his mouth. Marian, at the end of her shift, said his lungs don't sound as good as they did a couple of days ago.

Gail's back. This is Tina's last day. Dr. Meyer just put a new IV catheter in Jesse's left leg near his groin for dialysis and new stitches in the A line in his neck. A chest X-ray shows that the pleural effusion is worse.

Early afternoon. Dr Lanier made rounds. We stood by the door as he came out. He didn't want to talk to us, but he always feels obliged.

There's no substantial change since last week. We're still way out there. That little crack of light I told you about is a little bit larger.

Quiet now, early evening. Jesse sleeping. I'm thinking about superstition. It grew in me for a while then hit me on May 27, the day Superman fell, that it wasn't just me, that ICUs, high-tech medicine, and superstition go together. Christopher Reeve's fall was the biggest story in the country that day and no one mentioned it here. Of course we didn't tell Jesse and of course the nurses and doctors wouldn't want to talk about it around us, but I'd bet good money they didn't talk about it to each other, not on the unit and probably not off. To family and friends, maybe, miles away, but not here where a breeze that barely stirs the baby hairs at the base of a feather can throw you off your horse.

Mornings, going down the hallway from the transplant shelter, trying to decide on which side to pass the two brass pillars in the lobby, right or left, right and then left, or vice versa. For a long time, I stuck mostly to medical details in these notebooks, not editorializing about events or feelings or doubts. There's a practical side to this, since I could leave my notebook on a chair and a doctor might take a peek and find something to offend her. So, Dr. Atella was always Dr. Atella, not Atella the Hun. But practical or not, I didn't want to upset the delicate balance here, extending from Jesse's body to everyone and everything around him, by writing about it. Even letting go of that balance with jokes, clowning, dinner and drinks at the Three Gentlemen, had to be balanced. To laugh with full awareness of the danger, yes. But if I laughed and forgot, even for a moment, Jesse might slip away like a fish we were trying to bring into the boat.

Or looking at numbers on the liver charts and losing faith in appearances because I'd overworked them for answers they couldn't give. Interpreting gestures and tossed-off statements or facial expressions of doctors as if I'd lost my own inner compass. Even now there's constant work, wariness, watchfulness, a faked and false composure, a focused meditation to gain mental control, sticking flagpoles in the ground to orient myself and maintain sanity. Yesterday, Jesse bled from his tracheotomy and the pleural effusion was getting worse. I decided to decide that he wasn't going to make it. This wasn't fatalism, but a mental adjustment for facing the next moment. Hope for recovery, despair over what's happening, a *Que sera sera*, we're-here-to-be-with-Jesse-regardless-of-what-happens attitude, all are flagpoles. If he doesn't make it, I'll look back and see them waving at me and wonder which one marked the point of no return.

The other evening at the transplant shelter, I went out through the living room to call the front desk about the heavy bass rock music in the apartment above my room. A half dozen women asked me how Jesse was doing. I was irritated at having to figure out what to say, and afraid of giving the wrong answer.

He's OK. They're trying some feeds again.

Oh, good, that's a change. This from Sandra the seven-day liver transplant wonder, in and out and ready to go home and preach the gospel of organ donation.

Yes, I said. They hadn't done that for a few days.

I had to sound optimistic or I could hurt Jesse's chances. If I knew them better, trusted them and whatever thoughts they might send his way....

I fight it, too. I know that superstition can take me down. Fifteen-year old Valerie lay suffocating in Room A around the time of Jesse's second transplant. Her lungs were shrunken and crisp and unable to house air. I saw Jesse's image superimposed over hers in the window glass of her door pulled back toward Room B and looked away, then forced myself to look back. I try to avoid thinking or talking about nausea when Jesse doesn't have it so as not to jinx him, but I feel a contrary impulse to proclaim my sympathetic nausea by not eating lunch, or pointing out to others the sickening drone and squeak of the dialysis machine or the respirator's wheeze, or calling everyone I know and telling them about Jesse's intestines and inability to tolerate his meds, or reading Sartre's *Nausea*, or talking about nausea as a concept or universal fact, that someone in every borough, town, and city has it at any given moment, or organizing a delegation of nauseates to surround the building and raise a chant of retching sounds to exorcise the demons inside. If everyone else in the world pukes, maybe my son won't.

The little girl from India died during the night. Her parents withheld treatment. A cultural, religious difference between us? Or just different circumstances? We've wondered at times if we should withhold treatment from Jesse, or if that time might be coming. But withhold what? Dr. D says they don't withhold treatment from pediatric patients. Meaning, what? The liver team doesn't? Or all of them? General principle or a hard-and-fast rule? And what treatment was withheld from the little girl?

Positives and negatives for today. Positives. Good bowel sounds. Feeds restarted. They say Jesse's decreased alertness is partly due to Valium, not just liver and kidney malfunction. Splint made for right hand. The greenish secretions in his mouth may be material loosening up from the pleural effusion going away. They think the stomal bleeding is from the stoma itself, not from further back. Stoma was stitched. Like stitching a piece of bread. Negatives. Stomal bleeding profuse. Feeds stopped during the night. When restarted, only at 5 ccs. Have to ask Gail how much a cc is. Less alert today. Secretions in his mouth, even if from pleural effusion going away, can cause pneumonia.

Evening. We said goodbye to Tina. She told Jesse, who's barely awake, that she'd be back to see him, they'd be calling her in to work weekends sometimes, and she'd be thinking of him. He nodded and gave her a little smile. We gave her a little dog like the one we lay Jesse's right hand on to straighten his wrist.

Late, back at the shelter. About to leave for the night, Rachel looked at Jesse.

When I see him lying there quiet and calm, I think, that's the way he's going to make it.

July 15

Rachel is always here early. She's won the battle for who will be Jesse's primary caretaker while he's in the hospital.

Jesse had a good night. But he scratches himself constantly around his face. We help him. On my turn I try to picture myself immobile on a bed, eyes closed, able to guide the other's hand by thought. I watch for signs that I've touched the right spot and imagine how such a simple mercy could exceed any act of devotion or sacrifice we might perform for another human being. I feel the sensual pleasure of my pointer finger with a little bit of nail along the side of his nose, at the crease of its wings, around the soft skin of the eyelids, gently etching the outline of his cheekbones now almost visible under the thinning flesh.

Rachel tells me she called Leslie, baby Jessie's mother, at home yesterday. Leslie talked about what a terrible place this is but how she'd give anything to be back. I think of Don, who knocked over the newspaper stand, back on the road in his tractor trailer, hand on the trigger of the gearshift.

Dr. Jacoby the psychiatry resident just came by. Rachel, Will, and Gail long ago elected me to deal with her. This mainly involves having a question for her and trying to keep her away from them. Duty or not, she's a sensible person and easy to talk to, but every conversation, every gesture, every mood that people might read off us has strategic value now. In other words, I can't fully trust Dr. Jacoby. For whom is she here? The liver team? The patient and his family? From where I sit she's hopelessly compromised, an advocate for the patient and scout for the liver team. Or so she might be and so must be regarded. She shows signs of independence, such as saying they cut back on Jesse's meds too quickly after the second transplant. But instinct tells me that decisions about who gets a second or third transplant aren't made on objective assessments of the patient's condition alone. How the parents feel and how that gets reported back to the liver team by, say, a psychiatrist, might tip the scales one way or the other when a third transplant is a crapshoot from the start.

Jesse lets Ellie know when he needs to be suctioned. It's a private language the two of them have worked out, of eyes and winks and slightest movement of hand. There's so much love and sympathy and humor between the two of them now. But Ellie doesn't forget us. A little while ago, she gave him a bath with washcloths and Phisoderm soap in a green plastic bottle and warm water from a small plastic tub. Rachel out for a walk, Gail making phone calls, I felt like an intruder at the back of the room, but didn't mind being a distant onlooker to this intimacy, or didn't think so until Ellie spoke.

Sometimes we spend a lot of time together, don't we Jesse? It's good to have your father here.

He's strong and ingenious with her, with nods and half-smiles and little ways of helping. This is what we've waited for all his life, for him to let down his guard long enough to love and be loved. This morning, Rachel told me about meeting one of the OR nurses out on the street. Everyone here loves Jesse, she said. Deathly ill as he is, he always helps them move him onto the operating table. Yet there's a touch of patienthood that's hard to watch. Accepting his bath in bed, letting Ellie put his feet in the tub and wiggle his toes.

Dr. Sam is a likeable fellow. He's a GI fellow or a resident, we're not sure and are too polite to ask, since he seems to have so little authority here. He is Indian, and speaks excellent English with an accent that tells you he's not native-born American. He likes talking with us and likes Jesse. He's in awe of all the other doctors, especially Dr. Dorand, who appears not to notice him. He hears bowel sounds that only a saint could hear. We like him for that, but have to wonder whether his enthusiasm for Jesse's recovery gets the better of him. And congenial as he is, we have to run with the big dogs here, like Dr. Mellon. We drop Dr. Sam like a hot potato when she walks in, but it's alright, he drops us just as fast for her.

Dr. Mellon talked about getting Jesse fed, building him up slowly to a level that will do him some good, 5 ccs on the nasogastric feeds at quarter strength for a couple hours, then 7 ccs at 7 p.m., then 9 at 9, if they could find a pump that goes in increments of one instead of five. Ellie found one, maybe conjured it, since no one was sure such pumps even existed. We worship her. Dr. Mellon explained her strategy.

I want to increase strength, then volume. I'd like to get him to 10 ccs full strength by Monday, then go up 5 ccs a day. At this strength and volume it's mostly water, which you don't want.

She looked over at Jesse with a mixture of disbelief and admiration. It's become her signature look.

I'm glad I can be here this weekend to tell you that he's stable.

After she left I ask Gail how much a cc is. She held thumb and forefinger close together.

A cc on a syringe needle would be about this much.

A quarter inch?

She brought her fingers closer together.

No, not that much.

Late evening note, before leaving for the transplant shelter. Gail left late in the afternoon. A couple of hours ago, Dr. Boyd, all six-foot-six of him, strolled in alone on rounds. He looked at the liver chart on the door. He strolled into the room over to Jesse. He tipped his head toward him for a moment, then strolled back to us.

I have nothing to add or say.

And Rachel and I had nothing to ask him. Arrogant prick in his purple shirt. Rachel told me about Will's dream of holding Dr. Boyd's son Justin for hostage.

July 16

Lenore, a new nurse for Jesse, looks so wounded. She knows he doesn't like her but she can't accept it and keeps trying to figure out what she or he did wrong. He got angry when she woke him up last night, then wouldn't talk with her or respond in any way.

He wasn't in a daze, but he wasn't answering.

I've seen Jesse ice people, so I could feel for her if only she didn't whine at me with her eyes. I know it's understandable. She has just spent twelve hours with the Lord High Sheriff of Suffering and what does she get for it? Not so much as a drop-dead look. Does she not serve him in a hundred ways each night, giving him his meds, checking his temp and his SATs, suctioning him and dabbing at the secretions around his trach, changing his dressing, getting him the urinal and taking it away when he's through? Of course she does, and of course it's unjust that he prefers Marian, Jill, Terri, Ellie, and Tina to her. But that's baseball, Lenore!

Eden is new to Jesse, too, and he gave her a hard time the first night. But she's older and more confident than Lenore. She weathered the storm of Jesse's displeasure and agitation, his pulling out of IVs and tubes and his silent curses. She's tiny, friendly enough, and efficient. She's more authoritative with him than the other nurses, which rankled him at first. He seems to like her now, though. I've watched him. He takes to the motherly nurses, the sisterly ones, the loverly ones, and the strong and confident but not cold ones. Eden belongs in the last category. She pays no special homage to Jesse but understands that he's engaged in a struggle of epic Eggnogian proportions.

We've adjusted to Eden's style as well. She doesn't explain everything she does and doesn't confer with us before her every move or ask for our help. We were slightly offended at first, then we relaxed and accepted her. We don't prefer her to Marian or Jill, but when she's on we're just as confident that Jesse will make it through the night. Maybe that's what it is between Jesse and Lenore. She's tentative, unsure of herself, even fearful around him, and so he must choose contempt for her or succumb to his terror that she's not up to the job.

Afternoon. Jesse was awake a little while ago but not talking, and was too alert to be so unresponsive. I wondered if he was nauseated. I went out and had lunch across the street on a bench outside a playground in Central Park. Homeless people sat on the bench next to me and on other benches that circle the playground, watching the ceremony of innocence. I got back to the unit and Jesse looked an unhealthy brownish green. His mouth was set in a frown, from disapproval or perpetual itchiness, that gave him an expression infinitely sad, resigned, and hopeless. I thought of William Blake's life mask from the first Blake book I gave Jesse. His mouth, too, was set downward, frowning and wincing, the text informed us, at the touch of hot wax on skin. I went over to Jesse.

Don't get too discouraged Jess. You're going to walk out of here.

I'd said the same thing other times with the same words and others. This time I knew he was listening, because there was a conviction in my voice, or because he was looking for a boost, or because we got lucky. I said it was all right to get pissed off and discouraged, but not to forget the image of himself walking out of the hospital. He squeezed my hand.

Late afternoon. Dialysis and ultrafiltration. They took off four and a half pounds but had to give him albumin when his BP dropped. Dr. Mellon made rounds.

We're going to three-quarters strength on the feeds. His belly sounds aren't as good as yesterday but his intestines are moving. We need a minimum of three weeks to get Jesse ready for transplant.

July 17

Blood in Jesse's ostomy bag. Dr. Rand, the liver fellow with the swipe of hair in front who delivered the bad news on May 10th that Jesse had to go back to surgery four days after his first transplant, came in and put a stitch in his stoma, the red beacon of intestine peeking out of his side. Then the ostomy nurse came in and put powder and cream around it, anything that might lessen the trauma to the area and reduce the bleeding. I hatched the idea of building a cage out of gauze wound around wire mesh and taped to Jesse's belly with an opening for the plastic bag to accept the feces, to keep the stoma from getting bumped in the moving and turning and shifting that Jesse does or has done to him dozens of times a day. Dr. Meyer came in and I described the contraption to her. She said it was worth looking into, but with a quick look on her face that said, This man has spent too much time on the unit. Then she said that Jesse's decreased alertness may be due to kidney failure, to judge by his blood urea nitrogen, BUN, level.

But the liver produces BUN, so it must be doing something. Jesse needs dialysis, but we're having blood pressure problems for the first time now.

Dialysis. The dialysis nurse watched the upper and lower numbers drop on the monitor overhead to Jesse's left. The worry wrinkles on her face deepened until she finally stopped the machine. They gave him albumin and red blood cells to replace the blood he'd lost from his stoma. We waited for the blood to come through the tube from the blood bank so we could put it under our arms or sit on it with the fat part of our legs and then pass it to the nurse to hang on the pole and watch as the blood started dripping in and Jesse's BP started climbing on the monitor.

Late afternoon notes. Dr. Dorand made rounds at 4:00 p.m. Coming in, he saw the photo of Jesse in his bathrobe last Christmas morning in Norwalk, skinny and pale but pleased with himself with his new electric guitar slung over his shoulder. Will, who plays, got a good deal on a guitar and amp and we all went in on it. Dr. D stared at the photo. Something was puzzling him.

He's playing left-handed. That's unusual.

Yes.

I reminded him that Jimi Hendrix played left-handed. Dr. D positioned his hands in reverse, right hand on the frets and left hand fingering the notes.

That's right, he did. I play. I could play for Jesse. That's something I could do for him.

He'd like that.

I went down to the PICU lounge and called Dr. Gardner at the pay phone. She sounded pessimistic, her tone and the pauses she took more than her words.

Jesse needs several weeks of no crisis and good nutrition. The last perforation was clearly the result of steroids and a sick gut.

Back on the unit, Dr. Meyer came in before leaving for the day.

This has not been a good day for Jesse. I know that.

I went for a walk outside the hospital and looked for signs. At the drug store, an elderly woman paid for her things. The bill came to

$11.00 even. She didn't have enough. The cashier, young and attractive, rolled her eyes in frustration. The manager came and cancelled the order but was polite to the old woman. No sign here. Went to Richard's for dinner and had the chicken and fries platter. A woman in her 80s shuffled by me on her way to the bathroom, stopped and looked at my food.

Have you had the moussaka?

No, I haven't tried that.

You should, it's good.

She shuffled on to the bathroom. No sign. No Zen master paradox. No enlightenment. Or maybe I missed it.

Evening, and quiet for the moment. A few minutes ago, moving Jesse up on the bed with Marian, I remembered the picture of the Hiroshima mother bathing her daughter. The girl's spastic limbs and face are contorted from radiation, and, I suppose, from the fear of being moved, of being dropped in the water, of knowing that a knock could come at the door and her mother could go to answer it, forgetting her as she sank down into the tub full of water, or that an unheard knock might be made at a door inside her mother's head. Jesse's body is a bag of bones inside skin turned dark pumpkin. Is it fair to put him through this? Does he want this? Or would he if he were able to think straight without sedation and painkillers? Moving him with Marian, I thought of his alien killer, etched in my memory. He was about fourteen, I think, when he drew it on the back of old agency letterhead I'd brought home for scrap paper. A space alien in profile is about to execute a human prisoner in a pose he borrowed, I'm sure, from the famous photo of the South Vietnamese general executing the Vietcong soldier. The general has become an alien and the VC soldier a concentration camp prisoner. The alien is almost a ghost, probably because Jesse only sketched him in lightly, while the prisoner has the darker features of a second draft. The alien could be female. There's a feminine touch to the large right eye, the petite nose, the stylish flip of the back of its hairless head. It holds a square blocky gun in its right hand. The prisoner wears the crudely sewn sleeveless shirt of a concentration camp prisoner. His forehead is too high, even allowing for a receding hairline caused by poor nutrition not baldness, but this, along with his gaping mouth, bad teeth, and huge inhuman eyes enhances the fear in his visage. The left eye shows only the white, as though the pupil, hidden behind the lid, has been forced at gunpoint to witness the mind's terror that it projects onto the inside of his skull. The prisoner's stalk of a neck looks too weak to hold up his head for much longer than it will take for his executioner to blow it off. His pencil-thin arms make his chest narrowing to his waist look healthy by comparison. It is the body of a once-strong man. There's a suggestion of a doctor or a nurse wearing a surgical mask in the alien guard, and of the secret unspoken violation of the first time the thermometer gun was thrust in our ear and took our measure in a second as we marveled in obeisance at the ease and swiftness of the procedure and the nurse, smiling indulgently at the obedient praise she'd heard a thousand times before, released its hard plastic condom into the wastebasket.

July 18

I lay on my back in bed at the transplant shelter, then finally fell asleep, but woke up before 3. I read for a while then called Jill at 5. Jesse had vomited at 12:30 and 3, mostly mucus from his mouth that he wouldn't give up for suctioning. He peed on the pads under his butt and didn't want Jill to clean him up. He kicked at his sheets. She gave him a bolus of Valium and when that didn't work, a bolus of Fentanyl. I got up to go to the hospital and thought about Jesse in distress during the night while I was awake and on other nights while I lay here in a dead sleep, and wondered how we could get him to accept the mouth suctioning. He needs to be fed. We can't have him vomiting because he's holding on to the secretions and swallowing them, or letting their sickly juices trickle down his throat.

I got to the unit when Jill was going off her shift. She said she was amazed that Jesse was so alert with a BUN that should knock him out cold. He was alert all right, pissed off and not responding to us. I talked with him about letting the nurses suction his mouth.

Or we could do it for you if you want. Or you could do it yourself. I know you don't like it, but it can't feel good to have that stuff in your mouth.

No eye contact, no response.

Rachel's getting on my nerves, lifting his covers to check his dressing, interrupting my conversations with him. Take a walk! Dr. Sam comes up to me, smiling, and says, I hear good bowel sounds. Stuff it! Little Lisa the resident spins in and out on her Little Lisa half-heels, asking questions only of Rachel. Pardon me! More chest X-rays. The normal torture. They show pleural effusion. Ah well, another day, another murder to commit.

Late afternoon notes. I called my brother's wife in Arizona, a nurse who works with sick kids. She told me many people are praying for Jesse, that he's touched many lives. That gave me a lift. When I came back to the unit Dr. D was here on rounds with spleen on his mind.

Jesse's spleen may not be the cause of his decreased platelets and red blood cells, but it has been troublesome. It's so big it might be hard to close him up if we transplant him again. Taking it out would give us more space to work with.

Then he said something about connecting the donor's hepatic

artery directly to Jesse's aorta if they retransplant him. I didn't know what he meant, but I knew it wasn't standard operating procedure for transplants, and anything that's not SOP when you're that far out there, as Dr. Swanson says, makes me nervous. But Dr. D talked about the idea with confidence, even enthusiasm. Not an entirely scientific enthusiasm, I hoped. Then he turned another fifteen degrees toward me with a wry smile that meant I was about to hear an exit line.

But we probably shouldn't talk about the technical aspects. We don't want to jinx it.

July 19

Jesse awake this morning and appears confused. And he has a new IV in his left hand. They put it in during the night. Dr. Meyer says the chest X-rays still show pleural effusion. They could do chest PT, she says, which means pounding on his chest with the meat of the palm to loosen up the mucus and bring it up with suctioning, but that could cause internal bleeding with his clotting time so bad.

He rests his right arm on the pillow by his head, one of his favorite positions. He looks comfortable, but I hate to see it. It reminds me of my father at the hospice in Rochester. He took the same position near the end.

I wonder if I would take Jesse's place. I've wished so many times that I could, more fully than anything I've ever felt in my life. Love and parental impulse make me want to do this for him without even thinking about it. But that's the point. Love and impulse and the adrenaline of self-sacrifice would work fine on the spur of the moment. But in the cold gray steel of a longer moment, knowing what I know and seeing what I've seen, if the choice were real and no one was watching to register the fact that I'd made the right choice, would I calculate my worth against his, my contribution against what his might be someday? This I know, I am not good with illness, am a physical coward for it. Best guess? 60-40 I would lie down and take his place out of a sense of obligation and propriety, with full expectation of being praised for it. The love would still be there but would be largely irrelevant. Force of will would have to prevail. But at the moment of truth, could I manage even that? If the offer were made silently, only for my conscience and me, so that neither Jesse, nor Gail, nor Rachel, nor his brother and sister, nor the doctors and nurses could hear, would I study my feet as though I'd not heard the question and let the moment pass?

Fawn the social worker, so helpful two years ago with Jesse's colitis surgery, stands outside Room B talking to Dr. Lanier. She glances in here but doesn't make eye contact with me. Is it possible she doesn't know that Jesse's here? No, it's not possible. I may exaggerate his fame within the hospital for his superhuman struggle, but a social worker with the liver team? She knows he's here. His current social worker, Alice, really ours since she can't do a thing for Jesse, is going to talk to the transplant shelter about a lower rent for us. It's dirt-cheap now, especially for New York, but we're looking at months if things go well.

Dr. Lanier just left. He had no new ideas about how to stop the stomal bleeding. He said they've talked about doing an endoscopy, where they pass a scope down the throat and check for esophageal varices, but he's against it. The endoscopy itself can cause bleeding, he said, and it probably wouldn't change what they're doing.

The endoscopy wouldn't change what they're doing... Why not? I look for Dr. Lanier, but he's gone. Maybe Dr. Hall or Dr. Gardner will know. One of them calls us almost every day for report.

A NICU break, afternoon. Moving Jesse up on the bed, I forgot about the big line in his left leg near the groin still hooked up to the dialysis machine. Fortunately, the line held by its stitches and he slept through it. I walked around the room cursing myself. They're hard to put in a person with some fat on him, let alone a skinny kid whose blood won't clot. Only Dr. Meyer can be trusted to place a femoral line and she'll do anything to avoid it because of the danger of heavy bleeding. Then the alarm on the machine went off because the pediatric lines they're using to give him a gentler dialysis fooled the machine into thinking the pressure in the machine was too high. It woke him up. He pointed at the machine in terror and then, remembering his manners, looked fearfully, but did not point, at the dialysis nurse. And I, for the first time, was pissed off at him for not playing along with this circus of horrors.

Gail is back. I think this was her longest time with the kids since we came here. She brought Jesse's report card with marks ranging from A+ in English to D- in electronics. I read it to him, congratulating him on the good marks and making fun of electronics. The nurse changed his leads. They're round rubber pads with adhesive that stick to his chest with lines in the exposed side that lead to the box that measures his heart rate. I picked up an old one. There was a pre-life, swamplike feel to it. The nurse changed Jesse's ostomy bag, carefully cutting the hole for his stoma to keep the stiff cardboard at the base of the bag from rubbing against it and causing it to bleed. She turned him to wash his back. She changed the dressing over his surgical wound. She replaced the blue pads he'd just peed on.

Let's give you another diaper.

Is he a young man or not?! I wanted to scream at her.

Jesse was in agony during all this, being moved around so

much. If he gets better, we'll see this day as a painful bump on the road to recovery. If he doesn't, we'll see it as one more day when we and the finest medical science had to offer kept him on the rack. And what does a day like this do to the soul if the body does survive?

eleven

Sitting here on the basement stairs under the watchful gaze of Jesse's superhero and a few feet away from his bedroom door at my left, his carnivorous carrot hangs on the wall in front of me bold and colorful like his Skydiver but simpler, more one-dimensional, an enormous carrot bibbed like a fat man and dining on sautéed humans. Its body is bright orange. Its eyes are huge, with blue irises. Its green top in the shape of a just-exploded hydrogen bomb waves in a strong west wind. The table in front of it is reddish brown. The background is bright blue. The carrot's white bib is splotched with stains more like insect innards than the flesh and blood of boiled men such as those clumped in front of it like so many crayfish piled on a tabletop lined with newspapers. The fork it holds in its muscular right arm has pierced one poor soul. With its left hand it lifts a glass of turnip juice to wash down a person stuck in its thick red lips. A wadded-up napkin, bile-greenish, lies next to the glass. A joke on his semivegetarian father and strict vegetarian stepmother.

Back to July.

July 20

Late morning. Ellie gave Jesse a shampoo. It's amazing how much better he looks. Rachel read to him from *The Hidden Life of Dogs*. He loves animals and is fascinated by the debate over whether they have emotions or only instinctual reactions. He's a firm believer in the former. He read along with her and then grabbed the book with both hands and read for himself.

Dr. Vargas, a GI fellow, came in while Jesse was sitting up, awake and looking well. Vargas was shocked, delighted. But the attending nephrologist came in, too, and dashed one of our hopes. Kidney function and the amount of urine being put out have nothing to do with each other, she said. So all our tracking of golden drops of urine may be wasted effort and hope, and regardless of what Dr. D says we may be looking at a kidney transplant in the future.

Late afternoon notes. At 3 p.m. Dr. Dorand came onto the unit carrying a guitar case. He walked a little faster than usual past the nurse's station. He came into Room B without looking at us or saying anything and took out a 12-string guitar from the case. He adjusted the strap over his shoulder and tuned up. Rachel went over to Jesse.

Jesse, Dr. Dorand is here. He's come to play guitar for you. Remember?

He opened his eyes and nodded slowly.

Dr. D came over to the side of the bed by the window and put his foot up on the lower rail.

Jesse, I'm going to sing a song for you. It's the best I can do for you today.

He started, When you're down and troubled, too high for him, then found a lower range. His voice was a bit thin, but steady. Then another song in Yiddish, with a verse in English, Don't walk beside me, I may not lead, Don't walk behind me, I may not follow, Just walk beside me and be my friend. Then, Here Comes the Sun. Jesse nodded and smiled weakly. Dr. D put his guitar back in the case. I put my hand on his arm as he walked out of the room. Dr. Rand was with him. I was glad he was here to see this and would carry the memory of it with him when he became an attending surgeon himself. Dr. D was all business now.

I want Jesse to sit up again in a chair. It will be good for him for his overall condition and strength.

And he left, nodding as I thanked him.

6 p.m. Jesse active with physical therapy. After it's over, he kept it up, squeezing a nerf ball.

July 21

Jesse didn't sleep much last night. And he pulled out his nasogastric tube. He's bleeding from his stoma and itching constantly. Rachel stood at his side and leaned down to adjust his pillow. He leaned on his right shoulder and swung his left arm over her right shoulder. She smiled. Her eyes shone with tears that did not fall.

Oh, you want to give me a hug?

He nodded, yes. They hugged. Watching the arc of his arm and shoulder from the other side of the bed, it looked to me as though he was trying to use Rachel's shoulder as leverage to pull himself out of bed, but had the grace to recognize that, at this moment, her need was greater than his.

Daniel and Cassandra came with Gail's mother while I was out getting coffee. Gail said Daniel came over to the bed and took Jesse's hand again and Cassie had to leave the room again, crying. Later, Daniel said Jesse's hand looked like ET's, and it does. The fingers thin at the end of an arm that looks longer from emaciation, and fingers, hand, and arm all dark at the outer frontier of jaundice. Gail and I had agreed I should go home for a couple of days to be with the kids. Gail would stay here. When I said goodbye, Jesse fought back tears. I knew his tears were not for our leaving but that he couldn't go with us.

July 22

Afternoon in the NICU, first quiet moments to catch up on notes. Yesterday, at home, we sat in the living room. I read Daniel a book. Cassie sat nearby playing a game on the floor and listening. I couldn't have been home two hours when Gail called. Jesse'd had a major bleed, probably from esophageal varices, where the veins around the esophagus become engorged and develop weak spots that burst and bleed heavily after they've been forced to act as a bypass for the portal vein, backed up and swollen itself from a choked and hardening liver.

Should I come back?

I don't think you have to yet.

Stupid question, kind answer. I sat down with the children and explained that Jesse had a problem, that he was doing OK now but I might have to go back. Daniel walked away from me and went down to Jesse's room. I followed him down, then up and into one room after another as he kicked at things and said New York is hazardous to your health and There's no hope and I don't want to live anymore.

Gail called again. They were planning to take Jesse back to the OR to deal with the varices. They would probably take out his spleen. Gail suggested I ask our friends Dana and Laurie to drive me back, since I'd come back with Gail's mother and she would need her car here.

We drove on a hot muggy night on the parkways from

Connecticut into New York and past the George Washington Bridge over the Hudson. I wasn't thinking then of what this must be like for Dana, who'd had three brothers killed by drunk drivers when he was a child, two at one blow and the third a year later at the same corner a block from their house, all walking to school.

We parked on the street and went through the talking doors to the elevators and up to the surgical waiting room. It was eleven o' clock. The room was deserted. I thought Jesse must have... don't say it, or write it... and that Gail and Rachel had been too distraught to leave me a message, maybe taped to the reception desk where, during daytime hours, the imperious volunteers demand the name of the patient you're waiting to hear about and you have to be nice to them for fear they won't call you when your doctor comes and you aren't looking.

We took the long winding route down the elevators, across the pavilion under the glass rafters, down the escalator and along the tunnels to the elevator and up to the PICU. Jesse was sleeping. Dana saw him and was shaken. They had decided against surgery. We talked with Dana and Laurie for a while. I read the notes that Gail took yesterday, as promised.

3 p.m. The plan for the weekend is to turn the ventilator down and if Jesse tolerates that to turn it off for 1 to 2 minutes at a time.

6 p.m. Ellie brought in the big reclining chair around 4 p.m. She said, "Jesse is going to sit in a chair today and he's going to play Nintendo." She picked him up and put him in the chair. He looked worried and uncomfortable at first but then he seemed to like it. Ellie put his St. Louis Cardinals cap on his head and the recreation therapist set up the Nintendo and he played for a while. Everyone came in to see him. Funny, he didn't look as sick sitting in a chair. He looked at a book. After a while he wanted a blanket. He slept for a while. Ellie was so pleased!

10 p.m. Ellie picked up Jesse and put him back into bed a little after 6 p.m. He was awake and itchy. He was just falling asleep. It was about 7:15 and it just happened. He vomited 1,000 ccs of blood as far away as the wall by the windows. He was frightened, and frightened of all the people coming into the room. But he waved at everyone. There were doctors and nurses everywhere, running in and out. The doctors were debating about where the bleeding came from. They thought it must be from the upper body to come out through his mouth. If it had been from his lungs it would have come out through his trach. If it had been from his stomach it would have come out through his stoma.

They decided to do an endoscopy. They brought in the machine. Jesse was awake. Everyone was crowded around looking at the monitor. It was esophageal varices. You could see the veins on the monitor, huge. They said this was an indication of portal hypertension, because of the blood backing up from his liver. Dr. Butler the GI scarred one vein and sprayed the other with epinephrine to decrease the blood flow to them. They were planning to take him to the OR to remove his spleen and tie off the bleeding vessels. But then they decided not to. They thought it was too risky for Jesse. They started him on meds to decrease the blood flow to the veins, stomach, and small intestine. Dr. Butler said she didn't know how much this would set back getting Jesse's stomach and intestine in good shape.

Rachel tells me the liver team came yesterday before the big bleed, a huge contingent, surgeons, GIs, fellows, Cindy, and students. Both Dr. Swanson and Dr. Dorand were there and were arguing about something outside Room B. Ellie was washing Jesse when they came. Rachel and Gail shooed them out and Gail stayed with Jesse so Rachel could talk to them. Rachel went up to Dr. Swanson.

So what do you think?

I don't know.

Oh, come on you can do better than that.

Well, obviously he's in stark contrast to where he was two weeks ago.

Uh-huh. Based on the numbers, what do you think?

Well, I'm somewhat optimistic.

Well, I am too.

She looked around at the team. Dr. Swanson smiled and patted her on the shoulder. Then he lectured the team on how Jesse's clotting problem was due to DIC, disseminated intravascular coagulopathy, a kind of world-class clotting problem. Dr. Meyer talked to Rachel after he left. Evidently she saw Swanson's DIC comments as an attempt to fob off Jesse's bleeding problem onto the ICU docs and the GIs.

Jesse's not in DIC. We tested him. We can deal with internal bleeding, but if it continues it's a surgical problem and they have to do something about it.

Today is calmer. The immediate crisis has passed. Jesse's alert. I'm glad, but I'm tired of hearing ALERT on everyone's lips. Standing by him a little while ago, he looked at me and mouthed words. I leaned down close, trying to empty my mind of all thoughts that might cloud my already feeble lip-reading ability.

I want to die.

I leaned back, trying to show understanding with a slight nod, hoping I hadn't heard what I knew I'd heard and knowing that Rachel was watching us.

I understand, Jesse. I'm here with you.

Here with you! I took his hand for a moment. He closed his eyes. I walked away from the bed, nonchalant, and looked for my coffee, avoiding Rachel's gaze.

What did he say?

I don't know. I couldn't get it.

I lowered my voice to answer her, wanting to appear to her to be whispering so Jesse wouldn't know I hadn't understood what he said, and hoping he wouldn't hear my lie.

July 23

We got to the hospital at the same time as Rachel. She showed us another route through the basement. Marian was coming out of report at the end of her shift. She seemed angry. She told us she hadn't been able to get Jesse settled and that he had pulled out his nasogastric and respiratory tubes.

I was frustrated and angry with him for pulling out his tubes. I asked him why he was doing it. He told me he wanted to die. And I realized how small my own frustrations were compared to his.

But Marian said it with reproach in her eyes, mostly, I thought, toward me, closest to her of the four parents. As if it was my fault for letting him live too long. So what should I do, go in and smother him with a pillow? But I felt guilty, too, as though she was saying we were keeping Jesse alive not out of his own wishes, which had taken a detour in the last day or so toward peace, an end to climbing sand dunes, but out of our own needs.

Yet he's stronger, better coordinated, than before. This morning he helped Edward the nurse take his temperature, holding the thermometer for him. He's more awake than ever, reading comic books and talking a little against the vent.

Afternoon notes. We were outside Room B stretching our legs.

Ellie came over. She said Jesse had told her, Just shoot me. Then, a minute later, he had told her he wanted to go home. I went in to him.

Would you like a back rub Jesse?

Yes.

I rubbed his back for a few minutes.

Do you have hope?

Yes I do.

Do you get afraid sometimes that you won't get better?

Yes.

Do you sometimes feel that going through all this isn't worth it to get better?

No response. Fool! Two questions in one for someone with a tube in his throat and pumped up with Fentanyl to boot.

I said we were afraid sometimes, but were hopeful, too, because of all the progress he'd made. That everyone was amazed at him but that being so awake also meant being aware of his illness and of being in bed when he wanted to get out of here and go home. I said no one had expected what had happened to him. That it wasn't fair. That he had beaten all the odds and we were proud of him, but we knew he felt very discouraged now. I saw the relief in his eyes, and got a squeeze from him.

July 24

Jesse had a good night. This morning he's awake and was trying to get out of bed when we came in. He pointed to a chair and mouthed.

I want to sit in the chair again.

OK Jesse, you will, soon.

He brushes his teeth with a foam stick now. He holds a ball we bought for him to squeeze and transfers it from hand to hand. He holds up one finger when he wants to use the urinal and won't let anyone help him, except to take it away. He plays Punch me in the nose with Ellie.

He started tearing at his dog and I wondered if he was hallucinating. His face is impassive now, masklike, as if turning the pages of a newspaper to find an article he doesn't care whether he reads or not. Daniel, on his last visit here, wondered whether having a new liver would change Jesse's personality. He's young enough to voice the primitive thoughts we all have.

Rachel cleaned the secretions around his trach.

Thank you, he mouthed.

You're welcome.

Nodded.

Just keep fighting.

I am.

Then I came up.

I know how discouraged you feel.

He shook his head no as if to say, You can't know how discouraged I feel. You are standing.

Late afternoon. Jesse's most recent belly X-ray showed an air pocket near his stoma. It could be related to the dark bruise on his stomach. Dr. Lanier is worried about an obstruction. Jesse's belly was tense and shiny when he examined him. They stopped his feeds. Dr. Meyer came in many times. Dr. Dorand wants a CAT scan of Jesse's spleen. He wonders if there's an abscess in it.

Gail saw Jesse looking at her and mouthing and went up to him.

What is it, hon?

When can I go home?

As soon as you're better.

Nodded.

But I'm not going home either.

Yes.

Do you want to see Daniel and Cassandra again?

Yes.

I have a message from Daniel.

Nodded. Eyes opened a little wider.

You're the best brother I have in the whole world. You're also the only one.

He smiled. He has taught his little brother well.

Dr. Meyer tells us she heard they're talking about retransplant!

July 25

Jesse weepy today. Ellie came away from the bed toward us with her back to Jesse.

He's so depressed.

I'm happy, he mouthed.

He wants Ellie. She did physical therapy with him, moving his arms and legs. Rachel came over and helped. Then the resident came in and they wheeled him down for a CAT scan of his intestine and spleen.

Late afternoon notes. Dr. Dorand came by half an hour ago. The CAT scan showed large calcifications, dead areas without blood flow. Removing the spleen might help with the bleeding, he said. Dr. Rand stayed behind when Dr. D left. He said he didn't think the bruise near the stoma indicated a perforation because Jesse was not showing signs of sepsis. Still, he's not sure what it is. Dr. Meyer thinks it's a perforation. But the dye they used for the CAT scan went to his kidneys, she told us. This means the veins are patent, open, that there's blood flow through them. A good thing, I know, but haven't we heard this song before?

Outside Room B, the three of us conferred about the tricks Jesse's been playing on us. Gail talked about the few hours yesterday when he was NPO, or nothing by mouth.

He asked me for a swab to clean his teeth. He started sucking on it for the water.

He asked me for a tissue, I said, then he put it in front of his face and started pulling out his NG tube.

Yesterday he told me he wanted to be suctioned, said Rachel. His trach, not his mouth. I started to leave to get Ellie, but something made me look back at him. He was trying to pull out one of his IVs.

We smiled like conspirators, worried that Jesse might hurt himself but proud that he still has the juice to buck the program.

85, 88, 82, 79, 78, 79, 80, 79, 83, 93, 112, 120, 122, 121, 120, 115, 106, 96, 84, 76, 77. The changes in Jesse's heart rate on the monitor for one minute. It just happened, like that. It was fine a minute before. Blood gurgled out of his stoma for half an hour.

I went down to the NICU. Gail was alone with Jesse, standing by him. He turned to her.

I love you, he mouthed.

I love you, too.

I was happy for her after all the hard years of stepmother and stepson, and happy for Jesse too. And a little bit jealous.

Eden's on tonight. She's in a polite but no-nonsense mood, which is her usual mood. She makes it clear she can handle things quite well without us. We all go home to the transplant shelter at eleven, four hours after her shift began.

July 26

Late evening notes, first today except for jotted reminders, what with events of the day and being sick myself.

Eden came up to us as we approached Room B this morning. She looked almost beside herself.

Jesse was awake all night. He pulled out his NG tube three times and pulled the clip off his ostomy bag and pulled at the strings around his neck for his trach. He pleaded with me, Please help me to die. I said, Jesse, you know I can't do that. I read to him from the Book of Job. He's in agony. There's no reason he should have to go through this. You need to talk to the doctors.

About what? Giving him more drugs to ease his misery, or to put him out of it? I'm afraid to ask her. Job. I've thought of him many times during these weeks. I brought the beat-up King James Bible my father was given as a child, with its red-edged crinkly-thin rice paper and its black cloth cover. I've always loved the rolling Shakespearean language of Job, with Satan going to and fro in the earth and walking up and down in it. I tried to read it again during the first few days after May 10th but had to put it away. I had no use for a God whom only academic theologians could make right in his ways to man, letting Satan torture but not kill his servant Job. Job's choruslike friends with their ignorance of suffering and their religious bromides are contemptible, of course, but I had no patience for Job and his bellyaching, either. His grief over his children's death and his grief over his lost cattle seemed identical to me. Both were prized possessions, nothing more. And Job, at least, had language to comfort him. Jesse's suffering is greater.

I was sick, nauseated, this morning, the first time since we came here. I went to the NICU lounge to try to sleep it off. Rachel went out for a walk. Gail stayed with Jesse. It was quiet, midafternoon. She talked with him.

Hi Jess.

Nodded.

How are you doing?

No response.

Are you feeling angry?

Yes I am.

What are you angry about?

No response.

Are you angry about being sick?

Yes I am.

You're right to be angry. We're angry that you're sick, too.

Nodded.

Jesse.

He looked at her.

Do you trust me?

Yes.

She talked about knowing how upset and depressed he was. She told him how sick he had been but that he was better now. She got a squeeze. Later, I sat and talked with him. I said I knew he sometimes felt like dying, but that we still thought we was going to get better. He fell asleep with his leg on my chest.

The dam burst between Gail and Rachel today. Rachel came up to me. She had just talked to Dr. Jacoby the psychiatrist, who said we needed to be talking to each other about medical decisions. It was clear that Jacoby was pessimistic about Jesse's chances and had pulled away from the liver team. I suggested the three of us go to the PICU lounge. It was usually empty at this time of day. Rachel started to talk about her conversation with Dr. Jacoby. She got to the part about Making medical decisions, and Gail got up and walked out.

I'm not listening to this shit.

Rachel half-followed her out of the lounge shouting after her, You are not a better mother than I am!

I sat there, frozen in my seat. I knew what Gail was thinking. Her goal was the same now as it had been all along, to bring Jesse home alive. To even talk about the possibility of withdrawing care was to snip away at the rope that held his hammock to this side of the abyss. She had decided that Rachel was ready to let him go and that I was ready to go along with her.

Rachel came back in and talked about how she felt excluded in her role as a mother here, that we were belittling her, pushing her aside. I told her Gail and I had felt the same way for some time, that we could barely get a minute with Jesse.

Then Rachel left and I found Gail and persuaded her to come back to the lounge with me. She was furious with Rachel and not much less so with me. Then Dr. Dorand came in. He must have heard about the conversation with Dr. Jacoby because he started talking to us about the idea of withdrawing treatment.

You need to ignore the I want to die stuff. If Jesse's up in heaven and he could have been here, he'll wish he was, and if he makes it he'll thank you for not withholding treatment.

I thought that Dr. D must see both of us as having great faith because Gail did. No one could miss the quote about faith from St. Paul behind Jesse's bed, just beneath a photo of Jesse that Rachel had taken. In any case he was telling us to strap ourselves to the mast so we wouldn't act on a plea that was tearing us apart.

I was confused about what he meant by withholding treatment, when he'd said before that they wouldn't do that without a court order. And what would we withhold if we could? The respirator? He was not in a coma, for God's sake! We weren't going to watch him gasp for breath until he suffocated. The blood he was getting? We weren't going to let him bleed to death. Paddles during a code? Yes, that was life support. Anything short of that now was no more life support than a cane for a bum knee was life support.

Then he started talking about Dr. Giselle, Jesse's colitis surgeon. We had asked Dr. Meyer whether Giselle might be asked in to consult on Jesse's intestinal problems, and she must have passed on this message to Dr. D.

We work with Dr. Giselle all the time, but I don't think it would make sense for him to take over Jesse's case now.

I was shocked that this was the way he had interpreted our message, and I made sure my face registered it. The last thing we needed now was for Dr. D to think we lacked confidence in him. I told him we only thought that Dr. Giselle, with his expertise in gastrointestinal problems, might have some ideas, just as other specialists had been called in for consults, but that we had not thought about and did not want Giselle to take over Jesse's case.

Late afternoon. Jesse complained of belly pain. Terri gave him 2,000 ccs of Fentanyl and 10 ccs of Valium, enough to knock out a horse, she said. He was wide awake. Then she drew off blood through his nasogastric tube into a beaker to see how much fresh and how much old blood was in his stomach. A few minutes later we looked at the blood in the beaker. It had congealed like jello. Terri said she'd seen it only once before, with a liver patient. Then Jesse started to bleed from his mouth. The blood flowed lazily over his lower lip. We slipped into normal crisis mode, grabbing towels and blue pads to help Terri soak it up. Standing near the foot of the bed on the window side, I tossed a towel to land on his chest for Terri to grab and sponge blood with. It landed on Jesse's face and covered it. It was an accident, but I felt as though it had been a deliberate toss. How many more bleeds and tosses of the towel would it take before I could take the part of charwoman to Gregor Samsa and sweep Jesse out to make room for a patient who would play his part and get better?

Monk, my brother, called, in town to videotape a musician for his jazz archive. He'd had a hard time dealing with our father's illness and death and I knew it wouldn't be easy for him to come here. But he did, just as Marian came into Room B to start her shift.

Hello Jesse. It's me, Marian, hmm?

This was the busiest part of her shift. She had to check meds, start her flow chart, check and count supplies, check IV lines and straighten them out, check the settings on the respirator, and establish her presence in here. I wondered if we'd be in her way and if she would make that known. I saw my brother's face when he walked in, and, through his eyes, saw what outsiders saw when they came to visit.

Jesse, your Uncle Monk is here.

He opened his eyes and took my brother's hand. Monk held on, awkwardly. Jesse did not let go lightly now.

I'd like to play something for you, Jesse.

He took an alto saxophone from its case and played Moondance and Harlem Lullaby and Oh Canada, establishing the melody with the first few notes of each and then lifting off in jazz flight. Marian, Gail, and I stood around the bed with him. I caught Marian's eye but couldn't read her expression, whether of patience, annoyance, or interest. Afterward, she told me it was beautiful, and I realized she had stood there because she wanted to be part of this circle.

July 27

In the surgical waiting room. They took Jesse back into surgery, his eleventh overall but first in more than three weeks. I was hoping he'd be asleep when they took him out, but no, he was awake, impassive, after being told he was going back. We helped the nurses move furniture, then got out of the way as they wheeled out the bed and turned the corner into the hall toward the elevators. He looked at us, sadly. I hated myself.

A couple of hours into the surgery I walked back to the unit, the first time I'd broken the waiting room ritual. Go out and get something to eat, yes, or go out to bring back coffee for the two or three or four of us, but never back to the unit before we'd seen the surgeon, except for the time the liver fellow didn't show. I came back to hang a signed photo of Larry Bird the Celtics had sent by way of my sister's efforts and to get Gail's crossword puzzle book. I knew I had committed a transgression the moment I walked through the double doors. No one spoke or paid any attention to me. I may have been invisible, so out of place was my presence on this stage where the floor in Room B was being mopped, the bed was made, and other patients on the unit were being attended to. Jesse's only part now was to be waited for, and ours was to go through the double doors to the elevators, down to the basement, along the yellow-striped corridors to the escalator, up to the pavilion under the mighty glass rafters, and up the elevators to the surgical waiting room. Visible or not, I had been exposed as a motley fool stumbling onto the wrong scene and eliciting silence.

Later, in the NICU, from scribbled notes. They took Jesse's spleen. Dr. Dorand sat in a chair at the western end of the pavilion, our new spot. He held the thumb and forefinger of each hand apart from each other in a semicircle, then farther apart to reach the proper diameter, when we asked him how big the spleen was.

It was the size of a large handbag. We would have trouble closing him up with it inside him if we transplant him again. The area around it was oozing blood. It still is.

How do you get it to stop bleeding?
We packed it with clotting factors. It can take a while.
How much blood did he get?
He got a lot of blood.
You didn't find any perforations?
There were no perforations, no air pockets.

July 28

Jesse's in DIC, disseminated intravascular coagulopathy, again, the reason for all the bleeding. Dr. Meyer tells us he had a complete transfusion in the OR. She says they'll start his feeds again as soon as he has stool and bowel movements.

Late morning. Lots happening. Dr. D just left. He said he may want to go back in to check Jesse's bleeding and clotting. And the pain management team came. They started him on methadone and Dilaudid to replace the Fentanyl and Valium.

Jesse's awake and in pain. He waved to Gail. She just left to spend a few days at home. It doesn't work with Rachel and me both here, and Jesse's doing OK, she said. I assured her that we could make it work, and she and I are OK now after our fight, but the kids need her, too.

He goofed on Rachel, licking his lips, which looked dry. She came over to him.

Do you want a swab?
He puckered his lips.
Do you want a kiss?
Yes.
She bent down. He kissed her on the cheek.
Do you want me to kiss you?

No. Smiled. I want a swab.

He uses the alphabet card now, with difficulty. He opens his mouth for cleaning, no more holding on to secretions. He cracks his knuckles. Like the old Jesse, Daniel would say. Maybe the methadone is kicking in.

Dr. Stacy, a surgical fellow, just came by. She had nothing in particular to report but observed Jesse's activity with great interest. On the way out, she smiled broadly.

We're optimistic, right?

Cindy came in right after her.

There's never been anyone like this boy, right?

Never!

We're learning a lot from Jesse, she said.

We're all worried but amazed. A day after another major operation and he's doing better than he was before they took him down. His nose is driving him crazy, though, because of his NG tube. He puts a tissue over his face when he wants to cry. Sometimes he may just need to do that, Rachel says.

He mouthed something. We didn't get it at first. He was frustrated with us and with himself, and, as always, we hampered whatever lip-reading ability we did have by tensing up for fear we'd fail and drive up his frustration level. Between Rachel and me we figured out that he was saying he wanted the trach off so he could breath on his own and talk out loud.

I think of him at age three, shortly after Rachel and I split up. Gail was over for dinner. We were talking to each other. Jesse broke in.

I wanna taw.

What's that Jess?

I wanna taw.

I'm sorry, Jess. Say it again.

I wanna taw!

You want a toy?

I wanna taw!

You want to be tall?

I wanna taw!

We went around the house and picked up anything with a name beginning with T that might conceivably interest a three-year old. He got angrier, insisting with each desperate guess we made that he wanted a taw. A few years later over another dinner, Gail and I reminisced with Jesse about that night and how we were never able to figure out what he wanted. He looked up from his food.

I was saying I wanted to talk.

Rachel reached him today. I had gone out for a walk. The unit was quiet, before rounds, no immediate crisis to bring nurses and doctors running in and no X-rays to oppress him. They talked.

I know you're in a lot of pain.

Yes I am.

I know it must seem like it's never going to end.

Yes it does.

We can always talk about how you're feeling. We don't always have to talk about the future.

Maybe he just wants to deal with what's here and now, she told me, and not the future. It seemed like a wise thing to say. Then she told me that last night after Gail and I had gone back to the transplant shelter, Lenore went out of the room and Jill came in to say hello. Jesse took her hand and held it tight. When she turned to go he held her hand tighter. I wondered if he was apologizing for giving her a hard time a few nights ago. Or maybe he was trying to say, Don't leave me with Lenore!

July 29

Late morning notes. Jesse had a good night. I came in, put down my coffee, and went over to say hello. He mouthed and pointed.

Why the breathing tube?

That's to help you breathe, until you're stronger. You're breathing too, this just gives you a boost.

OK.

Then Ellie was over next to him. She checked out his lines and smoothed his sheets and talked to him as she worked.

Jesse Jesse Jesse. You've tangled up your lines again. What am I going to do with you?

Shrug.

What are you going to do when you get out of here?

Party.

Party? You're going to throw a party?

Yes.

Can I come?

Shrug. Maybe, maybe not.

Rachel came up. So you're thinking about a party, Jess? How are you feeling? Pretty good?

Metz-a-metz, with his hand.

How about Ellie? Is Ellie a good nurse?

Metz-a-metz.

1:30 p.m. I called my mother and told her things were going well. Came back and Jesse was bleeding from two sites at his surgical wound, dark blood advancing into white bandages. This, after an X-ray where he was raised and lowered. I stood next to him. He turned his head to look at me and mouthed words. I got closer.

I love you.

I thought that's what he said, but I wasn't sure, and didn't want to say I love you, too. If I'd misunderstood him he'd be frustrated that he'd failed to communicate again. I made a face that I thought would be an appropriate response, other than words, for someone who's just been told he is loved, and lowered my head and squeezed his hand. He nodded and closed his eyes.

Dr. Mellon was just in. She said it's amazing how much better Jesse looks compared to a few weeks ago. She wants to get him fed and then get him retransplanted. He'd been exercising his arms by lifting them up in the air and crossing one over the other and moving his hands and fingers, his own PT. Then he pointed to the TV, played with his hands and thumbs, mouthed N-I-N for Nintendo, and shoved me away as I was trying to read his lips.

I want to play.

The activity therapist brought in the Nintendo box and connected it to the TV. He played for a minute or two, then was tired.

Gail is back. She couldn't stay away. We went out and I got a haircut. Rachel talked to me when I got back. Jesse had motioned her over to him.

What is it, Jess?

Will you help me get out of here?

Yes honey, I'll help you.

He nodded, pleased.

What else can we say? It's what we hope for with all our hearts and minds. And he trusts us.

July 30

Notes at home, from scribbles. Jesse waved to us with both hands as we walked in first thing in the morning. I told him I might be going back to Naugatuck for the day with Gail. I avoided saying home, and felt foolish for such delicacy. As if he's not facing worse than plain talk! I told him I'd be staying for the night and wanted to check in at work in the morning, that he was doing well enough for me to do this.

But I'll be back tomorrow afternoon.

He fell asleep. We taped a note to the rail where he could read it.

The kids were surprised. They knew Gail was coming back but didn't expect both of us. We walked around the neighborhood, thankful that no one was outside to ask for an update. Rachel called, early evening. Jesse'd had a good day, sleeping a lot but lucid when awake. His weight is 43 kilos, the lowest it's been since he came in. Yes, he had read the note I left for him. Will's kids visited, she said. Jesse had a good time with them, especially John, the little one, and waved and smiled at people when they came in. The methadone is helping him, no doubt, but this is a Jesse we've seen only in bits and snatches before, now breaking through the ice.

July 31

On the train back to New York. I slept in my own bed for the first time in almost three months, a guilty pleasure. Gail drove me into work. Coming into New Haven I thought, this little corner of the world that has occupied so much of my time and energy, where my three children were born, is no longer the real world for me. Kind as the outreach staff have been, the silence around this experience is almost palpable. Only with Jenny, a nurse who's cared for sick kids and has one herself, did I feel as though I could peek over the wall and find someone peeking back. Katherine, the secretary, drove me to the train station in the early afternoon.

It says a lot about us as a country that we have these kinds of operations.

I wasn't sure whether she meant our technical genius or the value we place on individual life. I politely agreed with whichever sentiment she was expressing.

NICU notes, late. Coming back to the unit, I felt like a visitor who'd lost his ICU role and the small comforts, intimacies, and protective shell it offers in compensation for its damages. Having deserted the one true experience, I would be readmitted only after a reinitiation. No matter, Jesse was doing well. There's a feeling in the air, said Dr. Rousseau, the incoming GI attending, that he may be over the worst of this.

He had a lemon ice pop! I had bought several of them at Rich's and stuffed them as far back as I could in the tiny inefficient freezer of the patient refrigerator.

Ellie played with him.

Show me how you're going to wave goodbye when you get out of here.

He waved.

I cleaned the secretions under his trach. He thanked me several times. He's feisty, though, imperious when he wants to be, waving off Lenore coming in on the evening shift. Yet he looks so frail and skinny.

August 1

Bloody vomiting at 3:00 and 4:00 a.m. Feeds stopped. Again at 8:00 a.m. They may need to do an endoscopy. Jesse looks fairly well, but tired. He cups his hand to his ear when he doesn't hear us. A wry comment on our lip-reading illiteracy? He points to my hair.

Did I get a haircut?

Yes.

Yes I did. Down the street.

Smiles. Nods. Closes his eyes.

10:40 a.m. Why is his temperature so low? They put him under a heat lamp, shivering. The right side of his surgical wound is oozing. He's crying. He covers his face with his hospital gown and responds to my dumb question with, Yes I'm angry! His weight is up to 49 kilos. They'll hold his feeds for 24 hours and either scope him or feed him tomorrow.

Evening notes. I went out earlier and bought the cassette tape of Woodstock '94 and a book, *When Elephants Weep*, with money friends sent for him a while ago. I showed them to Jesse. He wanted to hold them. I let him, but not for long, as though he might drop them and hurt himself. Why was I treating him like a China doll that might break if a book tipped over onto it? He lay there in one more phase of his decline or recovery, so sick and almost so well. Suddenly I thought I should lift him up and carry him out, that, so close to being well, the true intervention now was to take him from this place of illness, sans IVs, sans respirator, sans dialysis, sans bags of blood from the blood bank, as though the illness that was in him had infected his room but was out of him for this brief moment, this crack of light that Dr. Lanier talked about, if only we could see it. Does Jesse know that this is so? Is this what he's been trying to tell us when we misread his lips?

Dr. Dorand made rounds at 6 p.m., late for him.

We may still want to go back in and clean him up and remove the blood clots in his abdomen and lungs. They're probably the source of the pleural effusion. I want to get a good couple of week's worth of feeding into him and prepare him for retransplant.

The liver is working for him. He's gotten better with it.

Jesse appears to be sleeping now, late evening, but he raises his arms and moves them around over his head as if conducting a symphony that has reached the movement of his own recovery.

August 2

Morning in Room B. Jesse has been sleeping since 5 a.m. Rachel says she saw one of the residents on the street this morning. She ran up to Rachel, excited, and told her she'd had a dream last night that Jesse was extubated and had all his tubes out and was sitting up in bed, ready to go home.

Gail is back. Jesse just woke up. He tried to put on his own socks. Used the call button for the nurse. The doctor said he could have an ice pop. If he keeps that down, she said, they'll start feeding him again. He spelled DAD, COMIC, and I WILL and PROMISE, about my pushing another ice pop on him, on the alphabet card. He teased Rachel with smiles and frowns. He gets her every time. I asked him about the volume on Woodstock '94. He nodded that it was good.

Afternoon. He had a little bit of ice pop but vomited shortly afterward. Then put on his glasses and watched some TV. Dr. Dorand, on rounds, said he was leaning toward re-exploration.

The reason for surgery is to get rid of the clots in his chest and abdomen that can cause infection, to get him ready for retransplant. The reasons to hold off are that he's doing all right, the antibiotics are covering him for infection, and surgery will delay getting him fed.

Evening. Jesse sat up in bed a little while ago with his glasses on and read some cards people have sent him, then a *Sports Illustrated*. Rachel stood next to him. He pointed to his arm.

Those arms, they're skinny?

Yes.

Yes, that's what we're working on now, getting you fattened up.

August 3

On the train. I got up early at the transplant shelter to put in another appearance at work. Gail got up to go to the hospital. Now, three months later and on my way to New Haven, I'm feeling what many parents must feel for their sick children, the anxiety, guilt, and dread of having to leave the hospital to go to work, take care of children, or do anything that does not involve one's physical presence with the ill one. Jesse's doing better now, but what about the ongoing nausea? What about varices? What about the pleural effusion? Any one of these could cause another crisis that takes him back to the OR. Why did I pick this day to go to work?

At work. Called the unit and talked to Rachel. Jesse's doing fine. He was nauseated earlier, but they're starting his feeds now. He spelled words on the alphabet card and teased Rachel.

Happy, he mouthed.

You're happy?

Not.

She frowned.

He smiled.

Here in my office in New Haven, away from the room in which reality is taking place, I reflect on the irony that this most private experience of Jesse's is marked by its lack of physical privacy, the unknown endlessly tested and measured and charted in and around Room B and explored, as they say, in the operating room. And Jesse? Room B, the ICU, the OR, his nurses and doctors, have become the daily round of his life. How real is home to him anymore?

August 4

Evening notes. Took the train from Naugatuck to New York City this morning, got off the elevator and saw Gail and Rachel talking in the NICU lounge. They told me Jesse was going back into surgery, that he'd lost a couple liters of blood from the right-hand side of his surgical wound. Dr. Dorand thinks it's old blood oozing. He told them he wants to clean Jesse out quickly and close him up, have him hold on to his feeds, sit in a chair, eat solid foods, and transplant him. No small goals, but I see Jesse's silent influence calling Dr. D to his side, as it has with so many others in his life. He wants to lift Jesse from his hammock and up to a minimal standard, but only that, to justify retransplant and give Jesse another chance.

Jesse vomited secretions at 1 AM. Dr. D, checking in before surgery, saw Jesse suction his mouth with the tube as though brushing his teeth, and was pleased. Walking down the hall with Jesse being wheeled to the elevator, the activity therapists looked at him with doelike pained expressions I wanted to wipe off their faces. I'm fed up with this place and these bullshit artists, including Dr. D with his Arizona Iced Tea and his dress shirt unbuttoned at the top two buttons and his casual manner as he talks about cutting my child again. There's a subtle complacency to Jesse's surgeries now. What's another operation for him? He always ends up better off the next day.

Gail and I went out for coffee. We came back and Rachel told me one of the nurses had tracked her down in the hall twenty minutes after they took Jesse down. They had forgotten to have us sign a consent form. So there he was, waiting on his bed wide awake to be taken in to surgery, and it was only luck that they found Rachel.

I cleaned up the surgical waiting room, dumping old newspapers and food. Dr. Dorand came in. He sat down, looking tired.

We took out four basins of blood. It was about what we expected.

Where was the blood?

It was oozing from raw vessels at the site where we took out his spleen.

Has it stopped?

It's slowed way down. It could ooze a little more. I think this could help him.

Were there any signs of infection?

They found staph epidermis in the cultures. Nothing serious. We pulled out one of his chest tubes. Feeding should start soon.

10:15 p.m. Temp 100.3. BP 79/41. He may get a couple units of blood.

Outside Room B at the nurse's station, I heard Tony the ICU resident on the phone to the liver surgeons.

Jesse is alert and in pain and his BP should be higher than it is.

Oh that my grief were thoroughly weighed and my calamity layed in the balance together! For now it would be heavier than the sand of the sea: therefore my words are swallowed up. For the arrows of the almighty are within me, the poison whereof drinketh up my spirit: the terrors of God do set themselves in array against me.

Job 6: 2-4

August 5

A restless night for Jesse. His weight is up and his face looks a bit puffy. And he's angry and upset, the first time I've seen him like this since he started on methadone, what, a week ago? Dr. Rousseau, the ICU attending, says he's concerned about a possible new infection.

They started dialysis but Jesse's BP dropped so they quit. Pain management came and increased the methadone. He's been sleeping a lot. Gail went home to spend the night with the kids. The plan is to bring them here tomorrow for the weekend, spend some time with Jesse, have lunch at the transplant shelter with them, and maybe go to the park if all goes well.

Afternoon. Jesse's weight is up 3 kilos from the a.m. Why? His temp is OK but his heart rate is up. His breathing is fast and shallow. He's awake and uncomfortable. His feeds are supposed to start again this evening.

He needs a new IV. They have to call the IV nurse, the resident screwed it up twice. Could we have some smooth sailing here? Rachel tells me about a device they can put in the trach to help patients speak while on the respirator. Passy-muir? She says it also speeds the transition from being on the respirator to getting off it. Sounds like a good idea, but if it's so great why haven't the docs brought it up by now? Because parents have to be around to win such small mercies for their children, like beds that weigh them instead of Tuna Scales? Or is this device such a tiny mercy that it's laughable to expect them to think about it now with the sand dune they see before them?

Jesse's hematocrit, the measure of red blood to whole blood, is at 32.5, the lower range of acceptable and down from 38 before surgery yesterday. Paula the resident says she's happy it isn't lower because it means the blood seeping from his wound may be blood-tinged rather than frank blood. She's going to talk to the doctors about new antibiotics. The infectious disease team and the surgeons are not eager to jump on new antibiotics the day after surgery. The GIs and Dr. Rivera, the new ICU attending, are interested in starting antibiotics. They'll talk and make a decision.

Chest sounds are coarse, Marian says. Temperature 101.7. Bandage oozing at both ends. Thick secretions in his mouth. Paula says it makes her lean more toward antibiotics. She's still waiting for calls. She's ordered a chest X-ray to rule out pneumonia. She shakes her head.

Something happened today and it's not doing Jesse any good.

The chest X-ray looks good, but Paula says Jesse could still have pneumonia that hasn't shown up yet. They start him on triple antibiotics.

An Orthodox Jewish family is across the hall from us in the open area. Their little girl is dying. The men are making lots of phone calls. The mother, dressed in black with a shawl over her shoulders, frets, walks around crazily, and lifts her hands and cries out.

9:15 p.m. Temp 100.9. Rachel just left for the transplant shelter. She plans to go home tomorrow for the weekend if all goes well.

A few minutes ago, Jesse was pissed off and didn't want me near him. I walked away and said to Marian, He's fed up. He doesn't want to hold my hand. I went downstairs to the vending machines off the main part of the cafeteria and got an ice cream sandwich. I walked around a bit and came back. Marian was standing by Jesse. He motioned to me. I came over. He took my hand.

10:00 p.m. Dr. Rand just left. I've seen his affection for Jesse grow over the past three months. I first noticed the change when he sided with Dr. Dorand after the Fourth of July and told me, If Jesse bleeds badly again, we will stop it. When he comes in now I see an air of confidence and determination and a fondness and admiration for Jesse. He did a belly exam. Jesse slept through it. We talked.

Do you have the results of the spleen biopsy?

No, not yet. I don't expect we'll learn much from that. We know about the calcifications. The liver's bad. We know that. But I think Jesse looks good. I don't think he's far away from retransplant.

No?

It's a balancing act now between getting him stronger and not waiting until he gets sicker.

What about the cultures? Any infection?

The staph epidermis is the only one I know of that's positive. That's nothing.

What about his incision? It's so bunched up and raw.

It looks worse than it is. It won't look like it does now when he leaves here, discolored, with these ridges and plastic noodles across it. It won't be a bikini scar, but it won't look like this.

He left. Jesse woke up in a Don't cross me mood. Marian started to turn him on his side. I went to help her. He pointed me to my chair.

10:45 p.m. Heart rate 129, BP 77/33, temp 100.6.

11:55 p.m. The little girl died. The rabbi carried her out, completely swaddled in a cloth.

August 6

12:55 a.m. BP 71/41, temp 100.2. Exhausted. Going down to the

NICU lounge for a nap. Told Marian to wake me up if anything happens.

6:20 a.m. Jesse's BP went as low as 68/38, then up with albumin. Marian thinks his decreased BP is a combination of fever and methadone. No blood has seeped through his dressings since they were changed at 10 last night, though, and his temp is normal.

7:00 a.m. He tried to spell on the alphabet card. His hands are shaky, his mouth moved as he tried to find the letters. Spelled DAD, and SWA for swab. Took the swab from me, then spit up cherry-flavored Tylenol from 10 p.m. last night. Why is his stomach not absorbing? How is he going to get fed like this?

Rachel came in with Will. They said goodbye to Jesse, then Rachel went home for the first time in three months. Stamford is less than an hour from here, so she can get back quickly if she needs to.

Jesse did physical therapy with me this a.m.

9:00 a.m. He's angry and upset. His temp is 96.4. They'll hold on feeds until they see how his BP does. When BP goes too low the blood does not suffuse the gut properly for feeds, Dr. Rivera tells me. If his BP decreases when they do dialysis they may give dopamine. Dopamine, the word like a summons from his first critical illness three months ago.

10:00 a.m. Gail and the kids arrived half an hour ago. Jesse waved to them and gave a little smile, then spit up secretions. Daniel took his hand, then Cassie. He had little energy for them, though.

To the transplant shelter to make lunch and spend time with the kids. We're all trying our best, but it doesn't work. We can't attend to Jesse and the kids at the same time.

Going back to the hospital. Gail staying with the kids. We agree on regular calls.

Dr. Reich just here. We talked. What do you think? I don't think he looks so good today.

I think he's OK. Bacteria get stirred up after surgery. That can be a short-term setback but a long-term gain.

What about his blood pressure going down? And his fever?

His blood pressure going down and the fever are a result of the surgery. His intestines look good on the X-ray. They're not inflamed.

He looks a little puffy to me.

The fluids he got in the OR cause the puffiness. The puffiness in his face is related to leaking capillaries after surgery. The capillaries should close up and the fluid should be removed in dialysis. And his blood pressure should go back up. The same with the bump in his clotting time and liver enzymes. That's caused by surgery. They should go back down, even with this liver.

Dialysis. Everyone is waiting to see how it goes with his BP.

BP 70s over 30s. Liver team called. Jesse's going to get a unit of blood. They just gave him albumin. Feels as though we're slipping backwards again.

He's oozing from his wound, blood and water. His hematocrit is drifting down. Paul and Tony, the ICU residents, and Maria and Terri, the nurses, are here. Jesse's going to get two units of blood. Should I call Rachel?

Dialysis stopped early. They couldn't remove any fluid. Jesse scared with all the activity.

Weight 48.6 kilos. Hematocrit 23. Tony pressed Jesse's left big toe to drive the blood out of it and make it white, then let go to see how long it took for the blood to flow back in and turn the toe red. The profusion is a little slow, he said.

6:35 p.m. BP 69/30. Tony pushing blood in. I try to warm up the bags, one under each arm. He starts squeezing the bag even before Maria has hung it on the pole. Dopamine at 10 ordered.

Called Rachel, said, Jesse's blood pressure is dropping. I think you'd better come back. Called Gail.

6:55 p.m. BP 62/29, hematocrit 21, very low. Jesse spit up secretions but has been unresponsive. Looks puffier. Putting on fluid.

Gail here with the kids. Put them in the nurse's lounge. They saw him earlier. Not now.

Jesse going down. Gail just came in, surveyed room, two docs and two nurses around the bed. Came up to Jesse.

JESSE HARLAN-ROWE!

Jesse, on his right side, turned his head, opened his eyes, and looked at her.

7:25 p.m. BP 73/34.

7:35 p.m. BP 44/20. Dr. Kostos, attending liver surgeon, called and is on his way. Long struggle to bring up BP. Jesse's eyes tracking, blinking. He's trying to talk. Terri checked the string around his neck that keeps the trach in position.

Jesse, I'm checking to see if your string is too tight.

Nodded.

Rachel and Will are back.

Late notes. Jesse coded around 9:00 p.m. Tony ordered epinephrine. Rachel and Terri were at the monitor at the foot of the bed trying to deflate the mattress for chest compressions. Rachel hit a couple of icons and the mattress popped flat. Tony did chest compressions. Maria counted for him. They brought him back. We love these people. They're kids, for God's sake.

10:00 p.m. or so. Gail's sister and daughter arrived to take the kids. We said goodbye to them and put on the best face we could about Jesse. Dr. Kostos arrived. They took Jesse down. We didn't leave the unit, for the first time. They brought him back with an open gut wound. He was too bloated to be closed up. They had packed clotting factors in the wound. A long, ugly, brutish, absurd tube stuck up from his throat.

What's that?

It will make it easier to suction him, Dr. Kostos said.

I went down the hall and paced as they settled Jesse in bed. Dr. Rand and Dr. Kostos came down the hall. Dr. Rand saw me and hung his head as he passed by.

twelve

Jesse had been shivering since sometime the day before and now his lips were shivering, too. We stood around the bed. Terri was in and out hanging blood and platelets and fresh frozen plasma. It had been a night and a day and a night from the evening of the sixth until the morning of the eighth and there had been little sleep for the three of us. We nodded off warming blood under our arms and legs to be hung on one of the three or four poles at the corners of the bed.

I wondered if I should be talking to Jesse about death, that it was all right to let go and the rest of it. But we hadn't talked about it before he came into the hospital. He seemed so young for that! Now he had no voice, and although I suspected he was thinking about his death, I couldn't be sure that speaking its name wouldn't frighten him, assuming he could hear me at all. So I told him he didn't need to be afraid and that we were all here with him and we loved him, but of course I had no way of knowing whether he had cause to be afraid or not. I could have talked with him about the past, his friends, the places we had lived, or picked up where we stopped on one of the mythical sagas we had created together, where one of us would start, take it to a certain point, and hand it off to the other. I may have thought about doing this and decided not to for fear he would take it as a sign that he was dying.

Gail asked the ICU resident to call Dr. Meyer. She came by in the morning and was shocked to see what had happened to Jesse.

Can you keep him comfortable? Gail asked her.

Yes. We can do that. We can keep him comfortable.

I had talked to my mother earlier. She wanted to fly here from Rochester and there was a flight leaving soon. I said, If you want to come to say goodbye to Jesse, and she interrupted, Oh no, as if she thought I would reproach her for having such a thought. I said, No, that would be a good reason to come, but she needed to understand there was very little hope for him, and to be prepared, because he no longer looked like Jesse.

I took few notes. Gail wrote some. She got through to him on the 7th.

8/7. I was standing by him a few minutes ago. His lips looked so dry.

> *Do you want me to put some chapstick on your lips?*
> *He nodded yes. I put it on. He puckered his lips.*
> *You remember how to do that, don't you?*
> *He nodded yes.*
> *Do you want me to smooth it around for you?*
> *He nodded yes.*

Even later than that, on the morning of the 8th, after the neurologist with the thick glasses and thick-soled black shoes had come in and pronounced him to be in a deep coma.

August 8. Jesse and I were talking and suddenly he began to tremble. He reached for my hand, grabbed it tightly with his fingers, and pulled it toward him.

I bet you have lots of things to tell us.

He nodded yes.

A lot of secret things?

He nodded yes.

Is God talking to you?

He nodded yes.

Has God given you a vision for your life?

He didn't reply. I told him when he was well I wanted him to tell me everything.

She still believed he'd get better, right up to the end.

I felt the bed rail sink a little to my left. It was Dr. Dorand. We spoke. Then he said he wanted to check something on the computer by the nurse's station. He came back in and Gail suggested that we go outside to talk. She and Rachel went out with him. I brushed back Jesse's hair and told him we were going to talk to Dr. Dorand but would be back soon.

Dr. Dorand stood at the far end of the nurse's station with Dr. Broward, the nephrologist from the CVVHD days. Rachel and Gail and I, Dr. Rivera, the ICU attending, and the ICU residents and nurses stood around them. We talked about whether anything could be done.

We could take him back into surgery to look for a discrete source of bleeding. I'm a surgeon, so that's my impulse. I want to do something. If I did it, it would be with some hope.

He paused. It was clear that he'd have a hard time mustering any hope for Jesse. Perhaps we could push the issue with him, perhaps not, but we were looking for guidance now.

If he were your child, what would you do?

There was silence. I wondered if the question was in poor taste, but then thought no, Dr. Dorand would understand that I had to ask it. He stood without speaking for what seemed like several minutes. He looked around, not at the others as though to be rescued, but behind them. I thought about breaking the silence by watering down the question, but something told me not to. I thought Dr. Broward might say something. He did not. Dr. Dorand put his fingers to his lips. Finally he looked back at me.

I would wait. I think it's more likely that the surgery would kill him than help him. I would wait for an opening.

Dr. Broward jumped in.

I agree. There's really nothing we can do for Jesse right now. We tried to dialyze him this morning with the ultrafiltration but we couldn't do it because his blood pressure dropped so quickly. It leaves us very little room. I agree with Dr. Dorand. The best thing to do now is wait and see if we can find some kind of an opening to take action. If his blood pressure stabilizes we can try to dialyze him and remove some of the fluid. Then we can look for another opening from there.

Rachel and Gail and I looked at each other and agreed.

What about the shaking? Rachel asked. Is there anything we can do about that? We were told it was flapping tremors from liver failure.

Dr. Dorand shrugged.

He's probably cold. When I'm cold I put on a blanket.

We said we'd try that. The meeting broke up and Dr. Dorand left for surgery. The three of us talked. We'd been agonizing about what to do and there was still tension between Gail and Rachel over whether we should allow them to call a code and try to bring Jesse back if he went into cardiac arrest. Of course, we had never established that we had the authority to keep them from calling a code even if we wanted to. In any case, things might be different an hour from now. Some new crisis or turn of events might call for action. But for now, we would wait. Rachel went back into Room B. I told Gail I had to go lie down in the NICU lounge.

Michael? I think you'd better come down to the room.

I must have slept for about half an hour. We didn't get back into Room B before the doctors and nurses rushed in. Gail and Rachel and I and the cleaning lady who always had a word for Jesse stood outside watching through the window behind the nurse's station and the open door. I saw that they weren't trying to collapse the bed. And no crash cart, no paddles. They didn't need them two days ago, but this is worse. Or is it just on TV that they use them? Dr. Rivera stood by Jesse with his hands on his chest. He turned to Terri.

We'll call it at 11:15?

She nodded. I looked at the clock. It was 11:00 a.m. Dr. Rivera began to pump, rhythmically but too fast, as Terri counted. Terri looked at him with alarm.

Slow down, John.

I was struck by how much better Tony the resident had been at this. We watched the blood pressure monitor. It showed 20 over 10, then showed numbers tumbling down to nothing, then racing back up, but not far enough, then tumbling back down again. Gail and I were holding hands. I looked over at Rachel and wondered if the three of us should hold hands. I wondered whether I'd be able to cry when it was all over. And then Dr. Rivera called it and everyone was out of the room in an instant. Terri brushed by us on her way out and let out a great sob.

We went in. After a few minutes others came in. We talked with Dr. Meyer. Dr. Rousseau, the GI attending, asked Rachel and me if we wanted an autopsy. If so, they couldn't remove all the tubes and IVs. We said no and they took them out. Cindy told us that

Jesse's body would be kept at the hospital morgue until our funeral director picked it up. I kept wondering if Dr. Dorand would come back.

We took down photos and cards from the walls and divided them up. Rachel took the photo of Jesse over the bed, waving and smiling. She was proud of it, and rightfully so. She had thought of it as an encouragement to his doctors to restore him to what he had been. I had seen it as Jesse waving goodbye. He looked like one of El Greco's gaunt saints, taller because he was so thin and because of the camera's angle, pointed up at him. He was pale against a dark background that I guessed to be their kitchen in Stamford. He smiled and waved toward the viewer with an arm that looked almost as long as the rest of him because of its closeness to the camera. I wish I had a copy of it now, but I have his Handman, a Druid-like priest in a robe with a hood drawn in the same position and from the same perspective, below the figure and with the hand as large as the rest of the body. I think it's an illustration for the episode in his George 10 saga where Ronanin releases a glowing ball that moves slowly toward George 10. The eyes are fixed downward on a puny approaching mortal, or their downward cast shows great sadness. The hand is outstretched in greeting or to warn interlopers from approaching. Or there is no such ambiguity and I make it so to keep things rich with him still.

My mother arrived. I think that was the worst part for me. I've never been sure why. Because she's my mother, or because she loved Jesse so much, as my father had, or because she was late, although it would have been worse for her to see the end. We moved away from the bed to let her say goodbye to him. Cindy walked over and stood with her. Which irritated me. Later, my mother told me she had to look at Jesse's beautiful brown hair because his body didn't look like him at all. Toward the end his hair, which had always been a rich brown, became a deep cranberry brown, the envy of all who saw it. That this was the effect of bile coursing through his body did not negate its beauty.

I walked past the nurse's station toward the PICU lounge. The neurologist tried to make eye contact with me and opened her mouth to give her condolences. I ignored her. I regretted it immediately, but the moment was gone. We both knew I had iced her. I went to the phone by the NICU lounge and left messages for Dr. Hall and Dr. Gardner. My mother took a taxi back to the airport. She'd been in the City for two hours.

We had our bags in the passageway outside Room B next to the nurse's station. Rachel and Will left. We agreed that we'd meet the next day for lunch midway between our hometowns to talk about the funeral service. I went back in. Jesse had changed. His body was heavier, denser than it had been just a few minutes before. No more blood was being pumped into it. If they had hoisted him on the Tuna Scale or Rachel had come in one more time to punch the correct icons at the foot of his bed, I suppose he'd have weighed the same. Still, he was heavier, more solid than before. If Elijah and Jesus really raised the dead, they knew how to lasso the wind and stuff it back down the bottleneck, but even they could not force anything that moved into this stone his body had become. So heavy, so dense. I think Blake was right. If he were alive today he might be the particle physicist who proves conclusively that energy is eternal delight, the free-floating stuff that clings to us and infects us down to our molecules and atoms and starts a dance in us that makes everything light. Heaviness is the end of the dance, and when the dance is over all is heaviness. I leaned down to kiss him on the forehead and marveled. After all that had happened to him, all his suffering, the tiny mole on his forehead that he'd had since he was a toddler was still there, visible on his burnt-red skin.

thirteen

Stuck to the refrigerator with a magnet and tucked in among blurbs that Gail has culled from magazines and newspapers, a Monro Muffler coupon card, an estimate from the dentist, a shopping pad, pizza coupons, a satirical letter on taxes from the 1930s, all held in place with Infoline, Carpet Guard, and local realtor magnets, is an unfinished Jesse drawing I brought up from his room last week. The disembodied head of a dark-haired man floats before a mountain with eyes and a mouth. The man looks toward an oracle like figure in the foreground with a large bloodshot eye, a large broken nose, and a wide smiling mouth with one large upper tooth. A curving intestine or umbilical cord that I first mistook for stylized clouds grows out of the top of its skull. I asked Gail, an artist herself, to fill in the man's half-erased left eye. She refused. Only the artist can do that, she said. I thought of sending it to Dr. Dorand when I found it. The man bears a faint resemblance to him and I wanted him to have one of Jesse's drawings. But I was sitting on the cusp between nostalgia and anger at the time, and soon jumped into anger.

Below the drawing is a narrow strip of paper snipped from a magazine. It reads, Nothing begins when you think it did. Lillian Hellman, from one of her memoirs or plays. Profound or pat, it turns my attention from these lawsuit folders, a pile separate from my hospital notebooks, to what prompted them. When did I begin to wonder if what happened to Jesse wasn't just bad luck? Talking to my friend the nurse just after coming back to work, still pitching my Jesse-as-warrior-beating-the-odds-so-many-times bit and getting stopped cold? It was she who made me face the brutal democracy of sepsis, which I had thought a special and exotic, though terrible, condition.

Once they perfed him, that was it. He was young and healthy, except for his liver. That's why he hung on as long as he did.

There was no miracle, then, no heroism to salvage from a case of very bad luck. But my doubts were festering before that. The call from our undertaker on August 10th. His associate in New York had gone to the hospital's morgue to pick up Jesse's body. It wasn't there. He was told that the hospital had sent a death notice to the Medical Examiner, who, when he saw Transplant written on it, had the body picked up and brought to the city morgue. Now, my undertaker in Naugatuck told me, the Medical Examiner was going to perform a full autopsy and Rachel or I would have to go in to identify the body before they would release it. One of my frantic calls went to Cindy. She or someone else at the hospital called and talked them out of doing the autopsy and into releasing the body. I called Dr. Meyer and asked her to find out how this had happened when we agreed there would be no autopsy and that Jesse's body would be in the morgue until we had it picked up. She said she would do that.

August 11th, the day before the funeral service. I was shaving at the bathroom sink with the door open. Out of the corner of my eye, I saw someone walking up the steps to the front door. More flowers, I thought. Good middle-class suburbanite, I went to our bedroom to put on a shirt. When I came back there was no one at the front door. I heard loud voices at the side of the house and went out through the glass doors off the kitchen. A state cop, a state detective, and a Naugatuck cop had come around the driveway with a warrant for a Gail Rowe ten years younger and four inches shorter than my Gail, who was putting a bag of garbage in a can when the state cop shouted, Don't move! and put his hand on his gun. By the time I came out, Gail had got their attention. The state detective was looking at the warrant and shaking his head. The three of them walked away sheepishly. It had nothing to do with Jesse, but it might as well have.

Waiting to hear from Dr. Dorand, amazed that he hadn't called. To say what? Hadn't he stood speechless before us the morning Jesse died? What could he add in a phone call? But such was the naiveté of my grief that I thought Jesse had changed us all and that this wedded us, somehow, for life. I see the same naiveté in the first letter Gail and I wrote to the liver team, in September. Knowing what you know now, would you have done things differently? Would you have acted more quickly to get Jesse back into surgery after his first transplant? Should you have turned down the second liver with its too-small hepatic artery? Did you miss signs of infection after the splenectomy near the end of July? I had even called to ask if Gail and I could attend the morbidity and mortality conference on Jesse, the quintessential secret society where doctors are encouraged to second-guess themselves and be second-guessed by their peers without opening themselves up to censure or lawsuit.

Cindy calling to set up a meeting with the liver team to go over our questions, So we can go on with our work and you can go on with your lives, she said. Poor Cindy. A truly decent person, she was no doubt trying to be helpful, giving a wake up call to the grieving parents who couldn't stop calling and sending letters, looking for satisfaction when there was no satisfaction to be had, but her comment, better left unsaid by anyone, was false and harder to take coming from her.

Dr. Meyer calling me back about the Medical Examiner fiasco with a complicated and contradictory tale about how my undertaker's associate in New York had picked up the body at the hospital morgue and then taken it upon himself to call the Medical Examiner's office when he saw Transplant on the death notice, thus setting in motion the whole train of events that followed. I called my undertaker in Naugatuck. He stuck by his story that it was the Medical Examiner's initiative, and it made sense. Why would his associate make more work for himself by calling the Medical Examiner when the hospital hadn't? And my undertaker was a smart businessman, a straight arrow with a reputation in town to uphold. It's unlikely he'd be fooled by a cock-and-bull story that his associate dreamed up to cover his mistakes or to squeeze more money out of the deal, or, even if he was so inclined, that he'd go along with a story he knew we could check out. Of the two versions, my guy's was the only plausible one. I concluded, and hoped, that someone in the hospital morgue had lied to Dr. Meyer to cover his own screw-up.

We took the train into the City in late September. Dr. Dorand had called after he got our letter and made a time to meet with us. If I had thought of Jesse and the PICU as gray during those three months, I had retained yet another image of light and life and energy bursting from everyone, including Jesse, during much of July and the first days of August. Today the unit was dull, empty, and dark. We had dreaded and longed for this visit and expected to be overcome with emotion. We were not. We saw a couple of the nurses, not the ones we knew best, and one of the residents. There was a little girl in Room B. We didn't see Jesse's drawing of Ozzie

Smith, the great St. Louis Cardinals shortstop. We had given it to Ellie at the funeral service to give to the PICU for Dr. Meyer and the nurses. Perhaps it was in the nurse's lounge. Or perhaps Ellie had taken it home. If so, she had earned it. Dr. Meyer was not in. We saw Dorinda, one of the PICU mothers. She had been living in the hospital for months, sleeping in the PICU lounge and eating trays of food the nurses ordered for her. Her son Corey, five years old, had got his heart and was doing well.

We walked to the pavilion and under its mighty glass rafters but were unimpressed. We walked through the talking doors and down the street to Rich's. The deli was almost empty, an off-peak hour. Rich looked at us from under black eyebrows with a mixture of dim recognition, puzzlement as to why these regulars had disappeared, and uncertainty as to whether he should welcome them back or make them earn their stripes all over again.

Do you remember us?

He smiled. Of course! Cappuccinos! And how is your son?

He wouldn't let us pay. We sat on a bench outside the park, then took the elevator up to Dr. Dorand's office. He was delayed, we were told, but would be here soon. We waited for about twenty minutes. Gail wanted to leave. Rich had saved the day, so why push our luck? I thought about asking whether Dr. Swanson, whom we had bumped into on our way up, could talk to us. Then Dr. Dorand walked in and took us into his office. Japanese prints and painted ceramic teacups sat on a teakwood breakfront, neat piles of folders on an L-shaped desk, and photographs of his children on top of a teakwood cabinet with glass doors.

We started with medical questions from our letter. No, he said, Jesse's low white blood count did not put him at greater risk for infection after his first transplant. About whether they should have transplanted Jesse in the first place, since his own liver had looked so good, he said Jesse's liver was firm and stippled, not soft and smooth as it should be. He insisted, threading his right index finger through the thumb and index finger of his left hand as he talked, that he had tested the hepatic artery of the second liver with a technique he had invented, and that it was fine when they transplanted Jesse. The second perforation was not, as Gail had hypothesized, the result of overly aggressive feeding. He shrugged.

I can't figure it out. There was no obstruction.

And the final infection that took him down? It was probably a translocation of bacteria from his bowel, which by then was paper thin from illness, he said. I wrote TRANSLOCATION in my notebook. The term seemed better suited for a science fiction novel or a Catholic saint than a medical conversation.

Or it could have originated at his stoma, Dr. Dorand said. Or in his respirator. The respiratory technician, I thought. A mercy killing? Then we talked about the lack of contact after Jesse died. He shook his head ruefully.

When I read your letter it was obvious to me that the family would want some contact after the patient's death. I'd never seen it that way before. There's a seductiveness to going on to the next patient. There's always a crisis, always a critical decision to be made.

He said he'd been thinking about starting a group, with members of the hospital's ethics committee and a few families, to come up with bereavement policies for the hospital's transplant programs. Would we be part of it? We said we'd certainly consider it. It was time for us to go.

Would you join me for a cup of tea? I make excellent tea.

We'd love to, but we need to leave time to catch our train.

He came over between us and hugged us. On the train ride home we agreed that we had to join Dr. Dorand's group. We had raised the issues and he had called us.

Then nothing for weeks. Now, I understand that my focus was

single and framed by the purity of grief while Dr. Dorand's was multiple and framed by the intensity of his work, if not by the ambivalence that might come with seeing the parents of a child who had died on his watch. But why suffer this silence from him? Why not treat it as I would an inflated doctor's bill and call his office until I got satisfaction? I did send him a note and called once over the course of a few weeks, but no, if Jesse must be dead then I must be under the spell of his death. To call again when I felt the call was due us would have been humiliating. From this vantage point my stance, and Gail's, look childish to me. Yet I hesitate, because I want to give those ones we were their due. We were fixed, standing in place outside the house where the feast was being held.

Gail asked me if I felt I hadn't protected Jesse. Yes, of course I felt that way. She said she thought our guilt was deeper because the doctors could not acknowledge their own sorrow or frustration, or not to us. Maybe that was it. I thought about how trust gives passage over disbelief, doubt, dark possibilities. Whatever the chain of events, the pattern was this. Lack of contact from Jesse's doctors looked to us like insensitivity. Stretched over time, insensitivity became a betrayal of trust delicately woven over the months of Jesse's illness. And finally, betrayal fueled speculation. What, other than insensitivity, might cause the doctors to sever contact with us? But in truth, our belief that we who had witnessed Jesse's struggle constituted a new society, and our suspicions about what had happened, were both there from the start. Only their relative weights changed on the seesaw.

If Jesse's suffering was avoidable, then the empathy we had sought for ourselves and others was a sham and his doctors at least had the good taste to shun it. I wrote a second letter in December, to the director of the hospital, recounting the whole sad story, the Medical Examiner, the calls not returned, the promises to meet not kept. I got a letter assuring a response to the issues I had raised. It never came. I sat with Gail at the kitchen table one morning in December. She put it bluntly.

We want to be paid. In Jesse, or in compassion, or in policy, or in explanation, or in money.

New Year's Day 1996. Before, we still lived in a year that Jesse had been alive in. No more. I had a waking image of him in his bed at the hospital. We stood outside the talking doors. They would not move. A few days later I received a note from Dr. Dorand. He had not forgotten about the committee, he wrote, and he would be in touch with us about it.

In mid-January I took the train in and sat in the Medical Records office in the basement with seven large blue binders filled with progress notes, doctor's orders, nurse's flow sheets, and radiology, lab, and operative reports stacked up on the table before me. I marked passages to be copied at seventy-five cents a page. I thought of Jack Nicholson studying a property transaction book at the Land Records office in *Chinatown* and coughing loud while ripping out a page that would lead him to the land grab, the murder, and the incest. It would have been a long day of coughing and tearing for me to bring home nothing so dramatic as that. I took notes and looked for a smoking gun. I read the progress notes for the first four days and had the impression that Jesse's doctors dozed off for a moment at the outset, then were hypervigilant for the next three months.

No danger of infection noted after the first transplant.

No stomach X-rays taken after May 6 until May 10, the day Jesse went back into surgery.

Radiology reports for only six of fourteen X-rays recorded in the progress notes from May 6 through May 10.

A note from Dr. Atella on the morning of May 10, the night after Jesse had been in agony and was pumped up with Fentanyl, which said he looked well.

A note from Dr. Atella on May 11, which said his antibiotics were discontinued on May 9 because he was feeling better and the surgical resident's exam was benign. I looked back at the surgical resident's note. It said the abdominal exam was difficult to assess. The resident recommended discontinuing the antibiotics but gave no reason. The nurse's progress note said the Fentanyl took a long time to touch Jesse's pain, that he was in extreme discomfort all night, had bile draining from his nasogastric tube, was getting puffy, and had coffee grounds feces in his bag, apparently a bad sign.

Deeper into the chart I found more. Some of it read like life and death stuff to me, some of it seemed to show a pattern of sloppiness or even deception.

A report on a stomach X-ray taken after the second transplant on June 8. It noted the possible presence of a sponge. No follow-up in the chart.

A report on a stomach X-ray taken after surgery on June 21 to look for a missing instrument. It was inconclusive. No follow-up in the chart.

A report on a chest X-ray of a sixty-six year-old man in Jesse's chart and under Jesse's name.

Both liver donors' names and identifying numbers recorded in the progress notes. Donor confidentiality is the holy of holies of organ transplantation.

Two operative reports for one surgery and none for another. Some operative reports dictated two or three months after the surgery, when, it seemed to me, any subsequent problems could be cleaned up retrospectively.

June 14, six days after the second transplant. A note from one of the GI fellows stating that Jesse had hepatic artery thrombosis, that is, that the hepatic artery was blocked, kaput. The next day the fellow qualified himself. I had the impression, from the careful wording of the second note, that he'd been told to. The discharge, or death, summary on August 8th referred to hepatic artery thrombosis on June 12th, four days after the second transplant.

No smoking gun here, but still... And Jesse? He was lost in a sea of details, reduced to numbers and procedures except for a few notes that drew him out. One was from Angela on the morning of May 9.

Pt found sitting up in bed yelling that he had to go to the bathroom but was still "tied down" by lines. Foley catheter found in bed. No bleeding noted. Placed back in supine position. Given Fentanyl. Stated, "I'm sorry. I forgot where I was for a while." When he was asked why he pulled out his Foley he stated "It was coming out anyway and I didn't feel as if I needed it anymore." Was instructed not to pull out any more lines as may damage self.

Why does this little note move me so? Because it's one of the last times Jesse spoke? Because Angela's phrasing, Didn't feel as if I needed it anymore, diction more formal than Jesse would have used, makes me hear his own voice and his own words?

A note from the young female social worker on May 5, the day we brought him in.

Jesse in excellent spirits. Talked excitedly about getting to work on the computer as soon as possible! Expressed interest in teaching me computer games over next few weeks.

I'll bet! I gave the clerk the pages I'd marked to be copied. At home, I showed them to Laura, the nurse down the street. She made a chart lining up columns for each section of the chart by date and time of day for May 6th through May 12th and entered information from each section so we could compare across columns. She gave me notes for each day that summarized key points, questioned decisions, and showed patterns, the number of times pain meds were given for stomach pain, the nausea and vomiting, the rising bilirubin. She pointed out that they started feeding Jesse after the first transplant when he had few, if any, bowel sounds, and that his need for pain meds increased and the vomiting started after he drank apple juice. About his hematocrit, the ratio of red blood to whole blood, dropping from just above acceptable to well below on May 7th, she wrote, Where did the blood go? She questioned why the surgical resident gave no reason for discontinuing the antibiotics on May 9th. She noted the coffee grounds feces in his bag. She marked a May 9th note that Angela had written in the nurse's flow sheets. It merely summarized the facts, that Jesse had been given triple antibiotics for a question of peritonitis and that they were discontinued after the first doses of each, per the surgical resident's instructions. Its tone seemed out of place, though, and its length was unusual for this section of the chart. Was Angela trying to leave us a message? Laura pointed out, with scorn, Dr. Atella's May 10th note about how well Jesse was feeling. It's true that Laura wasn't there, and medical charts can't tell you everything the doctors were thinking and doing, but she taught me how to read the chart with a critical eye.

I talked to a lawyer in town. He was in over his head. I called others in Connecticut and New York. I learned that, for legal purposes, organ transplants were still considered to be experimental procedures and so, malpractice suits involving them carried a higher burden of proof. I also learned that there was a limit of two years after death for medical malpractice suits, including the time it would take me to find a doctor to read the chart, let alone testify, and get an attorney to take the case. Most important, I learned that poor care is not malpractice. For that you must prove that poor care led directly to a poor outcome. If recovery after May 10th was unlikely, then bad hepatic arteries and sponges and instruments that may have been left inside Jesse and decisions based on reading the X-ray of a sixty-six year-old man, all coming several weeks after Jesse's first transplant, wouldn't matter in court. Slowly, after a detour into June and July, I circled, dropped, and picked away at the first four days. That was when his troubles started.

I talked to an attorney in the City who was skeptical but agreed to talk to a doctor if I could find one. I had copies of everything in the chart from the first five days. Now I needed X-rays and sonograms. Medical Records told me I'd have to get a court document verifying that I was the executor of Jesse's estate. I called the local probate court. The aide told me Rachel would have to sign off on such a document. I told her that was not feasible. Let's try something else, she said. I wrote a letter to the judge saying I wanted permission only to obtain Jesse's medical records. The judge issued a Petitioner's Probate Certificate. I sent it to the hospital. It worked.

I called the medical records and radiology departments and wrote letters. Everything went slowly. A bureaucratic system as tortuous as the hospital's underground passages poured salt in my wounds to keep me going. I got bills several times a week from doctors and specialists and every department in the hospital that had anything to do with Jesse, although, as I had learned, my insurance company had negotiated a set price for everything. I got bills addressed to Ms. Jessie Harlan-Rowe. I got a bill for $357,000 that said I could use my Master Card. I got a medication recall notice addressed to Jesse eight months after his death.

I learned that the sonograms of his liver taken on May 7, 8, and

9 were missing. About the radiologist's reports I'd identified as missing for X-rays taken from May 6 through May 10, I was told that only wet, or informal, readings had been done. Laura said there had to be formal reports somewhere. I never got them. I noted every discrepancy I found between progress notes and lab reports and available X-rays, every delay in responding to my letters or phone calls, every request for clarification on hospital procedure not answered. I was building a case not only for medical error but for missing records or lack of cooperation and all these might imply. I received the fourteen X-rays taken from May 6th through May 10th. One was a CAT scan of a Mr. R.A., a current patient at the hospital, taken the same day the package was postmarked. I wrote to the head of the radiology department, returning the CAT scan and asking for the missing X-ray and, again, for the missing sonograms. And may I suggest that you have your staff look in Mr. R.A.'s chart for these?

I found a doctor in the Midwest through a friend. He said he felt sick after reading the chart material I sent him and had to go out and run for miles. He thought the surgeons had waited too long to get Jesse back into surgery after his first transplant.

But I'm a pediatric neurologist. You need a gastroenterologist or a surgeon to say the same thing.

He showed the chart to a senior physician at the hospital where he was an attending, who told him, You don't turn on other doctors. He showed it to another doctor who said he thought Jesse's care had been adequate to good. He talked to another doctor who declined to look at the chart. He gave me the name of a gastroenterologist in Connecticut. I called her. She said she'd talk to a top GI at Yale and get back to me. She didn't. My Midwest doctor sent the material to a pediatric GI in Wisconsin.

At work in early August, the secretary's voice came over the intercom.

It's a Dr. Dorand for you?

He said he knew it had been a long time, but that he had finally got around to the committee we had talked about. It was short notice, he realized, but he called a meeting for tomorrow, and wondered if Gail and I could make it. I said tomorrow was the first anniversary of Jesse's death and we were planning to spend it at home.

Oh. I didn't know that.

He said he had worked with some others at the hospital on a draft of a bereavement policy. Would I be interested in taking a look at it? Sure. And he expected that the committee would be meeting again, after tomorrow, so if we would like to be involved in the future... I said I would talk to Gail about that and get back to him.

He faxed me the draft. It was good. I wrote back with a couple of suggestions and said we would not be able to participate on the committee but were glad he was moving ahead with it, and wished him success.

My attorney called and said he was ready to close out the case. I got him to agree to wait a few days, then called the GI's office in Wisconsin. His secretary told me he would get back to me within a week. I told her that was past my deadline. That Sunday, at the end of September, the doctor called me at home. Everyone else was out. I heard the rustling of papers on the other end of the line as we talked and had the impression he had just given the chart a quick look before calling me. He said he found some sloppiness, a general lack of order writing and X-ray reports, but wasn't sure there was much more than that. I felt him slipping away from me, calling long distance from the Midwest on what I supposed was his day off. I asked him to hold and ran downstairs to my study to find my notes. I came back and went down my list of questions one by one. He became more interested. He commented on Dr.

Atella's cheery May 10 note about how well Jesse looked.

It sounds overconfident. It could have contributed to a delay in getting Jesse back into surgery.

He wondered what the missing X-ray reports from May 10 would show.

Should they have recognized that there was a perforation? The pain suggests it. I think the surgical resident probably used poor judgment, but I'm not sure it constitutes negligence.

I told him I'd been waiting for someone to give me a logical explanation for why this resident recommended discontinuing the antibiotics on May 9th. I offered my own hypothesis. Jesse had been given the first dose of each of the antibiotics. Perhaps the first dose is the most important, I said, the one where you get the most effect, and the remaining two are mostly backup. Because antibiotics are hard on the liver, the resident might have made a judgment call that discontinuing them after the first dose would give Jesse good effect from the antibiotics and, at the same time, give his liver a break. There was a pause at the other end of the line.

I have no explanation for why he would do that.

I heard more rustling of pages. He referred to the surgical resident's chart note.

Did he read the most recent X-ray? If not, why not?

He puzzled over the antibiotics and asked out loud why no X-rays were ordered right then. He agreed that the pain meds the surgical resident ordered for Jesse would have helped to mask the perforation.

The course over the first few days was not usual. This could have been a tip off. The usual course would be to get better over the first couple days, then be extubated, then be fed and out of the ICU within seventy-two hours. A Fentanyl drip is not usual at this point. The increased need for it would indicate that something was going wrong. I think they were hung up on obstruction when, in fact, Jesse was perforating.

He agreed, when I asked him, that the intense pain Jesse felt the night of May 9 marked the point at which he was perforating, and thus that a day passed before they got him back into surgery. Then he hedged a little.

Perforations are hard to diagnose. It's not the kind of case that screams negligence. We talk about three levels of care in our quality-assurance reviews. First, there's consensus that the care was excellent and any good doctor would have done the same under the same circumstances. Second, there are questions about the care. Some doctors might have acted differently and some the same. Third, the care was negligent. Any reasonable physician would have acted differently. I think Jesse's care probably falls into the second category. I think you have grounds for a case, but whether it's worth it or not is another matter.

He promised to call my attorney. I got off the phone and walked around the house in a daze. I thought about Carol, the ICU resident who suspected a perforation the evening of May 9th and wanted to hold the pain meds until someone from the liver team had seen Jesse. She was smart, observant, and thorough. She probably called Dr. Meyer at home to question the surgical resident's assessment. She had acted correctly, and the structure of the situation constrained her. If she did call, Dr. Meyer probably reassured her or, at best, told her to follow the surgical resident's assessment but watch Jesse closely. Dr. Meyer was no autocrat. She encouraged her residents to think for themselves. But Carol, I thought, must have felt a subtle pressure to defer to her judgment, especially when the surgical resident, who had seniority in this situation, thought things were OK. For Carol to do more than she did, assuming she still had reservations, might have had a small or sizable impact on her career. I wondered if she wished she had pushed harder, and if one day she would save another life because of Jesse. I thought of Angela, who seemed to have her own doubts. She stood even lower on the totem pole than Carol but was not afraid to stand up to doctors, as she demonstrated on May 11 when the blond neurosurgical resident came to assess Jesse's shunt. I wondered if she wished she had spoken up two nights earlier. I thought of Dr. Meyer, who kept Jesse alive so many times but let him drink apple juice on May 8th when he had no, or almost no, belly sounds. I thought of Dr. Dorand, who smiled and said Jesse was ready to go up to the pediatric unit the day before the sky fell. And did he get a call from the surgical resident the night of the 9th? I thought of the surgical resident, and understood why his manner had changed the evening of the 11th when I was arguing with Dr. Atella over a call to Jesse's neurosurgeon in New Haven. He wanted to see if I had figured out what he'd done, and was satisfied, in my fuming over Dr. Atella's nonsense about the shunt, that I had not. And I thought of myself. What happened was not my fault, of course, but if one believes that advocacy is more than busywork to keep parents from going mad, then logic says it may be effective or ineffective, well or poorly timed, and may fall short of the mark because of fatigue or rationalization or fear of questioning doctors, or because of believing that one is best equipped to chart a course between challenge and accommodation, the right course in many situations but precisely the wrong one in this, where the more emphatic style of a Rachel or a Will, taking their turn at the transplant shelter that night, might have made all the difference for Jesse.

I lay on the living room couch and I was afraid, not that my attorney would decline but that he would accept the case. I imagined the outrage, real and tactical, that would flow from the doctors and the hospital. I saw them sleuthing into my past life and sins. I heard Rachel, who would have to be given the option to join a lawsuit, telling me I was crazy, that Jesse's care had been superb.

I wondered if I was right or if grief and rage had got the best of me. Then I thought of Jesse, of his great fear and great courage, and I realized that my work was done. Now my attorney had to do his, and if he said go, I would go. I would ask Gail, but she would say yes. Rachel could sign on or not by her own lights. I was learning, late, how things get done in this world, not by having unshakable faith but by going back to the well each time your faith is shaken, taking a draught, and going back into the arena.

I talked to the attorney the next day. He had talked to the doctor and had decided against taking the case.

You have a spitting chance, but I couldn't take this on.

I thanked him for considering it. It was over, nine months after it began, if that was when it began.

fourteen

The walls are eggshell blue and the carpeting is dark blue. The ceiling fixture has horizontal glass rods that refract the light, with one rod missing from the time Jesse kicked off a sneaker and broke it. Two metal posts framed with unvarnished pine divide the left-hand third of the room from the rest as you come in. The poles support a beam, running from the back to the front wall, with track lights attached to it. A framed copy of his self-portrait hangs on the left-hand wall above a bureau with maple wood veneer and faux black slate top. I never liked the bureau, and he was never attached to material things anyway, so it will be no great loss to knock it apart and toss it on the pile off the back deck. A canvas-sling wooden rocker fits sideways between the bureau and the front post. The sling, brass riveted at the top and bottom of the frame, is royal blue with BUFFALO BILLS and a Bills helmet on the upper half.

Next to the bureau on the front wall is a pressboard bookcase with drawing and sports books, science fiction novels, a book on Blake with his Ancient of Days on the cover, and other books. The color TV that sat on top has gone up to Daniel's room. To the right of the bureau is a closet built out from the left and rear walls. Some of his clothes still hang in here or are folded up in the bureau. Gradually, all but the most special are making their way out to the wardrobe in the unfinished part of the basement, casualties of our endless quest for closet space. His shoes are lined up in pairs on the closet floor. What is it about shoes? The intimacy of feet they suggest by hiding them?

His bed, or a bed occupying the space his did, juts out from the back wall between two end tables. I've switched mattress, box spring, and frame with Daniel's and Cassie's as theirs gave out on the way to buying new ones. A flannel Buffalo Bills blanket covers the mattress. I wonder if we overdid the Bills and if Jesse was moving away from them to other concerns. He talked about them less as we talked about them more. Once or twice when he came back from Rachel's on Sunday and I mentioned the game, asking him how they'd done or celebrating or commiserating with him if I knew the result, he hadn't watched. If his passion for them was waning, it's no surprise to me that he didn't say anything to spoil the fun we had rooting for him through them.

On the right-hand wall is a black and white poster, Scott Musgrove's Fat Dog Mendoza of Dark Horse Comics. Fat Dog and other mutant canines rush across the glossy paper on the trail of something that has already made it across. To the right of the small basement window is a picture frame filled with basketball stars, including signed photos my sister got for him while he was in the hospital. On the back wall over the bed are St. Louis Cardinals and Buffalo Bills pennants.

Newspaper and magazine clippings are tacked to the wooden posts. Here's a photo of Kurt Cobain. He liked Nirvana but did not romanticize Cobain's suicide. It was stupid for him to kill himself, he told Daniel, because he had a wife and baby. Here's an article clipped from the *Waterbury Republican-American.*

Lendl's ailing back forces him to retire.

He had one favorite player in each sport he paid any attention to. But why Lendl? His steadfast refusal to play to the crowd? His outsider status as a Czech-born U.S. Citizen? Or the lead sentence of the article.

Ivan Lendl found an opponent he couldn't beat: his own body.

Here are two articles about Superman coming back after DC Comics killed him off, in a series of four comics that I scouted around for and finally found for him. A color photo of Darth Vader cut from a comic book magazine, with aging glossy arms curling in on his body. A picture of George Lucas with a caption announcing that he's making three more Star Wars films. Daniel and I will go to see the new one this summer in Jesse's honor.

Daniel, who hates crowds, has decided he loves New Haven. We drive in and walk around town, along Broadway, down to Chapel Street and the shops, over to the Green and the new City Hall, and up Whitney Avenue to the Peabody Museum. We stopped at Cutler's Record Shop on Broadway last month. I half-heartedly flipped through titles and came across the CD of a tape Jesse brought with him to the hospital, which I had told myself I'd find one day and had carefully avoided hunting for. I couldn't remember the name of the group or the album, only the deep voice of the lead singer intoning Mmmm mmmm mmmm and the phrase, God shuffled his feet. I had to special-order the tape so I could play it in my car, cassette tapes now going the way of the dinosaur. The songs were filled with girls with birthmarks all over their bodies and people who wondered how ducks could tell their wives from all the other ducks and whether you had to get haircuts in heaven, and a foot-shuffling God who answered such questions with parables such as the one about the boy who woke up with blue hair and wondered if his friends would love or shun him for it. Quaint, that only four years ago a rock band could poke gentle fun at God and be called alternative. When I listen to it now, Jesse seems old-fashioned, too.

To the right of the door is a brown metal-top wooden table that we used in the dining room of our last apartment in New Haven. We talked about getting him a draftsman's table but he never cared what surface he drew on any more than he cared what kind of paper was at hand when he wanted to draw. A chair, a lamp on the desk, and a lamp on an end table by the bed. Other than the drawings, the basketball players, the pennants, and some vacuuming, the room looks much the same as Jesse left it. I took photos a few days ago. The posters and news clippings, everything that hangs, and the desk and Buffalo Bills chair and blanket will stay here for now. The bed, the bureau, the bookcase, and the end tables will go on the pile outside. The couch upstairs will come down here to make it a family room when the new one arrives for the living room. The thought has not escaped me that we are doing better now financially than we ever did while Jesse was alive. What would life have been like for him if he'd survived the wreckage of his body? Bedridden maybe, too weak to draw, getting out only to be carted back and forth to doctors or helped onto a lounge chair on the deck during good weather. Would Rachel and I have fought over who would take care of him? And fought to take that care or be relieved of it?

I brought Marian down here after the funeral service. Ellie and Tina came to the service together and had already left. Marian got lost trying to find the church and showed up at the reception afterward. I invited her back to the house. She said no, but I insisted. I knew it would be awkward for her with only family here, but it would be a pity for her to have driven four hours round trip for nothing. She followed us home. We went downstairs. I looked around the room and was embarrassed for having cleaned it, as though I'd cast Jesse out and stood convicted in this empty space. Marian looked around and then back at me.

Do you remember how Jesse's lips were moving so fast the last night and morning?

Of course I do.

I had the impression that he was praying. And I'm not a religious person.

I hadn't thought of that.

She smiled, and hesitated. You know, he told me he loved me.

He did?

But I think that was probably just the medication.

No, I don't think so. I think he did love you.

I keep these on the top shelf of his closet where I found them, faint rapid sketches on lined paper that he probably dashed off on the sly during two or three classes at school. He used such a light hand that his teachers could have mistaken them for blank paper from only a few feet away. I come down and look at them to chew on my doubts. He burned bright at the end, but what if he had lived? Would he have scoffed at the tender love he had learned and taught and have hidden himself away again, or been such a physical wreck that no emotional breakthrough could keep him from becoming embittered over what was left of him? Sitting here at his desk, I pull them out of their brown envelope and turn them over one by one. Here are amorphous figures with rounded oblong eyes angled toward their missing noses. Fire streams around the cloudy contours of their bodies. Here are half-drawn figures, hooded and masked, conferring with each other or facing the viewer, muscle-bound heroes without faces, and figures approaching each other for combat from either side of the page. Here is a large hooded figure above several smaller figures with the hopeless posture of captives. Here are four weather-beaten men, perhaps fishermen back from a long voyage that has failed to make its catch. Here is a Frog King drawn from the waist up with a beautiful webbed wing it unfurls like a peacock. The drawings are boring in their lack of illumination but fascinating with the promise of it. I still worry about what will become of Jesse.

The last two are more finished. I know they belong with the others, though, because they're drawn on the same lined paper and were stuck to the others by the same tangled shards left from when he ripped the pages from the notebook. The first is of a creature with a man's body, the outspread wings of a mythical beast, and a half-human half-demonic head. Its head is tipped back slightly toward the sky. Its mouth is turned down. Its closed eyes are human. Black marks like war paint highlight its cheekbones. A pointed horn grows from each side of its head, drawn dark and distinct with a flourish of hair like ceremonial feathers curving down over a medallion that shows the head of a wolf. The second is of a man with stiff arms and legs outspread and parachute straps unattached to any parachute. The head is too round at the top and too small, although it may be that the top of the forehead and side are covered by a not-yet-drawn aviator's cap. The nose looks like a clothespin. A flower grows out of the left eye socket. The first seems to mark, and the second to mock, the solemnity of death.

We're months away from a new century. We played the game that everyone played, how old we'd be in 2000, 2010, 2020. I tried it one more time with Jesse as May 5th approached, but it tasted false and cowardly on my lips. It's been three and a half years and sometimes I still can't believe he's gone.

They'll be home soon. Time to pick up in the kitchen, not that X-rays and charts and Jesse notebooks would faze my crew.

Here's one of my favorites, a bearded man in a wool patchwork shirt drawn on good thick paper. It hangs on the other side of the stairwell facing the bedroom and leading to the old part of the basement. I found it folded haphazardly on his closet shelf along with others I hadn't seen before. It tells a different story each time I walk by it. Shall I tell this one?

He finds himself on a beach in a harbor town, but it is not the northern harbor town of his youth. The light is different here, even before day. The air has a stronger sea smell from waves that roll in with a different motion than he recalls. But it has been years, and he is older now. His coat is made of many small diamonds, half-black, half-light, To remind you of the moon, said the woman who wove it for him, slowly, to entice him to stay. His hair, still dark, drips down in one curled wave over his forehead. His right hand, grown large from working the sails, forms a fist, ready but without fear. He sees his crew, on another beach where he left them weary of adventure, standing in the shadow of another light. Orion who shot phosphorescence in his wake is lost at sea. The tree of his youth that birds sang into fire is stripped and still. Even the wind ignores it. Unaccountably, wrapped up in battles with incredible beasts, fantastical monsters and demons each fiercer than the last, he has become a man and has learned the lesson, bitter as sea salt, that his mentor tried to teach him. A man may do all that is asked of him and be utterly ruined! the aged seafarer shouted at his back as he cast off. He laughed then, but a young man should, you know. To his left, boys and girls awaken and stretch their limbs into the sand. Like carousel ghosts they twirl their skirts revealing all, the girls who disappear down the beach selling oranges, the boys in bandanas shaking fists at the sky. Like smoke off a dream they flee the white horse with champagne-glass nostrils that he sees now at the other end of the beach. He laughs. For a moment he thought they were fleeing from him with his odd manners, too long at sea. He hears a murmuring and looks back. A procession of townspeople walks over a grassy ridge. He hears the murmuring still and looks down. The dread black ocean laps at his feet. Remember, he whispers, remember. With one eye, he looks inward. A darkening river beats slowly to the sea. With the other eye, he looks far away. The rosy fingers of dawn reach deep into the ancient waters.